Workbook for

Auto
Service & Repair

Servicing, Troubleshooting, and Repairing Modern Automobiles.
Applicable to All Makes and Models.

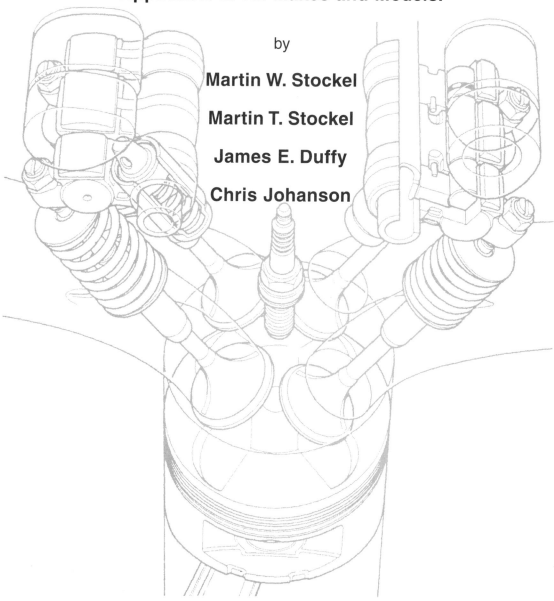

by

Martin W. Stockel

Martin T. Stockel

James E. Duffy

Chris Johanson

Publisher
The Goodheart-Willcox Company, Inc.
Tinley Park, Illinois

Introduction

The **Workbook for Auto Service and Repair** provides a thorough guide for the **Auto Service and Repair** text. It highlights important information, improves understanding, and simplifies the contents of the textbook.

The workbook contains many unique features designed to make learning easier and more interesting. It has two major types of exercises: *chapter quizzes* (in-text activities) and *jobs* (in-shop activities).

Each chapter quiz is correlated to and serves a study guide for a textbook chapter. You are lead through the text page by page, making sure you cover the most important material. The questions in the quizzes are organized by subject. A variety of questions are used, including multiple choice, completion, short answer, matching, and identification.

The workbook jobs supplement the contents of the textbook. The jobs give easy-to-follow instructions on various hands-on activities and help you develop the basic skills needed to service and repair automobiles.

As a student of automotive technology, you will find your workbook to be a valuable learning tool. Its use will make your learning experiences much more enjoyable.

Martin W. Stockel

Martin T. Stockel

James E. Duffy

Chris Johanson

Contents

Instructions for Answering Workbook Questions

Each chapter in this workbook directly correlates to the same chapter in the text. Before answering the questions in the workbook, study the assigned chapter in the text and answer the end-of-chapter review questions while referring to the text. Then, review the objectives at the beginning of each workbook chapter. This will help you review the important concepts presented in the chapter. Try to complete as many workbook questions as possible without referring to the textbook. Then, use the text to complete the remaining questions.

A variety of questions are used in the workbook, including multiple choice, identification, completion, and short answer. These questions should be answered in the following manner.

Multiple Choice

Select the best answer and write the corresponding letter in the blank.

1. Torrington bearings are a type of _____ bearing.
   (A) needle
   (B) ball
   (C) roller
   (D) None of the above.

1. ____A____

Identification

Identify the components indicated on the illustration or photograph accompanying the question.

2. Identify the parts of the injector illustrated below.

   (A) _flex hose_

   (B) _filter_

   (C) _winding_

   (D) _needle return spring_

   (E) _needle armature_

   (F) _sealing needle_

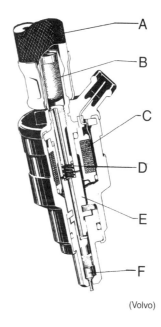

(Volvo)

5

Completion

In the blank provided, write the word or words that best complete the statement. In some cases you will be asked to draw missing parts or sections on an illustration. Use a ruler for all straight lines. Use colored pencils to help clarify your sketches.

3. On some vehicles with electronic fuel injection, the pulse _____ is increased when the engine is cold.

3. _____width_____

Short Answer

Provide complete responses to the statements.

4. What is the purpose of the turbocharger waste gate? __The turbocharger waste gate__ __prevents the turbocharger from developing too much pressure in the__ __intake manifold.__

Matching

Match the term in the left column with its description in the right column. Place the corresponding letter in the blank.

_C_	main pressure regulator	(A) driven by output shaft
_D_	manual valve	(B) redirect pressure to holding members
_B_	shift valves	(C) controls overall system pressure
_F_	throttle valve	(D) operated by driver
_A_	governor valve	(E) controls lockup clutch
_H_	filter	(F) operated by linkage or modulator
_G_	accumulator	(G) cushions shifts
_I_	servos	(H) removes dirt and metal
		(I) apply bands

Other Types of Questions

When other types of workbook questions are presented, follow the specific instructions that accompany the problems.

Instructions for Answering Workbook Jobs

Before starting any job, complete the related textbook and workbook chapters. Read the introduction, objective, and instructions for the job. Ask your instructor for any possible changes in the job procedures and for help as needed. Read and complete each step of the job carefully, while observing all safety rules. Always answer the job questions with complete sentences.

Name _____

Date _____ Period _____

Instructor _____

Score _____

Text pages 13-20

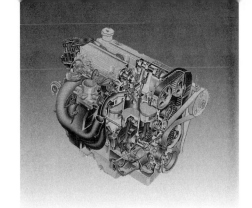

1

Safety and Environmental Protection

Objectives: After studying Chapter 1 in the textbook and completing this section of the workbook, you will be able to:

- Identify the major causes of accidents.
- Explain why accidents must be avoided.
- Recognize unsafe conditions in the shop.
- Give examples of unsafe work procedures.
- Use personal protective equipment.
- Describe types of environmental damage caused by improper auto shop practices.
- Identify ways to prevent environmental damage.

Tech Talk: Do you like working on cars and trucks? Do you want to be able to do it for several more years? Well, the easiest way to end your career as an automobile technician is to have a serious accident. Even minor accidents can cost you your health or your job. Always make sure that you do all repair procedures as safely as possible.

Instructions: Study Chapter 1 of the text; then answer the following questions in the spaces provided.

Preventing Accidents

1. The technician should always try to _____ accidents.

1. _____

2. Some accidents occur when technicians try to take _____.

2. _____

3. Technician A says that long-term exposure to certain chemicals can cause skin disorders. Technician B says that long-term exposure to some chemicals can cause lung damage. Who is right?
   (A) A only.
   (B) B only.
   (C) Both A & B.
   (D) Neither A nor B.

3. _____

4. The technician must keep _____ in mind at all times.

4. _____

5. Shopkeeping involves all of the following, EXCEPT:
   (A) keeping the shop premises in order.
   (B) identifying and correcting unsafe conditions.
   (C) keeping tools and equipment in working order.
   (D) None of the above.

5. _____

6. List several work procedures that should be followed when working in the automotive shop. _____

_____

_____

7. Describe the purpose of Material Data Safety Sheets (MSDS). _____

_____

_____

8. The technician should wear _____ when working on run-
   ning engines; using drills, grinders, or tire changers; or
   working around batteries or hot cooling systems.
   (A) respiratory protection
   (B) safety shoes
   (C) eye protection
   (D) All of the above.

8. _____

9. Falling parts or tools make _____ _____ necessary.

9. _____

10. Respiratory protection should be worn whenever you are
    working with _____.
    (A) starting system components
    (B) clutches
    (C) petroleum products
    (D) All of the above.

10. _____

11. When should the technician wear rubber gloves? _____

_____

Preventing Environmental Damage

12. Name the two ways that the automotive technician can cause environmental damage. _____

_____

_____

13. Technician A says that waste disposal guidelines are estab-
    lished and enforced by the Environmental Protection
    Agency. Technician B says that the Environmental
    Protection Agency recycles the hazardous wastes
    generated in the auto shop. Who is right?
    (A) A only.
    (B) B only.
    (C) Both A & B.
    (D) Neither A nor B.

13. _____

14. Automotive shop byproducts that can be recycled include   14. _____
_____.
 (A) scrap metal
 (B) tires
 (C) oil and antifreeze
 (D) All of the above.

15. The technician should never make any kind of vehicle   15. _____
adjustment without determining the effect on _____.
 (A) fuel economy
 (B) emissions
 (C) performance
 (D) All of the above.

• Describe how you would handle the following shop problems.

16. A radiator hose bursts, covering the shop floor with coolant and water._____

_____

_____

17. A can of used carburetor cleaner is discovered behind a workbench. _____

_____

_____

18. A vehicle is brought into the shop with some of the emission controls disconnected. _____

_____

_____

19. A vehicle is being operated in the shop when all windows and doors are closed. _____

_____

_____

20. A fellow technician throws a used alternator into the trash can. _____

_____

_____

Name _____

Date _____ Period _____

Instructor _____

Score _____

Text pages 21-44

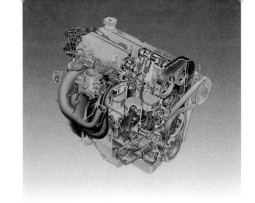

2

Basic Tools, Equipment, and Manuals

Objectives: After studying Chapter 2 in the textbook and completing this section of the workbook, you will be able to:

- Identify common automotive hand tools.
- Describe the proper use of automotive hand tools.
- List the safety rules for hand tools.
- Identify commonly used automotive service equipment.
- Describe the proper use of automotive service equipment.
- List the safety rules for automotive service equipment.
- Identify types of service manuals and training materials.
- Select and use the correct tools, equipment, and service manuals for a given job.

Tech Talk: Attempting to work on a car without the proper tools is like trying to fight a forest fire with a squirt gun—frustrating if not impossible. In a sense, hand tools serve as extensions of the human body. They increase the physical abilities of a technician's fingers, hands, arms, legs, eyes, ears, and back. Professional auto technicians often spend thousands of dollars on their tools. This is a wise investment. A well-selected set of tools will increase productivity, precision, and job satisfaction.

Instructions: Study Chapter 2 of the text; then answer the following questions in the spaces provided.

Buy Top-Quality Tools

1. The cheaper grades of tools are generally _____.
   (A) made of alloy steel
   (B) cumbersome
   (C) easy to clean
   (D) None of the above.

   1. _____

2. Fast, efficient work and _____ cannot exist together.

   2. _____

3. Technician A says that the time it takes to keep your tools clean and orderly is wasted time. Technician B says that open-end wrenches and box-end wrenches should never be stored together. Who is right?
   (A) A only.
   (B) B only.
   (C) Both A & B.
   (D) Neither A nor B.

   3. _____

4. The tools in the cabinet pictured below are arranged for _____ and normally fit into drawers.

4. _____

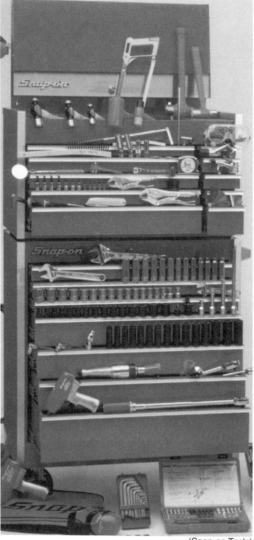

(Snap-on Tools)

Chisels and Punches

5. Chisels are used for _____.
   (A) cutting off rivet heads
   (B) driving pins from holes
   (C) aligning holes
   (D) All of the above.

5. _____

6. A few sections of round _____ _____ are useful when driving parts that may be damaged by steel punches.

6. _____

7. Explain the purpose of a starting punch. _____

_____

_____

8. A center punch is needed for _____.   8._____
    (A) marking parts before drilling
    (B) marking parts for reassembly
    (C) All of the above.
    (D) None of the above.

9. The aligning punch is used to _____.

10. When sharpening punches and chisels, _____ slowly and   10. _____
    _____ often to prevent drawing the temper

11. Draw the missing portions of the damaged chisels pictured below and identify the parts indicated.

    (A) _____

    (B) _____

    (C) _____

12. Identify the punches shown in the following illustration.

    (A) _____

    (B) _____

    (C) _____

Files

13. _____ files are commonly used in the auto shop.   13. _____
    (A) Flat mill
    (B) Round
    (C) Square
    (D) All of the above.

14. Be sure the file has a _____ firmly affixed to its tang before   14. _____
    use.

15. Coarse files are best for filing _____.
    (A) steel
    (B) brass
    (C) hard metals
    (D) None of the above.

15. _____

16. Fine files work well on _____.
    (A) brass
    (B) steel
    (C) aluminum
    (D) None of the above.

16. _____

17. Identify the files shown in the following illustration.

    (A) _____

    (B) _____

    (C) _____

    (D) _____

A   B   C   D

(Deere & Co.)

Grinders, Sanders, Wire Wheels

18. The tool shown in the following illustration is a(n) _____.
    Label the parts indicated.

    (A) _____

    (B) _____

    (C) _____

    (D) _____

    (E) _____

18. _____

(Ingersoll-Rand)

Drills

19. Quality drill bits are made of _____.
    (A) carbon steel
    (B) high-speed steel
    (C) brass
    (D) All of the above.

19. _____

20. Cutting oil is not necessary when drilling _____.
    (A) steel
    (B) cast iron
    (C) aluminum
    (D) None of the above.

20. _____

21. The tool pictured below is a typical _____. Label the parts indicated.

21. _____

    (A) _____

    (B) _____

    (C) _____

    (D) _____

    (E) _____

    (F) _____

Reamers, Taps, and Drills

22. Reamers are used to accurately_____.

23. _____ are used for cutting internal threads.
    (A) Taps
    (B) Dies
    (C) Heli-coils
    (D) None of the above.

23. _____

24. _____ are used to cut external threads on bolts, screws, and pipe.

24. _____

25. Name the four types of taps that are commonly used in the automotive shop. _____

    _____

    _____

    _____

26. The plug tap should be used first. When it strikes bottom, the _____ tap should be used.
    (A) finishing
    (B) pipe
    (C) bottoming
    (D) None of the above.

26. _____

27. Identify the taps shown in the following illustration.

    (A) _____

    (B) _____

    (C) _____

    (D) _____

(Starret Co.)

28. Fill in the missing numbers on tap and drill selection.

Hole Size	Threads Per Inch	Tap Size
(A) 9/16	12	
(B)	28	14
(C) 3/4	10	
(D)	28	3
(E) 3/8	16	

Hacksaw

29. A hacksaw is used to cut _____.
    (A) tubing
    (B) bolts
    (C) sheet metal
    (D) All of the above.

29. _____

30. The 18-tooth blade is used for cutting _____.

30. _____

31. The 32-tooth blade is used for cutting _____.

31. _____

32. A special hacksaw, termed a _____ saw, will cut in tight
    quarters.
    (A) jab
    (B) coping
    (C) hole
    (D) None of the above

32. _____

33. A _____ saw is handy for cutting large holes in sheet metal.

33. _____

34. The tool pictured below is a(n) _____ frame. Label the parts
    indicated.

34. _____

    (A) _____

    (B) _____

    (C) _____

    (D) _____

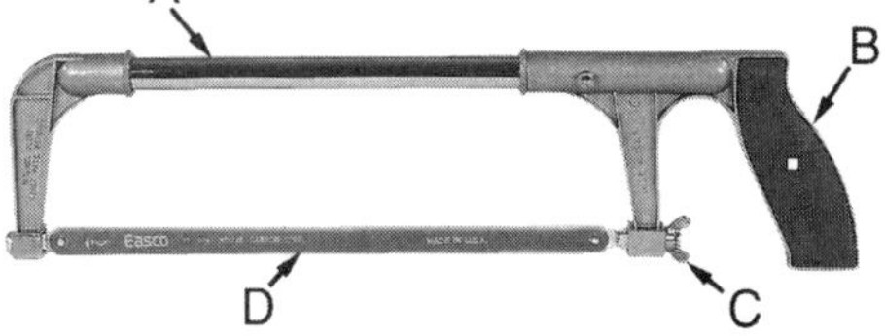

(Owatonna Tool Corp.)

35. The tool pictured in the following illustration is a(n) _____-
    type saw. Label the parts indicated.

35. _____

    (A) _____

    (B) _____

    (C) _____

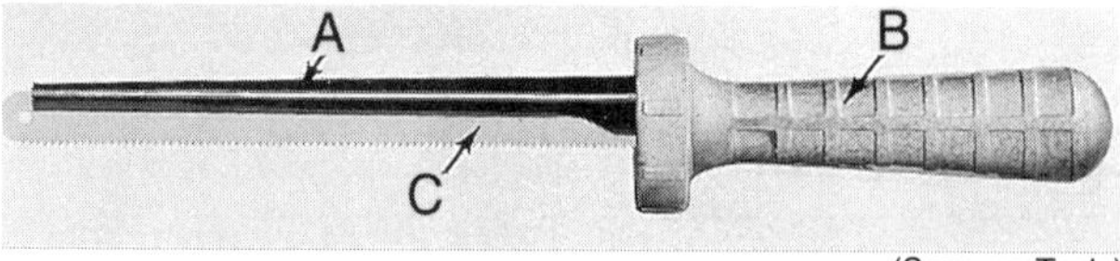

(Snap-on Tools)

Screwdrivers and Pliers

36. List the types of screwdrivers that should be owned by the automotive technician? _____

_____

37. The _____ screwdriver is useful in tight quarters where even a "stubby" cannot be used.
    (A) Torx®
    (B) clutch
    (C) offset
    (D) None of the above.

37. _____

38. When grinding a new tip on the standard tip screwdriver, maintain the _____.

38. _____

39. Pliers are used for _____.
    (A) tightening nuts
    (B) loosening tubing fittings
    (C) crimping
    (D) None of the above.

39. _____

40. Avoid cutting _____ with pliers.
    (A) tubing
    (B) wire
    (C) hardened bolts
    (D) None of the above.

40. _____

41. Identify the screwdrivers shown in the following illustration.

    (A) _____

    (B) _____

    (C) _____

    (D) _____

42. Identify the pliers shown in the following illustration.

    (A) _____

    (B) _____

    (C) _____

    (D) _____

(Utica and Proto Tools)

Wrenches

43. Box-end wrenches are available with _____-point openings.
    (A) 6
    (B) 12
    (C) Both A & B.
    (D) Neither A nor B.

43. _____

44. Carburetor, vacuum, and brake fittings should be loosened and tightened with a(n) _____ wrench.
    (A) Torx
    (B) offset
    (C) flare
    (D) None of the above.

44. _____

45. Double offset wrenches give more handle _____.

45. _____

Socket Wrenches

46. Sockets are available with _____-point openings.
    (A) 10
    (B) 12
    (C) 18
    (D) All of the above.

46. _____

47. Define drive size. _____

_____

_____

48. The ratchet handle allows both heavy _____ force and _____.

48. _____

49. Flex handles of different lengths _____.
    (A) are used exclusively in areas where limited swing is necessary
    (B) are used in the same manner as screwdrivers
    (C) provide heavy turning leverage
    (D) None of the above.

49. _____

50. The reach of a socket set can be increased by using a(n)_____.
    (A) extension
    (B) impact socket
    (C) T handle
    (D) None of the above.

50. _____

51. Sockets of one particular drive size can be turned with the handles of another size by using a(n)_____.
    (A) transition piece
    (B) adaptor
    (C) universal fitting
    (D) None of the above.

51. _____

52. Identify the tools shown in the following illustration.

(A) _____

(B) _____

(C) _____

(D) _____

(E) _____

(F) _____

(G) _____

Special Wrenches

53. Technician A says that an adjustable wrench tends to loosen and slip. Technician B says that an adjustable wrench should be used in place of an open-end wrench whenever possible. Who is right?
    (A) A only.
    (B) B only.
    (C) Both A & B.
    (D) Neither A nor B.

53. _____

54. When using any type wrench, it is important to _____ on the handle.

54. _____

55. Identify the specialty wrenches shown in the following illustration.

    (A) _____
    (B) _____
    (C) _____
    (D) _____
    (E) _____
    (F) Wedge-type_____

56. The illustration below shows a(n) _____-type impact wrench. These wrenches almost always have a(n) _____" drive.

56. _____

57. The impact wrench shown below is powered by a(n) _____ pack.

57. _____

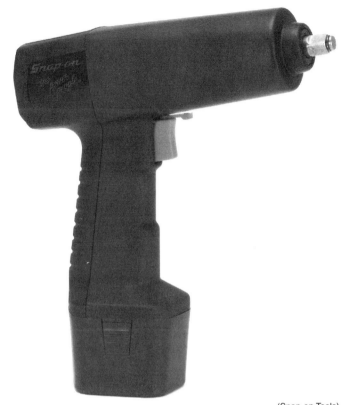

(Snap-on Tools)

Mark Your Tools

58. As tools are obtained, they should be marked in areas that are difficult to _____ _____.

58. _____

Service Information

59. Technician A says that a factory manual contains information on one make and model of vehicle for a given year. Technician B says that a factory manual contains detailed procedures for diagnosing specific problems and making repairs to any part of a vehicle. Who is right?
    (A) A only.
    (B) B only.
    (C) Both A & B.
    (D) Neither A nor B.

59. _____

60. _____ manuals cover one common system for many vehicle makes and models.

60. _____

Name _____

Date _____ Period _____

Instructor _____

Score _____

Text pages 45-62

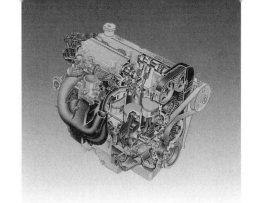

3

Precision Measurement Tools and Equipment

Objectives: After studying Chapter 3 in the textbook and completing this section of the workbook, you will be able to:
- Identify common measuring tools.
- Select the appropriate measuring tool for a given job.
- Use precision measuring tools.
- Properly maintain precision measuring tools.

Tech Talk: A competent automotive technician uses precision measuring tools on the job. The ability to use these tools properly distinguishes the good technician from the "parts changer." Knowing when, where, and how to measure is essential to anyone seeking a career as an automotive technician.

Instructions: Study Chapter 3 of the text; then answer the following questions in the spaces provided.

Tool Storage

1. Technician A says that measuring tools should be kept in a protective case. Technician B says that measuring tools should be stored in an area that will not be subjected to excessive moisture. Who is right?
   (A) A only.
   (B) B only.
   (C) Both A & B.
   (D) Neither A nor B.

1. _____

Outside Micrometers

2. The outside micrometer can be used to check the diameter of all of the following, EXCEPT:
   (A) piston pins.
   (B) cylinder bores.
   (C) crankshaft journals.
   (D) pistons.

2. _____

3. Individual micrometers are designed to produce readings over a range of _____.

3. _____

4. Micrometers are made so that every full turn of the thimble moves the spindle _____.
   (A) 0.010″
   (B) 0.100″
   (C) 0.001″
   (D) 0.025″

4. _____

5. Each line on the micrometer's thimble edge equals _____ inches.

5. _____

6. List the four steps that should be followed when reading a micrometer.

   (A) _____

   _____

   (B) _____

   _____

   (C) _____

   _____

   (D) _____

   _____

7. Identify the parts of the micrometer shown in the following illustration.

   (A) _____
   (B) _____
   (C) _____
   (D) _____
   (E) _____
   (F) _____
   (G) _____
   (H) _____
   (I) _____

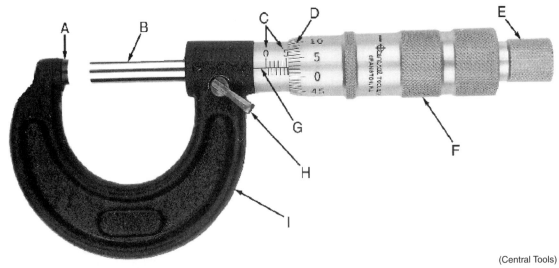

(Central Tools)

Special Micrometers

8. The inside micrometer is used for making measurements in _____.

8. _____

9. The micrometer depth gauge is a handy tool for reading the depth of _____.
   (A) slots
   (B) splines
   (C) counterbores
   (D) All of the above.

9. _____

10. Technician A says that a dial indicator is commonly used to check end play. Technician B says that a dial indicator is commonly used to measure cylinder diameter. Who is right?
    (A) A only.
    (B) B only.
    (C) Both A & B.
    (D) Neither A nor B.

10. _____

11. When using a dial indicator, be certain that it is mounted firmly and that the actuating rod is _____ to the plane movement to be measured.

11. _____

12. The _____ micrometer pictured below is accurate to one one-thousandth of an inch.

12. _____

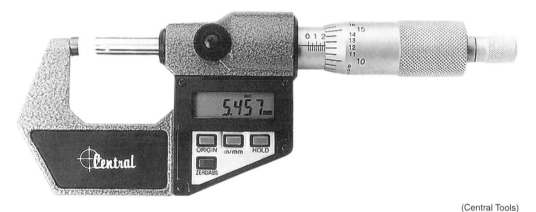

(Central Tools)

13. The tool shown below is used to check all of the following, EXCEPT:
    (A) cylinder bores.
    (B) brake drums.
    (C) brake rotors.
    (D) large bushings.

13. _____

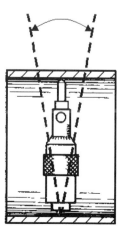

14. The tool shown below is a(n) _____-type micrometer. Label the parts indicated.

14. _____

(A) _____

(B) _____

(C) _____

(D) _____

(E) _____

(F) _____

(G) _____

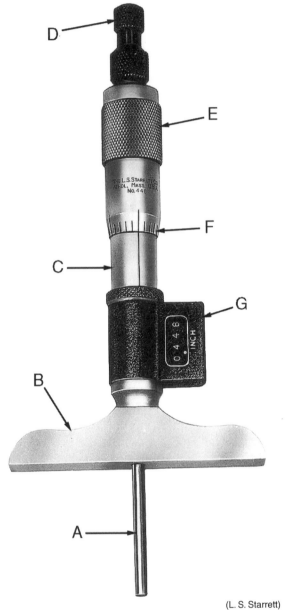

(L. S. Starrett)

Calipers, Gauges, Straightedges

15. When accuracy is not critical, inside and outside _____ are useful tools for quick measurements.

15. _____

16. Technician A says that the inside caliper can be used to accurately measure the diameter of holes. Technician B says that an outside caliper is frequently used to measure the diameter of holes. Who is right?
    (A) A only.
    (B) B only.
    (C) Both A & B.
    (D) Neither A nor B.

16. _____

17. Dividers are handy for _____.   17. _____
    (A) taking surface measurements
    (B) making circles
    (C) Both A & B.
    (D) Neither A nor B.

18. Define thickness gauges._____

    _____

    _____

19. The _____ gauge is excellent for checking the gap of used   19. _____
    spark plugs.

20. The telescoping gauge is an accurate tool for measuring   20. _____
    _____.
    (A) connecting rod bores
    (B) main bearing bores
    (C) valve guide diameters
    (D) All of the above.

21. A steel straightedge can be used for _____.   21. _____

22. Remember that all metals expand and contract in direct pro- 22. _____
    portion to their _____.
    (A) size
    (B) weight
    (C) temperature
    (D) None of the above.

23. The tool shown below is used to check all of the following, 23. _____
    EXCEPT:
    (A) shaft end play.
    (B) shaft diameter.
    (C) gear backlash.
    (D) cylinder taper.

(Central Tools)

24. Identify the measuring tools shown in the following illustrations.

(A) _____

(B) _____

(C) _____

(D) _____

(E) _____

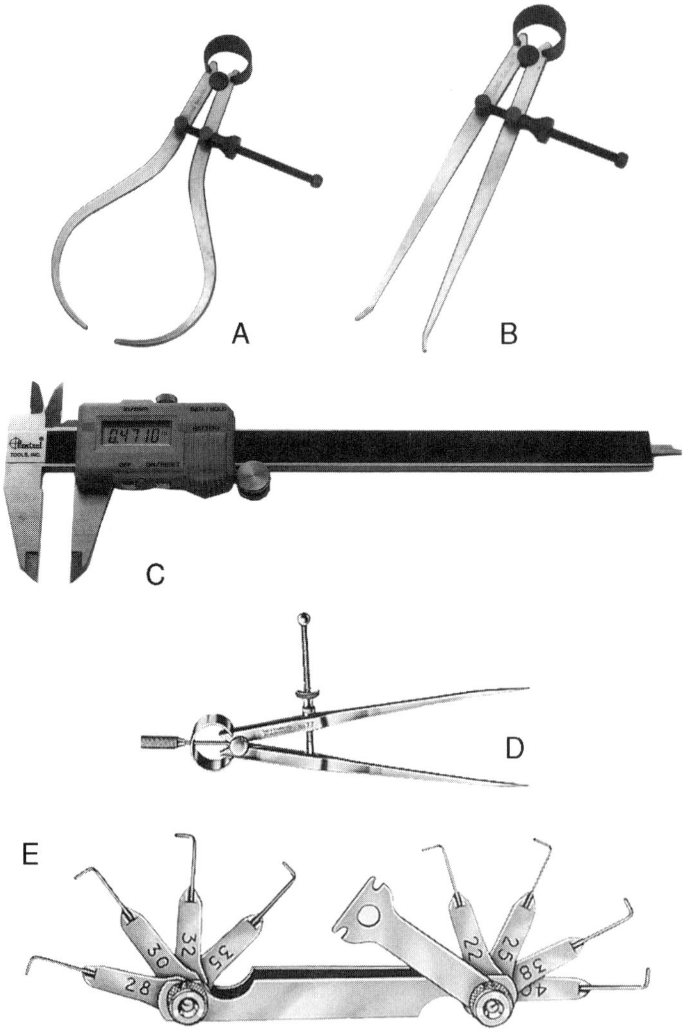

A

B

C

D

E

Other Automotive Measuring Equipment

25. The compression gauge measures the pressure developed   25. _____
    in the engine _____.

26. An oil pressure tester can measure the pressure developed by the oil pumps of which three engine systems?

(A) _____

(B) _____

(C) _____

27. Technician A says that the fuel pressure tester can be used to check for a defective fuel pump or clogged fuel filter. Technician B says that the fuel pressure tester is only used on carbureted engines. Who is right?
   (A) A only.
   (B) B only.
   (C) Both A & B.
   (D) Neither A nor B.

27. _____

28. An ohmmeter measures the electrical value known as _____, which is the opposition to current flow.
   (A) resistance
   (B) impedance
   (C) capacitance
   (D) None of the above.

28. _____

29. When using an ohmmeter, _____ is not important unless a diode is being checked.
   (A) voltage
   (B) current
   (C) polarity
   (D) None of the above.

29. _____

30. A voltmeter is used to check the electrical potential between two points in a circuit that is _____.

30. _____

31. An ammeter is used to check the electrical property known as _____.

31. _____

32. Multimeters can be used to measure _____.
   (A) resistance
   (B) voltage
   (C) current
   (D) All of the above.

32. _____

33. A tachometer measures engine speed through two leads that connect to the primary side of the ignition coil and _____.

33. _____

34. The gauge shown below measures _____ air pressure.

34. _____

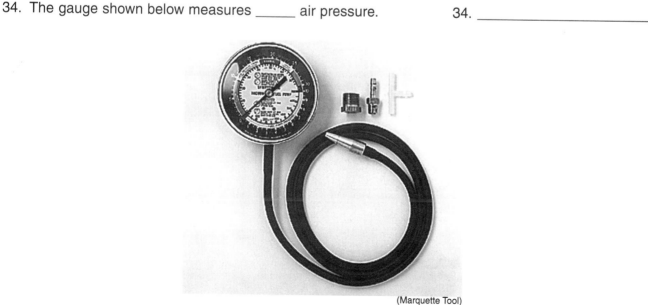

(Marquette Tool)

35. The bulb in the test light shown below is designed to operate on _____ volts. In addition to the parts shown in the illustration, a powered test light contains an internal _____.

35. _____

_____

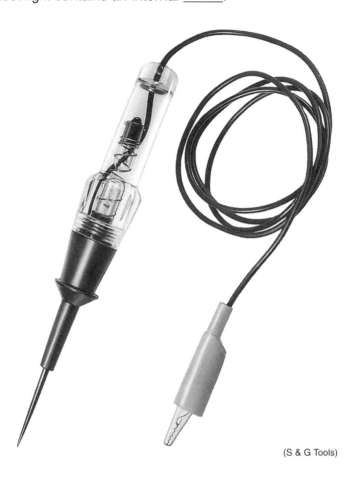

(S & G Tools)

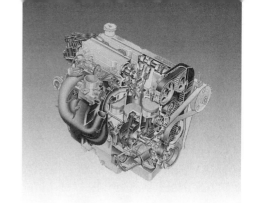

Name _____

Date _____ Period _____

Instructor_____

Score_____

Text pages 63-72

4

Jacks, Lifts, and Holding Fixtures

Objectives: After studying Chapter 4 in the textbook and completing this section of the workbook, you will be able to:

- List the most commonly used lifting and holding equipment.
- Select the correct type of lifting or holding equipment for the job.
- Describe safety precautions for jacks, lifts, and holding fixtures.

Tech Talk: If used correctly, jacks, lifts, hoists, and repair stands can make a potentially cumbersome and tiring job easy. On the other hand, if used improperly, this same equipment can injure or kill. Tons of force can be exerted by a jack or lift. This force can crush your hand or foot, or it can cause severe vehicle or equipment damage. Improperly used hoists or repair stands can cause an engine block or transmission to fall, causing personal injury or ruining parts. Learn to use lifting equipment and holding fixtures properly.

Instructions: Study Chapter 4 of the text; then answer the following questions in the spaces provided.

Lifting Equipment

1. Technician A says that a hydraulic hand jack should never be used to raise a vehicle. Technician B says that a hydraulic jack can be used to bend parts. Who is right?
   (A) A only.
   (B) B only.
   (C) Both A & B.
   (D) Neither A nor B.

1. _____

2. A floor jack can be used to raise the _____ of a car.
   (A) front
   (B) rear
   (C) side
   (D) All of the above.

2. _____

3. Technician A says that it is acceptable to lift a vehicle by positioning a jack under the oil pan. Technician B says that it is acceptable to lift a vehicle by positioning a jack under the transmission housing. Who is right?
   (A) A only.
   (B) B only.
   (C) Both A & B.
   (D) Neither A nor B.

3. _____

4. Never work under a vehicle supported only by a(n) _____.

4. _____

5. The end lift can be operated by _____ pressure.
   (A) pneumatic
   (B) hydraulic
   (C) Both A & B.
   (D) Neither A nor B.

5. _____

6. A(n) _____ _____ lift raises the car while leaving both the front and rear of the vehicle completely exposed.

6. _____

7. The _____ _____ lift eliminates the single central post, leaving the central portion of the car more accessible.

7. _____

8. Remember that many cars weigh _____ or more.

8. _____

9. Identify the parts of the single-post frame lift shown below.

   (A) _____
   (B) _____
   (C) _____

Specialty Lifting Equipment

10. A(n) _____ _____ is essential to the safe, efficient removal and installation of automatic transmissions.

10. _____

11. Technician A says that a portable crane and a chain hoist can be used to remove an engine from a vehicle. Technician B says that a portable crane can be used to place heavy objects on a workbench. Who is correct?
    (A) A only.
    (B) B only.
    (C) Both A & B.
    (D) Neither A nor B.

11. _____

12. A large repair stand can be used to hold _____ for repairs.
    (A) engine blocks
    (B) differentials
    (C) transmissions
    (D) All of the above.

12. _____

13. Small bench-top repair stands are useful for holding _____   13. _____
_____ in place on the workbench.

14. What is the one vital rule to remember when using a repair stand? _____

_____

15. Identify the parts of the transmission jack shown below.

(A) _____

(B) _____

(C) _____

(D) _____

(E) _____

(F) _____

(G) _____

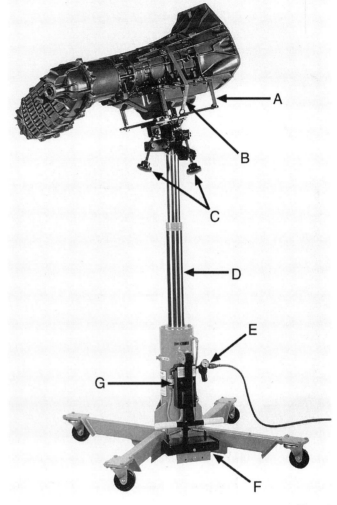

(Weaver)

Name _____

Date _____ Period _____

Instructor _____

Score_____

Text pages 73-81

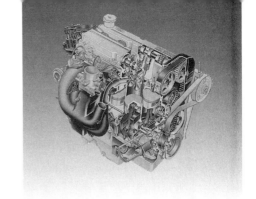

5

Cleaning Equipment and Techniques

Objectives: After studying Chapter 5 in the textbook and completing this section of the workbook, you will be able to:

- List the most common automotive cleaning techniques.
- Compare the advantages and disadvantages of different cleaning methods.
- Select the correct cleaning method for a given job.
- Describe the safety rules that apply to various cleaning techniques.

Tech Talk: A professional auto technician understands the importance of part cleanliness. Although cleaning is time consuming, it is vital. When working with precision components, the smallest amount of dirt can cause a mechanical failure. A particle of metal the size of a pinhead can damage a cylinder wall or engine bearing, cause an automatic transmission valve or a hydraulic lifter to stick, or clog a carburetor passage or fuel injector nozzle. A quality technician will make sure that all parts are perfectly clean before installing them.

Instructions: Study Chapter 5 of the text; then answer the following questions in the spaces provided.

Types of Cleaning Equipment

1. Careless cleaning of parts during teardowns of engines, transmissions, and rear ends may ruin the job and cause _____.

   1. _____

2. All the following components are subject to accumulations of hard carbon, EXCEPT:
   (A) piston heads.
   (B) valves.
   (C) main bearings.
   (D) combustion chambers.

   2. _____

3. Technician A says that a rotary wire brush can be used to clean deposits from cylinder heads and valves. Technician B says that a rotary wire brush can be used to clean deposits from pistons and bearings. Who is right?
   (A) A only.
   (B) B only.
   (C) Both A & B.
   (D) Neither A nor B.

   3. _____

4. Identify the items indicated in the following illustration.

(A) _____

(B) _____

(C) _____

Cleaning Solutions Can Be Dangerous

5. Gasoline can be used to clean all of the following parts, EXCEPT:
   (A) crankshaft bearings.
   (B) valves.
   (C) transmission parts.
   (D) None of the above.

5. _____

6. Technician A says that goggles or a face shield should be worn when using cleaning solvents. Technician B says that cleaning solutions should be used in well-ventilated areas. Who is right?
   (A) A only.
   (B) B only.
   (C) Both A & B.
   (D) Neither A nor B.

6. _____

7. Why is it important to use a solvent with a high flash point? _____

_____

8. Why should technicians thoroughly wash their hands and arms when a cleaning job is finished?

_____

Parts Washers and Hot Tank Cleaners

9. Although small parts can be cleaned in a can or a bucket, a far more efficient job can be accomplished by using a(n) _____.

9. _____

10. After rinsing components in a parts washer, let the parts _____ and then blow them dry with compressed air.

10. _____

11. Large shops that specialize in rebuilding usually have a hot   11. _____
    tank for heavy cleaning of _____.
    (A) engine blocks
    (B) transmission cases
    (C) radiators
    (D) All of the above.

12. Identify the parts of the cold solution parts washer pictured in the following illustration.

    (A) _____

    (B) _____

    (C) _____

    (D) _____

    (E) _____

    (F) _____

    (G) _____

    (H) _____

    (I) _____

    (J) _____

    (K) _____

    (L) _____

(Graymills)

Steam and Pressure Cleaning

13. The steam cleaner is used for cleaning _____.   13. _____

14. List two of the safety rules for steam cleaning.

    (A) _____

    (B) _____

15. High-pressure spray cleaning equipment uses _____ water.   15. _____

16. Pressure at the nozzle of a high-pressure spray cleaner can   16. _____
    reach approximately _____ psi.
    (A) 500
    (B) 1000
    (C) 1500
    (D) None of the above.

17. A low-pressure spray cleaning gun is operated by _____   17. _____
    pressure.

18. Technician A says that the solution in a vapor cleaner must   18. _____
    be heated to clean parts. Technician B says that a cold soak
    solution requires that the parts be suspended in the clean-
    ing solution. Who is right ?
    (A) A only.
    (B) B only.
    (C) Both A & B.
    (D) Neither A nor B.

19. Automotive body and welding shops occasionally use a(n) _____ to remove rust, paint, or welding scale.

19. _____

20. A bead blast cleaner differs from a conventional sandblaster in that the blaster unit is placed in a(n) _____.

20. _____

Name _____

Date _____ Period _____

Instructor _____

Score _____

Text pages 83-95

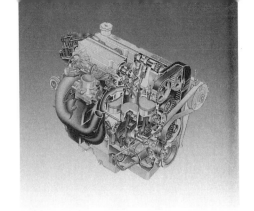

6

Welding Equipment and Techniques

Objectives: After studying Chapter 6 in the textbook and completing this section of the workbook, you will be able to:

- Describe the equipment needed for welding metal.
- Describe the equipment needed for brazing metal.
- Describe the procedures for brazing metal.

Tech Talk: The technician is often called on to perform welding jobs. Although most welding is performed by auto body technicians, skill in welding is often necessary to repair cracked brackets or aluminum castings. Welding skills are also needed to install trailer hitches. Brazing is often used to repair sheet metal parts, such as oil pans or timing covers. The skilled technician will make the effort to learn the basics of welding and brazing.

Instructions: Study Chapter 6 of the text; then answer the following questions in the spaces provided.

Gas Welding

1. Welding is a(n) _____ process.

2. The regulators reduce _____ _____ to a usable level.

3. Technician A says that all oxyacetylene hose fittings should be greased before they are attached. Technician B says that the lines should be purged before lighting the torch. Who is right?
   (A) A only.
   (B) B only.
   (C) Both A & B.
   (D) Neither A nor B.

4. The acetylene hose is normally _____ in color.

5. The oxygen hose is generally _____ in color.

1. _____

2. _____

3. _____

4. _____

5. _____

6. Technician A says that cylinder valves should be opened as rapidly as possible. Technician A says that it is important to know what type of material you will be welding before starting the welding process. Who is right?
   (A) A only.
   (B) B only.
   (C) Both A & B.
   (D) Neither A nor B.

6. _____

7. Technician A says a neutral flame is used for gas welding. Technician B says an oxidizing flame is recommended for gas welding. Who is right?
   (A) A only.
   (B) B only.
   (C) Both A & B.
   (D) Neither A nor B.

7. _____

8. A carburizing flame has too much _____ in the mixture.
   (A) oxygen
   (B) acetylene
   (C) Both A & B.
   (D) Neither A nor B.

8. _____

9. If the flame is anything other than neutral, the resulting weld will be _____.

9. _____

10. When backhand welding, the torch tip is _____ the direction of travel.

10. _____

11. The weld should _____ through the joint.

11. _____

12. While using an oxyacetylene cutting torch, the _____ _____ lever should be depressed when the spot has been heated to a bright red.

12. _____

13. The technician should always wear protective equipment when welding. Examples of safety equipment are _____ and _____.

13. _____
    _____

14. Weld only in areas where there is good _____.

14. _____

15. Technician A says that a leaking oxygen hose should be replaced. Technician B says that a leaking oxygen hose can be repaired. Who is right?
    (A) A only.
    (B) B only.
    (C) Both A & B.
    (D) Neither A nor B.

15. _____

16. Complete the following statements about welding joints based on the illustration at the top of the following page.

    (A) A(n) _____ joint is used when metal thickness is _____ (_____).

    (B) A(n) _____ joint may be used on parts not exceeding _____(_____).

    (C) A(n) _____ type joint is often used on thin metal _____ (_____) of an inch or less.

    (D) A(n) _____ joint is used when thickness ranges from _____ to _____(_____ to _____).

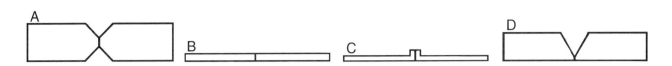

17. Identify the welding methods shown in the following illustrations.

(A) _____

(B) _____

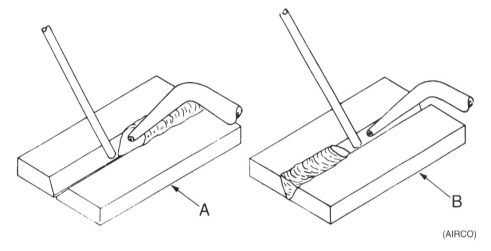

(AIRCO)

Arc Welding

18. Define *arc welding.* _____

_____

19. Welding rods are usually _____ to provide a gaseous shield around the arc.

19. _____

20. When using an arc welder, always wear a(n) _____ to protect your eyes and face.

20. _____

21. Your eyes can suffer damage from the _____ produced during arc welding.

21. _____

22. Define *striking an arc.* _____

_____

23. A good arc has a sound like _____.

23. _____

24. Technician A says that a short arc will make a humming noise. Technician B says that a short arc will tend to cause the rod to stick to the workpiece. Who is right?
(A) A only.
(B) B only.
(C) Both A & B.
(D) Neither A nor B.

24. _____

25. Excessive arc length will cause a(n) _____ noise with a lot of _____.

25. _____

_____

26. Define *slag*. _____

_____

_____

27. TIG and MIG are two types of welding in which the welding joint is protected by a shield of _____ gas.

27. _____

28. A ferrous metal contains _____.
    (A) aluminum
    (B) carbon
    (C) iron
    (D) None of the above.

28. _____

29. The TIG or MIG filler wire passes through the center of the _____ _____ as welding takes place.

29. _____

30. Technician A says that before welding, the welding machine must be properly grounded. Technician B says that arc welding equipment should never be used when standing in water. Who is right?
    (A) A only.
    (B) B only.
    (C) Both A & B.
    (D) Neither A nor B.

30. _____

31. Some metal _____ may produce deadly gases when welded.

31. _____

32. The following illustration shows the tip of an electric arc welder during use. Identify the parts indicated.

    (A) _____

    (B) _____

    (C) _____

    (D) _____

    (E) _____

33. Identify the parts of the arc welding setup shown in the following illustration.

(A) _____

(B) _____

(C) _____

(D) _____

(E) _____

(F) _____

(G) _____

(H) _____

(I) _____

(Lincoln Electric Co.)

34. Brazing consists of melting the _____ without melting the _____.

34. _____
_____

35. Define *capillary action*._____
_____
_____

36. Parts should be held together during brazing and cooling to avoid internal _____.

36. _____

37. A regular bronze or manganese bronze rod can be used to braze all of the following, EXCEPT:
(A) steel
(B) cast iron
(C) malleable iron
(D) stainless steel

37. _____

38. Brazing flux should be compatible with the type of _____ being used.

38. _____

39. An uncoated bronze rod is heated and dipped in _____.

39. _____

40. What type equipment will produce sufficient heat for brazing? _____
_____
_____

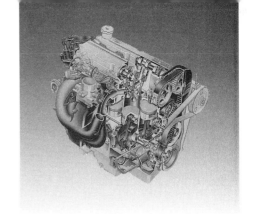

Name _____

Date _____ Period _____

Instructor _____

Score_____

Text pages 97-130

7

Fasteners, Gaskets, Sealants

Objectives: After studying Chapter 7 in the textbook and completing this section of the workbook, you will be able to:

• Identify automotive fasteners.

• Properly select fasteners.

• Torque fasteners to specifications when needed.

• Repair damaged or broken fasteners.

• Describe gasket construction, materials, and application.

• Describe the construction and installation of seals.

• Describe the types and selection of sealants and adhesives.

Tech Talk: Fasteners, such as bolts, nuts, screws, and clips, hold the parts of a vehicle together. Thousands of fasteners are used in the construction of the average vehicle. A technician must constantly remove, install, and repair fasteners when performing any type of automotive work. To prevent an improper repair job, threaded fasteners must be carefully selected according to diameter, thread pitch, and strength. Many fasteners must be carefully tightened to the correct torque values. Non-threaded fasteners must also be used for the intended fastening job.

Modern vehicles rely on gaskets, sealants, seals, and adhesives to hold parts together and prevent leaks of engine oil, brake fluid, gear oil, greases, transmission fluid, power steering fluid, and coolant. Defective gaskets can cause loss of engine compression or intake manifold vacuum.

Anyone seeking a career as an automotive technician must have a thorough knowledge of automotive fasteners, gaskets, and sealers. This includes both their description and proper installation.

Instructions: Study Chapter 7 of the text; then answer the following questions in the spaces provided.

Types of Fasteners

1. Machine screws are used without _____.

2. Technician A says that sheet metal screws are used to hold thin metal parts together. Technician B says that sheet metal screws are used with standard nuts. Who is right?
   (A) A only.
   (B) B only.
   (C) Both A & B.
   (D) Neither A nor B.

1. _____

2. _____

3. When using a sheet metal screw, why should you punch, rather than drill, the hole? _____

_____

_____

4. A stud is a metal rod that is _____.   4. _____

5. Technician A says that if a portion of a broken bolt protrudes   5. _____
from its hole, the bolt may be removed by gripping the pro-
truding portion with vise grip pliers and turning it out.
Technician B says that if a portion of a broken bolt does not
protrude from its hole, the bolt can be removed by driving it
counterclockwise with a punch. Who is right?
(A) A only.
(B) B only.
(C) Both A & B.
(D) Neither A nor B.

6. Partially stripped threads can be cleaned up and repaired   6. _____
through the use of a thread _____ or _____.   _____

7. Summarize the three procedures that can be used when threads in holes are damaged beyond
repair.

(A) _____

(B) _____

(C) _____

8. Bolts and screws may be identified by all of the following,   8. _____
EXCEPT:
(A) length.
(B) tensile strength.
(C) malleability.
(D) thread pitch.

9. Define bolt head markings. _____

_____

_____

10. Technician A says that Unified National Coarse threads are   10. _____
used in all automotive applications. Technician B says that
Metric fasteners do not have separate fine and coarse des-
ignations. Who is right?
(A) A only.
(B) B only.
(C) Both A & B.
(D) Neither A nor B.

11. Nuts for automotive use are generally _____ in shape.   11. _____

12. All self-locking nuts use the same basic principle, the cre-   12. _____
ation of _____ between two fasteners.

13. Define pallnut. _____

_____

14. _____ are used to attach gears and pulleys to shafts.   14. _____
    (A) Keys
    (B) Splines
    (C) Pins
    (D) All of the above.

15. Technician A says that snap rings are made of aluminum.   15. _____
    Technician B says that snap ring pliers should be used to
    install and remove snap rings. Who is right?
    (A) A only.
    (B) B only.
    (C) Both A & B.
    (D) Neither A nor B.

16. When a setscrew is used, the shaft will usually have a(n)   16. _____
    _____ spot to accept the screw tip.

17. Sketch the missing screw heads in the following illustration.

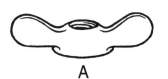

HEX   FLAT   OVAL   FILLISTER   ROUND

18. Identify the fastener drive types shown in the following illustration.

    (A) _____

    (B) _____

    (C) _____

    (D) _____

A   B   C   D

19. Label the fasteners and fastener parts in the following illustration.

    (A) _____

    (B) _____

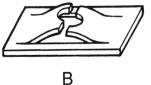

A   B

20. The following illustration shows several methods used to remove broken studs. Describe each operation shown.

(A) _____

(B) _____

(C) _____

(D) _____

(E) _____

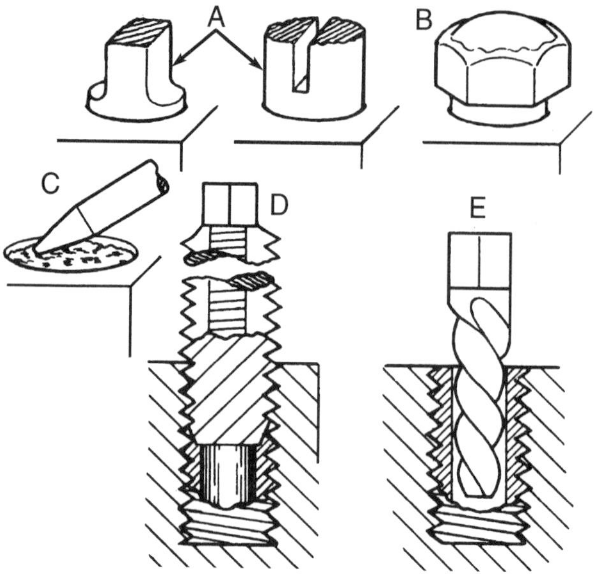

21. The following illustration shows a common method for repairing stripped threads. Identify the parts indicated.

(A) _____

(B) _____

(C) _____

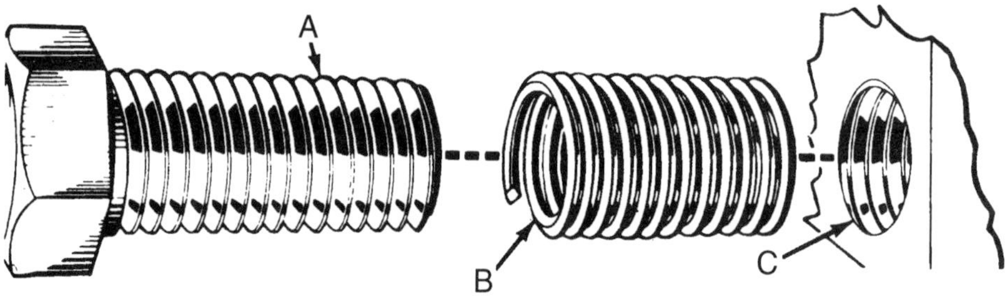

(Chrysler)

22. Label the fastener parts in the following illustration.

(A) _____

(B) _____

(C) _____

(D) _____

(E) _____

(F) _____

(G) _____

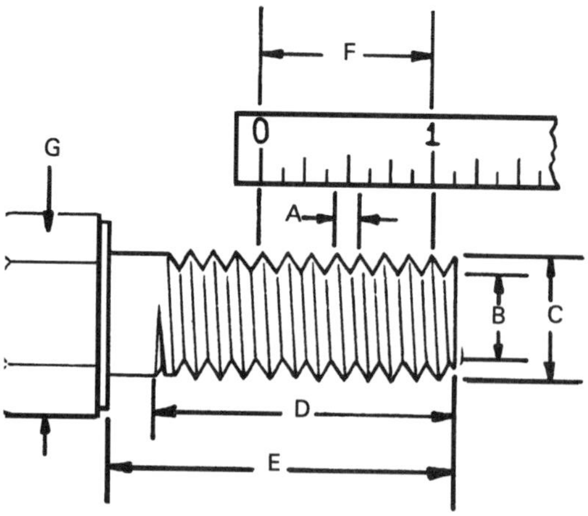

23. Label the fasteners and fastener parts in the following illustration.

(A) _____

(B) _____

(C) _____

(D) _____

(E) _____

(F) _____

(G) _____

(H) _____

(I) _____

Torquing Fasteners

24. List seven problems that can occur when fasteners are torqued improperly.

(A) _____

(B) _____

(C) _____

(D) _____

(E) _____

(F) _____

(G) _____

25. The torque wrench will measure the _____ force that is applied to the fastener.

25. _____

26. If the center of pull on the handle of a torque wrench is exactly one foot from the center of the head, a one pound pull on the handle would produce _____ of torque applied to the fastener.
    (A) 1 ft./lb.
    (B) 12 in./lb.
    (C) Both A & B.
    (D) Neither A nor B.

26. _____

27. When installing fasteners, always check for _____

_____.

28. Where a number of fasteners are used to secure a part, the proper tightening _____ should be followed.

28. _____

29. If no sequence or tightening chart is available, it is usually advisable to start tightening in the _____ and work _____.

29. _____

_____

30. During bolt tightening on some assemblies, it is advisable to use a(n) _____ and always avoid _____.

30. _____

    _____

31. Draw the crisscross tightening pattern on the following illustration using lines and arrows. Also, show the tightening sequence numbers.

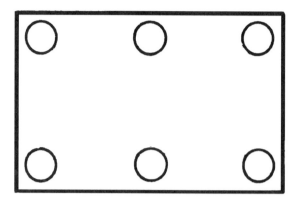

32. Draw the crisscross tightening pattern on the following illustration using lines and arrows. Also, show the tightening sequence numbers.

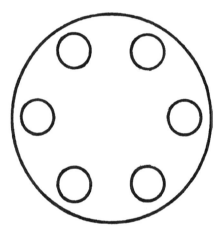

Gaskets and Sealants

33. Technician A says that gaskets and seals are used throughout the engine to confine fuel and oil. Technician B says that gaskets and seals can be used to confine air and vacuum. Who is right?
    (A) A only.
    (B) B only.
    (C) Both A & B.
    (D) Neither A nor B.

33. _____

34. Define *gasket*. _____

    _____

    _____

    _____

35. Some of the materials used in the construction of gaskets   35. _____
    include _____.
    (A) rubber
    (B) copper
    (C) paper
    (D) All of the above.

36. If a gasket is reused, it will fail to compress and _____   36. _____
    properly.

37. After thorough cleaning, always inspect both part _____   37. _____
    surfaces to detect any nicks, dents, etc.

38. On more complicated gaskets, such as cylinder head gaskets, make certain the gasket is _____

    _____.

39. Many head gaskets have the word _____ and occasionally   39. _____
    the word _____ stamped on them.   _____

40. A shrunken or expanded gasket condition can be corrected by _____

    _____

    _____.

41. Carefully inspect gaskets for _____

    _____.

42. A simple paper or combination cork and rubber gasket can be made. Explain how. _____

    _____

    _____

    _____

    _____

43. Screw holes can be made in gaskets by _____

    _____

    _____

    _____.

44. Technician A says that the use of sealant will help hold a   44. _____
    gasket in place during installation. Technician B says that
    sealant helps seal small cracks and surface imperfections.
    Who is right?
    (A) A only.
    (B) B only.
    (C) Both A & B.
    (D) Neither A nor B.

45. Rubber gaskets are highly _____.   45. _____

46. When a relatively thin, stamped part is bent along its part-   46. _____
    ing edge, it must be _____ before installation.

47. To straighten stamped parts, the parting edge on a smooth,   47. _____
    _____ surface and gently _____ to straighten bent areas.   _____

48. Name five defects that should be checked for on gasket mating surfaces.

   (A) _____

   (B) _____

   (C) _____

   (D) _____

   (E) _____

49. Before installing a new gasket, check it for _____.

   49. _____

50. Technician A says that sealant should be applied to both sides of a gasket before installation. Technician B says that sealant should be applied to only one side of a gasket. Who is right?
   (A) A only.
   (B) B only.
   (C) Both A & B.
   (D) Neither A nor B.

   50. _____

51. When installing a gasket, fasteners should always be torqued in the proper _____.

   51. _____

52. Identify the labeled parts of the following illustration.

   (A) _____

   (B) _____

   (C) _____

   (D) _____

   (E) _____

   (F) _____

53. Identify the types of head gaskets and installation information in the following illustrations.

   (A) _____

   (B) _____

A

B

(Victor, McCord)

54. The following illustration shows a technician making a simple gasket. Identify the parts indicated.

    (A) _____

    (B) _____

Oil Seals

55. Technician A says that seals are used to confine fluids.   55. _____
    Technician B says that seals prevent the entry of foreign
    materials. Who is right?
    (A) A only.
    (B) B only.
    (C) Both A & B.
    (D) Neither A nor B.

56. An oil seal is secured to one part while the sealing lip allows   56. _____
    the other part to _____ or reciprocate (move) without
    leakage.

57. All the following components are part of a seal, EXCEPT: 57. _____
    (A) garter spring.
    (B) metal case.
    (C) retainer.
    (D) sealing element.

58. After preparing the seal counterbore with sealer, place the   58. _____
    seal squarely against the opening with the seal lip facing

    _____.

59. If a seal driving set is not available, a section of _____ of the   59. _____
    correct diameter can be used to install (drive in) a seal.

60. If a hammer and punch are used to install a seal, be careful   60. _____
    to strike at different _____ and near the _____ edge of the   _____
    seal.

61. If a seal begins to tip during installation, strike the _____.   61. _____
    (A) low side
    (B) sealing tip
    (C) high side
    (D) counterbore

62. O-rings are usually round and _____.

62. _____

63. An O-ring must be slightly _____ to properly seal.

63. _____

64. A static part is non-_____.

64. _____

65. Sealers that can be used in place of a precut gasket are called _____ _____ _____ gaskets.

65. _____

66. Why is it a bad idea to use too much sealer? _____

_____

67. Technician A says that sealer must be used sparingly on carburetors and throttle bodies. Technician B says that sealer should never be used on transmission valve bodies. Who is right?
    (A) A only.
    (B) B only.
    (C) Both A & B.
    (D) Neither A nor B.

67. _____

68. Identify the parts of the oil seal shown in the following illustration.

    (A) _____

    (B) _____

    (C) _____

    (D) _____

    (E) _____

69. The following illustration shows various methods of seal removal. Identify the parts indicated.

    (A) _____

    (B) _____

    (C) _____

    (D) _____

    (E) _____

70. Identify the conditions in the following oil seal illustrations.
    (A) Seal has been installed _____ and is leaking.
    (B) Seal is correctly installed with the lip facing _____.

70. _____

_____

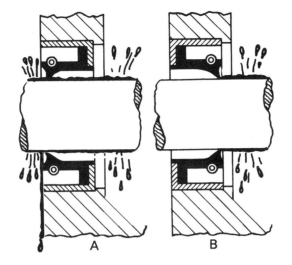

A   B

Name _____

Date _____ Period _____

Instructor _____

Score_____

Text pages 131-149

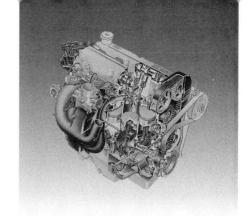

8

Tubing and Hose

Objectives: After studying Chapter 8 in the textbook and completing this section of the workbook, you will be able to:

* Identify different types of tubing, hose, and fittings.
* Select the correct type of tubing, hose, or fitting for the job.
* Properly install new tubing and hose.

Tech Talk: A vehicle's metal and plastic tubing and rubber hoses serve the same purpose as human arteries and veins: they carry critically needed fluid to various parts of the car. A failure of an "artery" (fuel line, brake line, water hose, power steering hose, transmission cooler line) may cause serious mechanical problems. The car could stop "dead" in the road. A complete understanding of hoses and tubing, as well as their related connectors and fittings, is essential if you plan to be a good technician.

Instructions: Study Chapter 8 of the text; then answer the following questions in the spaces provided.

Tubing Material

1. Most automotive tubing is made of _____ or _____.

   1. _____
      _____

2. Copper tubing is _____, easy to _____, and forms good joints.

   2. _____
      _____

3. Technician A says that copper tubing is commonly used for brake lines. Technician B says that copper tubing should never be used for fuel lines. Who is right?
   (A) A only.
   (B) B only.
   (C) Both A & B.
   (D) Neither A nor B.

   3. _____

4. Although a hacksaw can be used to cut tubing, a faster and better method is to use a(n) _____ _____.

   4. _____

5. Label the cut tubing shown in the following illustration.

(A) _____

(B) _____

(C) _____

(D) _____

WRONG   A

WRONG   B

RIGHT   C

D

6. Identify the parts of the tubing cutter shown in the following illustration.

(A) _____

(B) _____

A

B

(Dodge)

Tubing Fittings and Connectors

7. All of the following are basic tubing connections, EXCEPT:
   (A) flare.
   (B) pipe.
   (C) compression.
   (D) interference.

7. _____

8. In a flare connection, the tubing _____ securely grasps both sides of the flare, producing a leakproof seal.

8. _____

9. List the five rules that should be followed when installing tubing. (They are given as the chapter headings.)

   (A) _____

   (B) _____

   (C) _____

   (D) _____

   (E) _____

10. Technician A says that flared fittings should be used on high-pressure automotive applications. Technician B says that compression fittings can be used on high-pressure automotive applications. Who is right?
    (A) A only.
    (B) B only.
    (C) Both A & B.
    (D) Neither A nor B.

10. _____

11. The pipe fitting uses a(n) _____ thread that produces a leakproof seal when fully tightened.

11. _____

12. Technician A says that connectors are used to attach tubing to a unit. Technician B says that connectors are used to join two or more sections of tubing. Who is right?
    (A) A only.
    (B) B only.
    (C) Both A & B.
    (D) Neither A nor B.

12. _____

13. Define *unions*. _____

_____

_____

14. Explain the use of *elbows*._____

_____

_____

15. When several branch lines are served by a single feeder line, a(n) _____ block can be used.

15. _____

16. The _____-_____ ____ is used to stop flow through a line.

16. _____

17. A(n) _____ _____ is used to draw off the liquid contents of a tank.

17. _____

18. Label the parts of the I.S.O. fitting shown in the following illustration.

    (A) _____

    (B) _____

    (C) _____

    (D) _____

(Chevrolet)

19. The following illustration shows a flare being formed. Label the parts indicated.

    (A) _____

    (B) _____

    (C) _____

(Dodge)

20. The following illustration shows a(n) _____ fitting. Label the parts indicated.

    (A) _____

    (B) _____

    (C) _____

    (D) _____

20. _____

21. The following figure shows a type of _____-_____ fitting.

21. _____

22. The fitting shown below is usually called a(n) _____ _____ fitting.

(Kia Motors)

22. _____

23. Label and draw the tube cross sections on the following drawing.

    (A) _____

    (B) _____

    (C) _____

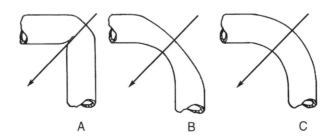

       A   B   C

Hose

24. Flexible hose is used in the following systems of a car: _____

_____.

25. The _____ radiator hose is particularly susceptible to collapse due to the vacuum created by the water pump.

25. _____

26. Power steering and brake hose must withstand pressures exceeding _____.
    (A) 500 psi
    (B) 750 psi
    (C) 1000 psi
    (D) None of the above.

26. _____

27. In determining how sharp a hose bend may be, figure that the radius of the bend should be _____ times the diameter of the hose.

27. _____

28. Any hose that shows signs of _____, _____, or _____ should be replaced.

28. _____

_____

29. Hoses often deteriorate _____, causing portions to break loose and producing partial or even complete blockage.

29. _____

30. The following figure shows the fuel system being _____.
    (A) bled
    (B) drained
    (C) depressurized
    (D) repressurized

30. _____

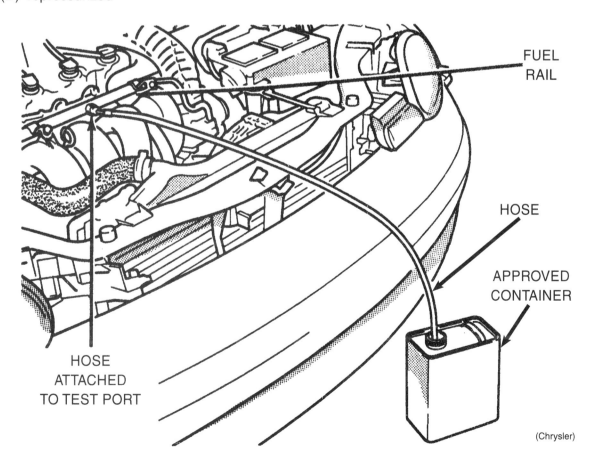

FUEL RAIL

HOSE

APPROVED CONTAINER

HOSE ATTACHED TO TEST PORT

(Chrysler)

Name _____

Date _____ Period _____

Instructor _____

Score_____

Text pages 151-166

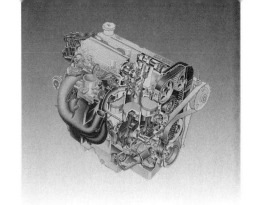

9

Wire and Wiring

Objectives: After studying Chapter 9 in the textbook and completing this section of the workbook, you will be able to:

- Identify different types of automotive wiring.
- Select the correct type of wiring for the job.
- Make basic wiring repairs.
- Read wiring diagrams.
- Perform basic circuit tests.

Tech Talk: Early automobiles had only a few feet of wire connecting the headlights, taillights, starter and generator, and the ignition system. Modern automobiles and trucks have hundreds of feet of wire connecting hundreds of different electrical and electronic components. It is almost impossible to work on any part of a vehicle without handling an electrical component or connection. For this reason, the automotive technician must learn the basics of automotive wire and wiring.

Instructions: Study Chapter 9 of the text; then answer the following questions in the spaces provided.

Primary Wire

1. Each conductor size is assigned a number. The larger the number, the _____ the wire.

1. _____

2. As wire size increases, electrical resistance _____.

2. _____

3. All the following are factors in determining correct wire size, EXCEPT:
   (A) conductor location.
   (B) line voltage.
   (C) electrical load.
   (D) wire length.

3. _____

4. A wiring harness has several wires either pulled through a(n) _____or_____ together.

4. _____

   _____

5. Explain why wire color coding is used. _____

   _____

   _____

6. Define *wiring diagram.* _____

_____

_____

_____

_____

7. Primary terminals include _____ -type terminals.   7. _____
   (A) blade
   (B) lug
   (C) bullet
   (D) All of the above.

8. Plug-in connectors are designed with _____ lugs to ensure   8. _____
   that they are not improperly connected.

9. Plug-in connectors used on many computer-controlled vehi-   9. _____
   cles have rubber _____ with as many as three sealing rings
   to protect the connection from moisture.

10. Technician A says that a terminal block serves as a common   10. _____
    connection point for a number of wires. Technician B says
    that the junction block supplies current to several circuits
    from one feeder source. Who is right?
    (A) A only.
    (B) B only.
    (C) Both A & B.
    (D) Neither A nor B.

11. Define *soldering.* _____

_____

_____

_____

12. Technician A says that acid core solder is excellent for sol-   12. _____
    dering wires. Technician B says that rosin core solder must
    be used for all electrical work. Who is right?
    (A) A only.
    (B) B only.
    (C) Both A & B.
    (D) Neither A nor B.

13. It is the job of flux to remove _____ and prevent it from   13. _____
    reforming.

14. Before soldering, all traces of _____, _____, _____, and   14. _____
    _____ must be removed from the pieces to be joined.   _____

15. To allow for good heat transfer from the iron tip to the work,   15. _____
    the soldering iron tip should be _____ and _____.   _____

16. Pieces to be joined by soldering should be _____ so the sol-   16. _____
    der is melted by the _____ in the metals to be soldered   _____
    together.

17. The illustration below shows the two types of wire used in an automobile. Complete the following statements and identify the parts indicated.

(A) This is _____ wire.

(B) This is _____ wire.

(C) _____

(D) _____

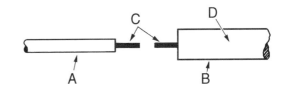

18. Identify the electrical symbols in the following illustration.

(A) _____

(B) _____

(C) _____

(D) _____

(E) _____

(F) _____

(G) _____

(H) _____

(I) _____

(J) _____

(K) _____

(L) _____

(M) _____

(N) _____

(O) _____

(P) _____

(Q) _____

(R) _____

(S) _____

(T) _____

(U) _____

(V) _____

(W)_____

(X) _____

(Chrysler)

19. Identify the primary wire terminals shown in the following illustration.

(A) ______________________________
(B) ______________________________
(C) ______________________________
(D) ______________________________
(E) ______________________________
(F) ______________________________
(G) ______________________________
(H) ______________________________
(I) ______________________________
(J) ______________________________
(K) ______________________________
(L) ______________________________
(M) ______________________________
(N) ______________________________
(O) ______________________________

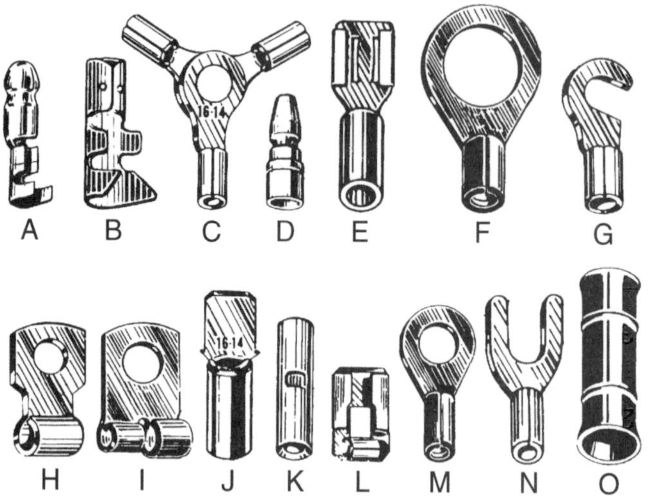
A
B
C
D
E
F
G
16-14
H
I
J
K
L
M
N
O
(Belden Mfg. Co.)

20. Draw the missing soldering iron tips on the following illustrations.

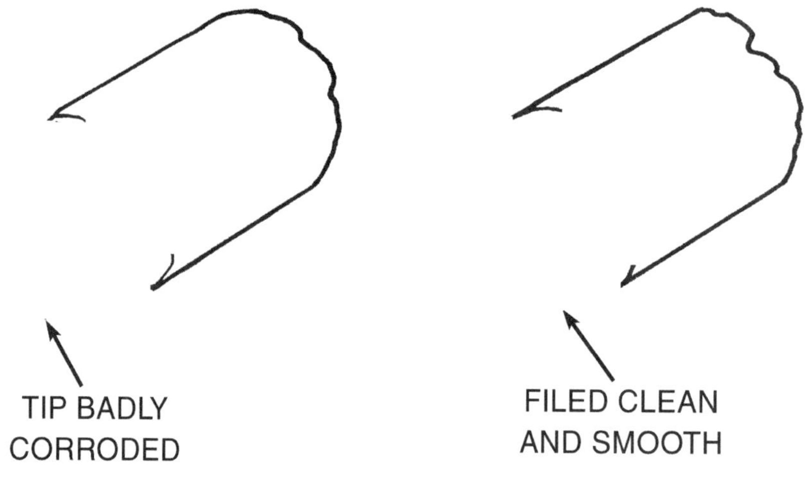
TIP BADLY CORRODED
FILED CLEAN AND SMOOTH

21. Identify the soldering tip conditions indicated in the following drawings.

(A) ______________________________
(B) ______________________________

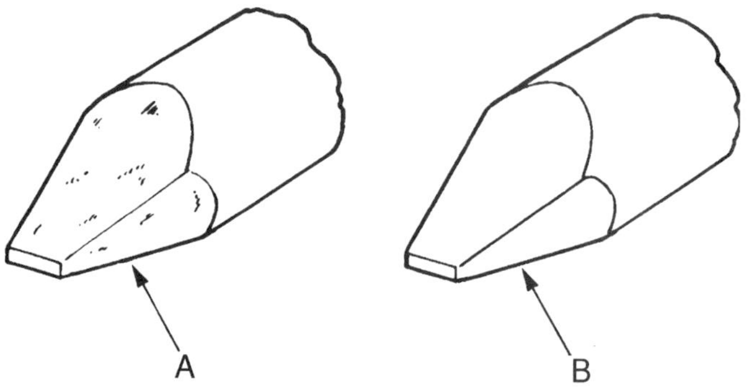
A
B

22. Complete the following statements based on the illustration below.

    (A) This soldering tip position is wrong because _____.

    (B) This position is right because the tip is in _____.

23. Label the parts indicated in the following illustration.

    (A) _____

    (B) _____

Secondary Wire

24. Technician A says that primary wire handles battery voltage.   24. _____
    Technician B says that secondary wire is used in the high-
    tension circuit. Who is right?
    (A) A only.
    (B) B only.
    (C) Both A & B.
    (D) Neither A nor B.

25. What causes crossfiring in secondary wires? _____

    _____

    _____

26. Resistance is built into modern secondary wires to reduce   26. _____

    _____ _____.

Printed Circuits

27. Define *printed circuit.* _____

    _____

    _____

28. The printed circuit eliminates the use of individual _____.   28. _____

Troubleshooting Wiring

29. List three wiring problems that commonly occur in automobiles.

(A) _____

(B) _____

(C) _____

30. A small test light can be used to check wires for _____.   30. _____
    (A) impedance
    (B) resistance
    (C) continuity
    (D) None of the above.

Name _____

Date _____ Period _____

Instructor _____

Score _____

Text pages 167-189

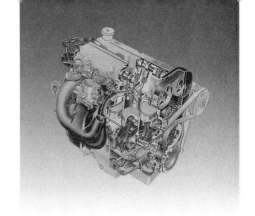

10

Friction and Antifriction Bearings

Objectives: After studying Chapter 10 in the textbook and completing this section of the workbook, you will be able to:

- Compare the differences between friction and antifriction bearings.
- Explain the application of different bearing designs.
- Properly install friction bearings.
- Diagnose common reasons for bearing failures.
- List the different kinds of antifriction bearings.
- Explain the advantages of each type of antifriction bearing.
- Describe service procedures for antifriction bearings.

Tech Talk: Friction and antifriction bearings are used throughout the vehicle. Friction bearings are used as engine connecting rod and main bearings, camshaft bearings, starter bushings, transmission bushings, etc. Worn friction bearings can cause a wide range of problems, such as oil leakage and part knocking.

Antifriction bearings are also used throughout the modern vehicle. These bearings are used in transmissions, differentials, wheel bearings, alternators, and other assemblies. If serviced improperly, antifriction bearings can become noisy. If the noisy bearings are ignored, they can lock up, causing serious mechanical damage.

It is important to understand the design, operating principles, and service of both friction and antifriction bearings.

Instructions: Study Chapter 10 of the text; then answer the following questions in the spaces provided.

Major Classes of Bearings

1. Technician A says that friction bearings slide against a portion of a shaft. Technician B says that antifriction bearings eliminate friction. Who is right?
   (A) A only.
   (B) B only.
   (C) Both A & B.
   (D) Neither A nor B.

1. _____

2. Define *journal*. _____

_____

_____

_____

3. Friction type bearings are used on the _____.
   (A) crankshaft
   (B) camshaft
   (C) connecting rods
   (D) All of the above.

3. '_____

4. Define *bushings*. _____

_____

_____

_____

5. Technician A says that radial loads are parallel to the axis of
   the bearing. Technician B says the thrust loads occur at right
   angles to the axis of the bearing. Who is right?
   (A) A only.
   (B) B only.
   (C) Both A & B.
   (D) Neither A nor B.

5. _____

6. Identify the bearing types shown in the following illustration.

   (A)_____type bearing.

   (B)_____type bearing.

7. Identify the types of forces applied to the bearings illustrated below.

   (A) _____

   (B) _____

   (C) _____

Friction Bearings

8. Technician A says that excessive clearance in a bearing   8. _____
   insert will cause increased oil pressure. Technician B says
   that excessive bearing clearance can cause increased oil
   consumption. Who is right?
   (A) A only.
   (B) B only.
   (C) Both A & B.
   (D) Neither A nor B.

9. All of the following can cause bearing failure, EXCEPT: 9. _____
   (A) insufficient clearance.
   (B) dirt.
   (C) a bowed crankcase.
   (D) high oil pressure.

10. Define *thrust flange.* _____

    _____

    _____

11. Bearing spread causes the insert diameter across the part-   11. _____
    ing edges to be slightly larger than the _____.

12. Define *bearing crush.* _____

    _____

    _____

13. Insert halves come in _____. It is important that they not be   13. _____
    _____.   _____

14. One of the most widely used methods of measuring bearing   14. _____
    clearances involves the use of a(n) _____.
    (A) outside micrometer
    (B) steel rule
    (C) Plastigage
    (D) None of the above.

15. The bearing shown in the following illustration is a(n) _____-   15. _____
    type bearing. Label the parts indicated.

    (A) _____

    (B) _____

    (C) _____

    (D) _____

    (E) _____

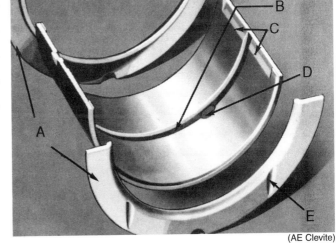

(AE Clevite)

Antifriction Bearings

16. The antifriction bearing uses _____ elements to reduce friction.

16. _____

17. All of the following are common antifriction bearings, EXCEPT:
    (A) needle bearings.
    (B) self-aligning bearings.
    (C) precision insert bearings.
    (D) roller bearings.

17. _____

18. By using two or more bearings facing in opposite directions, _____ in either direction can be handled.

18. _____

19. Technician A says that the deep groove ball bearing will handle heavy thrust loads and moderate radial loads. Technician B says that straight roller bearings are designed to handle heavy radial loads and heavy thrust loads. Who is right?
    (A) A only.
    (B) B only.
    (C) Both A & B.
    (D) Neither A nor B.

19. _____

20. The spherical roller will handle _____ loads.

20. _____

21. The tapered roller is the most common of the roller bearings. It will carry _____ loads.
    (A) thrust
    (B) radial
    (C) Both A & B.
    (D) Neither A nor B.

21. _____

22. Torrington bearings are a type of _____ bearing.
    (A) needle
    (B) ball
    (C) roller
    (D) None of the above.

22. _____

23. Define bearing identification. _____
_____
_____

24. Define nonseparable bearing inspection. _____
_____
_____

25. For separable bearings, carefully inspect the _____ and each _____ element.

25. _____
_____

26. Fine dirt wear will cause _____
_____
_____.

27. Technician A says that spalling can be caused by foreign particles, overloading, or normal wear. Technician B says that once spalling starts, iron oxide powder is formed. Who is right?
(A) A only.
(B) B only.
(C) Both A & B.
(D) Neither A nor B.

27. _____

28. Define *brinelling*. _____

_____

_____.

29. Overheating will break down the _____ _____ of bearings and cause rapid failure.

29. _____

30. If any oil or grease seals are related to the job at hand, _____ and, if necessary, _____ them at this time.

30. _____

_____

31. To facilitate installation, the outer race of large bearings can be placed in _____ _____

31. _____

32. Identify the parts of the ball bearing assembly pictured below.

(A) _____

(B) _____

(C) _____

(D) _____

(E) _____

(F) _____

(G) _____

(H) _____

(I) _____

(J) _____

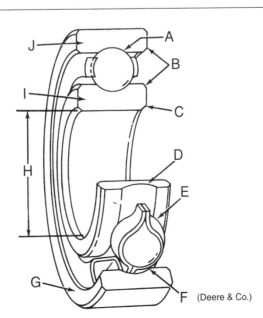

(Deere & Co.)

33. Identify the parts of the straight roller bearing pictured below.

(A) _____

(B) _____

(C) _____

(D) _____

(E) _____

(F) _____

(G) _____

(H) _____

(I) _____

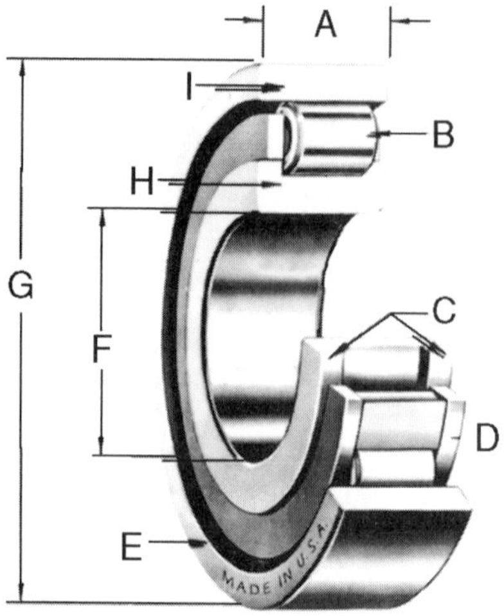

(AFBMA)

34. Identify the right and wrong way of pressing the bearing.

(A) _____

(B) _____

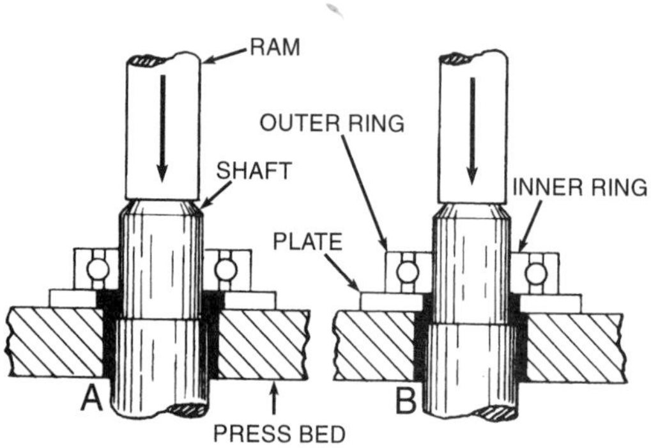

RAM

OUTER RING

SHAFT

INNER RING

PLATE

A

B

PRESS BED

35. The following illustration shows the procedure for removing a bearing retaining race. Label the parts indicated.

(A) _____

(B) _____

(C) _____

(D) _____

(E) _____

(F) _____

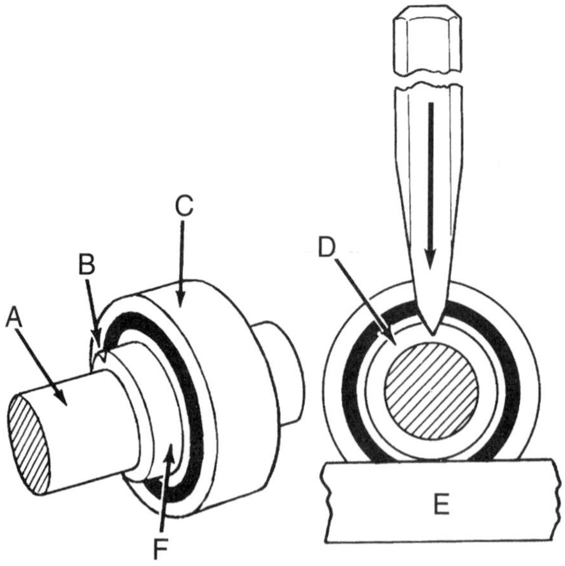

C

B

A

D

E

F

Name _____

Date _____ Period _____

Instructor _____

Score_____

Text pages 191-203

11

Engine Mechanical Troubleshooting

Objectives: After studying Chapter 11 in the textbook and completing this section of the workbook, you will be able to:

- Summarize preliminary test steps.
- Perform a compression test.
- Use a cylinder leakage detector.
- Perform a vacuum test.
- Check engine oil pressure.
- Diagnose engine mechanical problems.

Tech Talk: The importance of working logically when diagnosing an engine problem cannot be overemphasized. Jumping to conclusions will only prolong the job, wasting both time and money. The best way to diagnose an engine problem is to consider all possible sources of the problem and to check the basic engine components and systems before testing the more complex systems.

Instructions: Study Chapter 11 of the text; then answer the following questions in the spaces provided.

Steps to Diagnosing Engine Problems

1. The technician should begin engine diagnosis by asking the _____ to describe the problem.

   1. _____

2. All of the following should be checked before checking engine mechanical condition, EXCEPT:
   (A) oil and coolant levels.
   (B) compression.
   (C) air and fuel filters.
   (D) computer trouble codes.

   2. _____

3. Explain how to make a compression test. _____

_____

_____

_____

_____

_____

4. Technician A says that on most engines, the compression of the lowest cylinder should not be more than 25% less than the compression of the highest cylinder. Technician B says that checking compression in one or two cylinders is generally sufficient. Who is right?
   (A) A only.
   (B) B only.
   (C) Both A & B.
   (D) Neither A nor B.

   4. _____

5. Low compression has _____ (more or less) effect on engine performance than uneven compression.

   5. _____

6. If compression on a cylinder goes up after oil is added to the cylinder, the _____ are probably worn.

   6. _____

7. Cleaners should never be poured into the carburetor or throttle body if the vehicle has a(n) _____ _____.

   7. _____

8. A cylinder leakage detector can be used to pinpoint the cause of low _____.

   8. _____

9. At idle speed, a vacuum gauge should read about _____ to _____ inches of mercury.

   9. _____
      _____

10. Technician A says that oil level should be checked before testing oil pressure. Technician B says that idle speed should be checked before testing oil pressure. Who is right?
    (A) A only.
    (B) B only.
    (C) Both A & B.
    (D) Neither A nor B.

    10. _____

11. To test oil pressure, the oil pressure gauge can be installed in place of the oil pressure _____.

    11. _____

- Identify the engine problems associated with the vacuum gauge readings shown in the following illustrations.

   12. _____

   13. _____

   14. _____

   (Nissan)

Engine and Engine System Problem Diagnosis Charts

15. All of the following are possible causes of low oil pressure, EXCEPT:
    (A) internal leaks in the lubrication system.
    (B) clogged oil pickup.
    (C) high idle speed.
    (D) pressure regulator stuck open.

15. _____

16. Technician A says that excessively high oil pressure can be caused by an oil that is too heavy. Technician B says that excessively high oil pressure can be caused by a stuck pressure regulator. Who is right?
    (A) A only.
    (B) B only.
    (C) Both A & B.
    (D) Neither A nor B.

16. _____

17. Oil that is too light or diluted could cause excessive _____.

17. _____

18. Engine mechanical problems that can cause _____ in the intake manifold include improper intake valve seating and incorrect valve timing.

18. _____

19. If an engine has hydrostatic lock, there is _____ in the combustion chamber.

19. _____

20. Noise in a power steering pump or alternator can be isolated by disconnecting the related _____ _____.

20. _____

21. Exhaust leaks are often mistaken for _____ _____ noise.

21. _____

22. A technician's _____ is helpful in pinpointing the source of an engine noise.

22. _____

23. For diagnosis, bearing knocks can be quieted and therefore isolated by _____ spark plugs.

23. _____

24. Technician A says that loose piston pins will cause a sharp double knock. Technician B says that the noise created by loose piston pins is most noticeable during periods of heavy acceleration. Who is right?
    (A) A only.
    (B) B only.
    (C) Both A & B.
    (D) Neither A nor B.

24. _____

25. The two classes of combustion knocks are _____ and _____.

25. _____
    _____

Name _____

Date _____ Period _____

Instructor _____

Score_____

Text pages 205-215

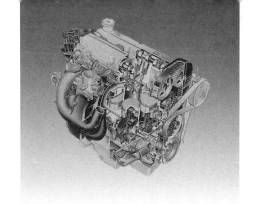

12

Engine Removal, Disassembly, and Inspection

Objectives: After studying Chapter 12 in the textbook and completing this section of the workbook, you will be able to:

- Describe general procedures for removing an engine from a car.
- Explain the use of engine removal equipment.
- List safety rules that apply to engine removal.
- Describe general procedures for disassembling an engine.
- Explain how to make visual checks of major engine parts.

Tech Talk: Removing an engine from a late-model vehicle requires skill and patience. Engine removal on modern vehicles involves many variables, including engine size, front or transverse (sideways) engine mounting, engine mount locations, transmission and transaxle variations, emission control placement, and accessory equipment location. Engine disassembly is further complicated by the vast range of engine designs available.

Any of the above variables can complicate engine removal and disassembly. If you are unprepared, a considerable amount of time and effort can be wasted. However, you can make engine removal and disassembly a quick and easy job by studying the material in this chapter.

Instructions: Study Chapter 12 of the text; then answer the following questions in the spaces provided.

General Removal Procedures

1. If just the engine is to be removed, be certain to support the _____.

   1. _____

2. Once a wire, control rod, or other part has been removed, it is good practice to put the _____ back into place.

   2. _____

3. When lifting any heavy assembly, make certain that the fastener is threaded into the hole for a distance of at least _____ its diameter.
   (A) 1/2
   (B) 1
   (C) 1 1/2
   (D) None of the above.

   3. _____

4. Attach the puller so that the weight of the engine, or engine and transmission, will be _____ at the desired angle.

   4. _____

5. After removing the engine from the car, immediately _____ it until it is _____ the floor.

5. _____

_____

6. The wire in the following illustration has been _____ to facilitate reinstallation.

6. _____

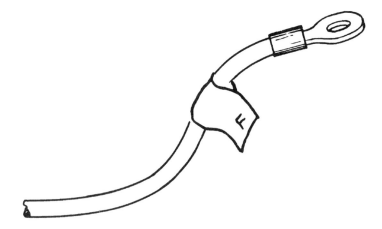

7. Identify the parts of the lifting device shown in the following illustration.

(A) _____

(B) _____

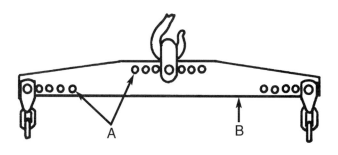

Engine Disassembly and Inspection

8. Technician A says that waiting for an engine to cool before removing a cylinder head is a waste of time. Technician B says that waiting for an engine to cool before removing the head will prevent warpage. Who is right?
(A) A only.
(B) B only.
(C) Both A & B.
(D) Neither A nor B.

8. _____

9. Describe how to remove a shaft-type rocker arm assembly. _____

_____

_____

10. To remove the rocker arms on engines using ball stud type rockers, loosen each ball nut until the rocker arm can be _____ _____ to clear the pushrod.

10. _____

11. To remove a cylinder head, _____ the order of the recommended tightening sequence and crack each cylinder head cap screw.

11. _____

12. If the cylinder head is stuck, carefully use _____ to free it   12. _____
    from the engine.
    (A) pry bars
    (B) screwdrivers
    (C) Either A or B.
    (D) Neither A nor B.

13. Avoid jamming any tapered object between the _____ and   13. _____
    _____, as the slightest nick or dent can cause serious   _____
    damage.

14. After removal, the cylinder head should be placed in a(n)   14. _____
    _____ _____.

15. Technician A says that before removing the main bearing   15. _____
    caps, each cap and the corresponding crankshaft web
    should be marked with a punch or a number stamp.
    Technician B says that marking main bearing caps is not
    necessary because the caps are interchangeable. Who is
    right?
    (A) A only.
    (B) B only.
    (C) Both A & B.
    (D) Neither A nor B.

16. When removing a crankshaft, lift it straight up, being careful   16. _____
    to avoid any damage to the _____ surfaces.

17. After removal, study the crankshaft _____ to detect any   17. _____
    damage.

18. Technician A says that some camshaft timing mechanisms   18. _____
    contain only gears. Technician B says that all timing mecha-
    nisms use a chain or a belt. Who is right?
    (A) A only.
    (B) B only.
    (C) Both A & B.
    (D) Neither A nor B.

19. To remove the camshaft timing mechanism from the engine,   19. _____
    the _____ must usually be removed first, followed by the
    timing cover.

20. When any timing gear part shows wear or damage, it must   20. _____
    be _____.

21. When it is necessary to replace any timing mechanism part, what else should be replaced? _____

    _____

    _____

22. After removing the timing mechanism but before removing   22. _____
    the camshaft, you may have to remove the following addi-
    tional engine parts, EXCEPT:
    (A) oil pump.
    (B) fuel pump.
    (C) cylinder head(s).
    (D) distributor.

23. A cylinder that is worn or scored past the maximum boring   23. _____
   dimension can be saved by _____.
   (A) careful welding
   (B) installing a sleeve
   (C) Either A or B.
   (D) Neither A nor B.

24. A block that is _____ must usually be discarded.   24. _____

25. Removing the oil pump may affect ignition _____.   25. _____

26. If the oil pump gear drives the distributor, pulling the pump   26. _____
   will allow the distributor to _____ _____.

27. Identify the parts of the engine shown in the following illustration.

   (A) _____

   (B) _____

   (C) _____

   (D) _____

   (E) _____

(Chevrolet)

28. When is the process shown in the following illustration not performed? _____

_____

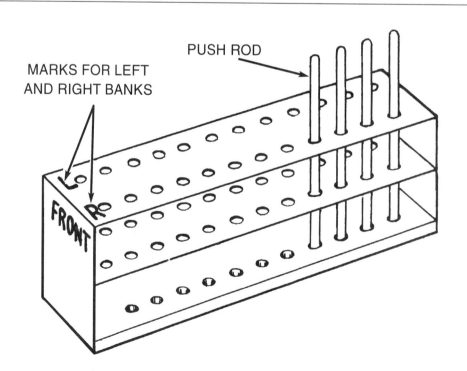

MARKS FOR LEFT
AND RIGHT BANKS

PUSH ROD

FRONT

29. The tool shown below is a(n) _____ _____.

29. _____

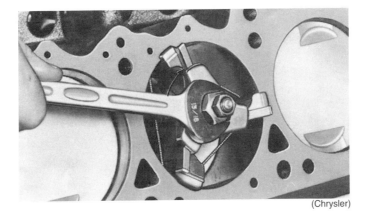

(Chrysler)

30. Circle the illustration below that shows a properly removed ring ridge.

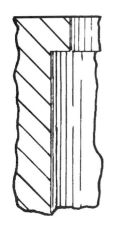 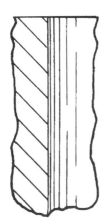 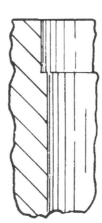 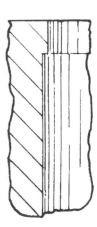

Name _____

Date _____ Period _____

Instructor _____

Score_____

Text pages 217-239

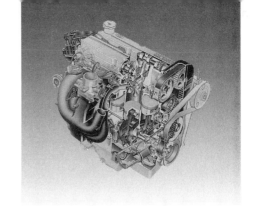

13

Cylinder Head and Valve Service

Objectives: After studying Chapter 13 in the textbook and completing this section of the workbook, you will be able to:

- Properly disassemble a cylinder head.
- Inspect the cylinder head and valve train for signs of trouble.
- Properly grind valve seats and valves.
- Test valve springs.
- Service valve guides.
- Reassemble and install a cylinder head.

Tech Talk: The valves are among the hardest working parts in the engine. They must be able to open and close in a fraction of a second while sealing tremendously hot, high-pressure combustion gases. Therefore, the valves must be very carefully cleaned, inspected, refaced, and reinstalled. Carelessness can cause a quick comeback.

Instructions: Study Chapter 13 of the text; then answer the following questions in the spaces provided.

Cylinder Head and Valve Service

1. As the valves are removed from the head, place the valves in a(n) _____ so they may be replaced in their original guides.

1. _____

2. If the cylinder head coolant passages are badly clogged, give the head an initial cleaning in a(n) _____ _____.

2. _____

3. The following illustration shows a technician removing carbon from a cylinder head. Identify the parts indicated.

(A) _____

(B) _____

(C) _____

(D) _____

(E) _____

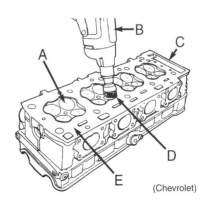

(Chevrolet)

Valve Reconditioning

4. Technician A says that heavy carbon deposits under the head of an intake valve may indicate worn valve guides. Technician B says that heavy carbon deposits under the head of an intake valve may be a sign of clogged oil drain holes in the cylinder head. Who is right?
   (A) A only.
   (B) B only.
   (C) Both A & B.
   (D) Neither A nor B.

4. _____

5. All _____ valves should be discarded.
   (A) burned
   (B) warped
   (C) cracked
   (D) All of the above.

5. _____

6. The stones on a valve grinder must be _____ to the correct angle.

6. _____

7. A(n) _____ angle provides a narrow contact area between the valve and the seat.

7. _____

8. The margin on a valve should be approximately _____.
   (A) 1/32″
   (B) 1/16″
   (C) 3/32″
   (D) None of the above.

8. _____

9. The valve stem should always be trued by _____.

9. _____

10. Never remove more than _____ from the end of a valve stem.

10. _____

11. Label the following illustration showing a valve face angle.

    (A) _____
    (B) _____
    (C) _____
    (D) _____
    (E) _____
    (F) _____
    (G) _____

12. Identify the parts of the grinding machine shown in the following illustration.

(A) _____

(B) _____

(C) _____

(D) _____

(E) _____

(F) _____

(G) _____

(H) _____

(Kwik-Way)

13. Label the following valve grinding illustrations.

(A) _____

(B) _____

(C) _____

(D) _____

(E) _____

CORRECT   INCORRECT

Cylinder Head Reconditioning

14. Technician A says that excessive valve guide clearance will often promote excess oil consumption. Technician B says that valve guide clearance is greatest in the center of the guide. Who is right?
    (A) A only.
    (B) B only.
    (C) Both A & B.
    (D) Neither A nor B.

14. _____

15. Valve stem clearance is generally considered excessive when it exceeds _____.

15. _____

16. There are two common types of valve seals. Name them.

(A) _____

(B) _____

17. The valve seat must be the correct _____ and engage the _____ of the valve near its central portion.

17. _____

_____

18. Seat width varies but will average around _____ for both the intake and exhaust valves.

18. _____

19. To narrow a valve seat, you must remove metal from the _____ portion of the seat.
    (A) lower
    (B) middle
    (C) upper
    (D) All of the above.

19. _____

20. When grinding seats, remember that the finished seat will be only as accurate as the _____.

20. _____

21. Valve lapping involves using lapping _____ between the valve face and the seat.

21. _____

22. To check the concentricity of the seat and valve face, _____ rubbed on the valve face or _____ marks about 1/4″ (6.35 mm) apart can be used.

22. _____
    _____

23. After extended service, valve springs tend to lose _____.

23. _____

24. Valve stem height must be checked on engines with no provision for valve _____ .

24. _____

25. Technician A says that if valve spring squareness does not meet specifications, the spring can be bent back into shape. Technician B says that if valve spring compressed pressure is not within specifications, the spring must be replaced. Who is right?
    (A) A only.
    (B) B only.
    (C) Both A & B.
    (D) Neither A nor B.

25. _____

26. A weak valve spring may cause valve _____.

26. _____

27. Identify the parts of the valve seat recess cutter in the following illustration.

    (A) _____

    (B) _____

    (C) _____

    (D) _____

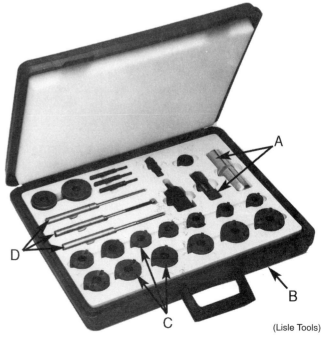

(Lisle Tools)

28. The following illustration shows correct and incorrect valve seating. Label the parts indicated.

(A) _____

(B) _____

(C) _____

(D) _____

(E) _____

(F) _____

(G) _____

(H) _____

(I) _____

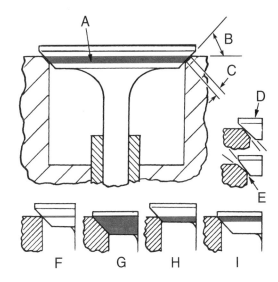

29. The following figure shows pencil marks being used to check valve seat _____.

29. _____

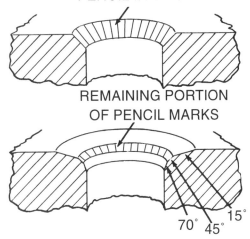

PENCIL MARKS

REMAINING PORTION OF PENCIL MARKS

70° 45° 15°

30. The device in the following illustration is called a valve seat _____. It is used in place of valve seat _____.

30. _____
_____

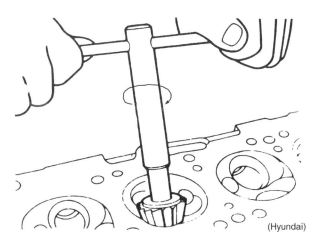

(Hyundai)

31. The following illustration shows valve spring tension being tested. Identify the parts indicated.

(A) _____

(B) _____

(C) _____

B—

A

—C

(Chrysler)

Cylinder Head Assembly

32. Excessive valve spring installed height can be corrected by the use of _____ installed between the spring and head.

32. _____

33. When installing heads that do not have guide pins, make them by _____

_____.

34. Torque-plus-angle tightening is used on engines with _____ blocks and _____ heads.

34. _____

_____

35. Label the parts of the valve spring assembly shown in the following illustration.

(A) _____

(B) _____

(C) _____

(D) _____

(E) _____

A—

B—

C—

D—

E—

(Buick)

Name _____

Date _____ Period _____

Instructor _____

Score_____

Text pages 241-272

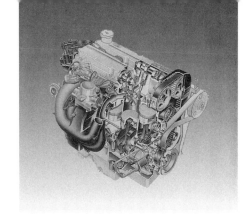

14

Engine Block and Lubrication System Service

Objectives: After studying Chapter 14 in the textbook and completing this section of the workbook, you will be able to:

- Check the condition of a cylinder block.
- Check for a cracked cylinder block.
- Measure cylinder wear.
- Hone a cylinder wall.
- Describe cylinder reboring.
- Service connecting rods.
- Service automotive pistons.
- Properly install piston rings.
- Correctly install a piston and rod assembly in its cylinder.
- Measure bearing clearance with Plastigage.
- Service engine oil pumps.

Tech Talk: It is amazing that the average engine is as durable as it is. Each piston accelerates from zero to 60 mph and then decelerates back to zero on every stroke. This process occurs in less than four inches of piston travel and is repeated thousands of times every minute at highway speeds. It occurs millions of times during the life of the engine. For this reason, the block, pistons, rods, and bearings must be serviced properly and reassembled carefully. If the technician is careless, an overhauled engine can literally "blow up" (parts break and fly apart) in a matter of minutes.

Instructions: Study Chapter 14 of the text; then answer the following questions in the spaces provided.

Engine Block Service

1. The engine block is the _____ on which other engine components are assembled.

1. _____

2. Technician A says that a cylinder block can be checked for warpage with a steel straight edge and a feeler gauge. Technician B says the block surfaces should be flat and true within .050″ in a 6″ span. Who is right?
   (A) A only.
   (B) B only.
   (C) Both A & B.
   (D) Neither A nor B.

2. _____

3. When resurfacing a block, a minimum amount of metal
should be removed to avoid changing the _____.
(A) compression ratio
(B) piston-to-valve clearance
(C) lifter-to-rocker-arm clearance
(D) All of the above.

3. _____

4. List the three main types of engine block cracks.

(A) _____

(B) _____

(C) _____

5. Crack detection using dye penetrants will work on _____
and _____ metals.

5. _____

_____

6. The three ways that a crack can be repaired are _____

_____

_____.

7. After extended use, engine cylinders may become _____
and _____ to the extent that machining is required.

7. _____

_____

8. Heavy scoring of a cylinder (scoring beyond maximum
reboring) will require the installation of a(n) _____.

8. _____

9. To order the correct new rings, it is essential that the cylinder _____ be determined.

9. _____

10. All of the following cause heavy wear to occur at the top of
the cylinder, EXCEPT:
(A) poor lubrication at the top of the cylinder.
(B) pressure of the rings.
(C) the cooling effect of the fuel.
(D) combustion pressure.

10. _____

11. Define *ring float.* _____

_____

_____

12. Define *piston slap.* _____

_____

_____

13. A(n) _____ _____ can be used to quickly and accurately
check a cylinder for taper and out-of-roundness.

13. _____

14. If the cylinder is not scored, cracked, or scuffed, taper up to
a maximum of _____ is permissible.

14. _____

15. Cylinder out-of-roundness should not exceed _____.
(A) .005″
(B) .025″
(C) .05″
(D) None of the above.

15. _____

16. Cylinders with minor taper and out-of-roundness can be deglazed by using a(n) _____.

16. _____

17. List three reasons that deglazing is commonly accepted as good practice.

    (A) _____

    (B) _____

    (C) _____

18. When cylinder wear has almost reached maximum acceptable taper and out-of-roundness, the adjustable _____ hone should be used.

18. _____

19. Never pull a spinning hone out of a cylinder. Parts can _____.

19. _____

20. Technician A says that after honing, the cylinder should be cleaned with hot, soapy water. Technician B says that after cleaning, cylinders should be wiped down with engine oil. Who is right?
    (A) A only.
    (B) B only.
    (C) Both A & B.
    (D) Neither A nor B.

20. _____

21. The following illustration shows one method used to check a cylinder head for cracks. Identify the parts indicated.

    (A) _____

    (B) _____

    (C) _____

    (D) _____

(Storm-Vulcan)

22. Label the cylinder wear patterns shown in the following illustrations.

    (A) _____

    (B) _____

    (C) _____

    (D) _____

    (E) _____

23. What is being performed in the following illustration? _____

_____

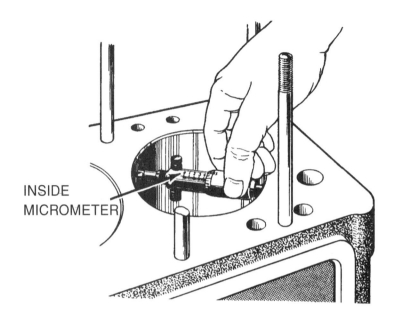

INSIDE
MICROMETER

24. Identify the parts and describe what is happening to the piston rings in the illustrations below.

(A) _____

(B) _____

(C) _____

(D) Before rings can _____ .

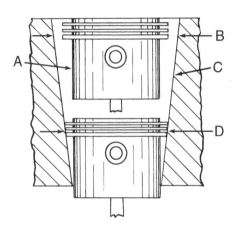

25. The following illustration shows a piston that is so loose in the cylinder that tipping occurs. Identify the parts indicated.

(A) _____

(B) _____

(C) _____

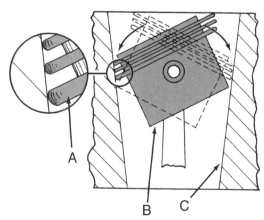

Connecting Rod Service

26. Before removing any rods, check to see that all rods are _____ and that both upper and lower bearing halves are marked with the _____.

26. _____
_____

27. When cleaning a piston, remove the _____ and soak the piston and rod assembly in a carbon-removing solvent.

27. _____

28. Connecting rods should always be checked for _____ and _____.

28. _____
_____

29. Connecting rod bore out-of-roundness should not exceed _____.
(A) .0005″
(B) .001″
(C) .015″
(D) None of the above.

29. _____

Piston Service

30. Pistons must be of the correct _____, _____, and _____.

30. _____

31. When pistons show signs of corrosion, look carefully for possible _____ leaks.

31. _____

32. Technician A says that all ring grooves should be examined for burrs, dented edges, and side wear. Technician B says that particular attention should be given to the oil control ring grooves. Who is right?
(A) A only.
(B) B only.
(C) Both A & B.
(D) Neither A nor B.

32. _____

33. Explain how ring groove width should be checked. _____
_____
_____

34. The ring groove may be reconditioned by cutting a wider groove and inserting a ring groove _____ on the _____ edge.

34. _____
_____

35. One way to resize pistons is to have the thrust areas of the pistons _____.

35. _____

36. Technician A says that an oiled feeler gauge strip and a spring scale can be used to fit pistons in their cylinders. Technician B says that piston-to-cylinder clearance can be determined by carefully measuring both the piston and the cylinder. Who is right?
(A) A only.
(B) B only.
(C) Both A & B.
(D) Neither A nor B.

36. _____

37. A piston pin must have ample _____ for oil; yet it must not have looseness that will result in pin knock and ultimate failure.

37. _____

38. Since pin-to-piston clearances are extremely small, proper _____ is an exacting job.

38. _____

39. Proper pin clearances depend on all of the following, EXCEPT:
   (A) pin diameter.
   (B) piston material.
   (C) pin length.
   (D) piston operating temperature.

39. _____

40. Expanding the connecting rod bushing tightly into the connecting rod bore is called _____.

40. _____

41. On full-floating pin installation, make certain the _____ are not _____ and check that they are _____ in their grooves.

41. _____

_____

42. Name the two basic piston ring types.

   (A) _____

   (B) _____

43. It is advisable to allow at least _____ of ring gap for each inch (25.4 mm) of cylinder diameter.

43. _____

44. Explain the procedure for checking ring side clearance. _____

_____

_____

45. Be careful to install the rings with the correct side _____.

45. _____

46. If rubber hoses are not slipped over the connecting rod bolts before piston installation, the _____ _____ can be damaged.

46. _____

47. To check connecting rod bearing clearance, a(n) _____ should be placed across the insert.

47. _____

48. In the following illustration, piston-to-cylinder _____ is being checked. Label the parts indicated.

48. _____

   (A) _____

   (B) _____

   (C) _____

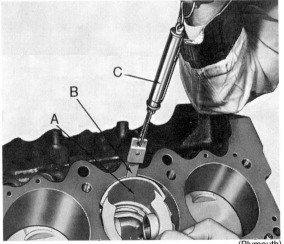

(Plymouth)

49. Identify the parts in the following illustration.

(A) _____

(B) _____

(C) _____

(D) _____

(E) _____

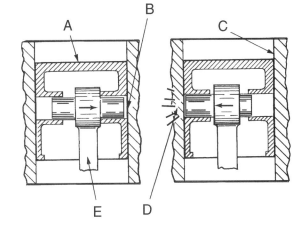

50. Label parts of the piston assembly shown in the following illustration.

(A) _____

(B) _____

(C) _____

(D) _____

(E) _____

(F) _____

(G) _____

(H) _____

(I) _____

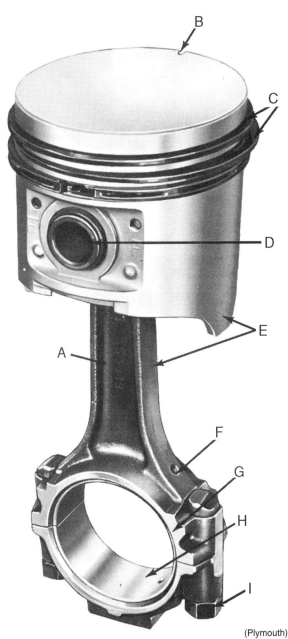

(Plymouth)

51. The following illustration shows a piston being installed in a cylinder. Identify the items indicated.

   (A) _____

   (B) _____

   (C) _____

   (D) _____

   (E) _____

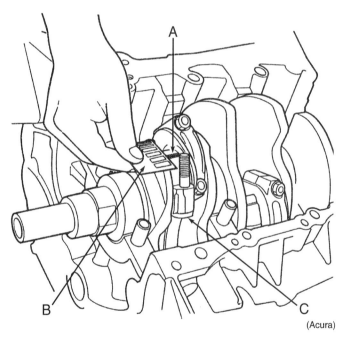

(Acura)

52. The following illustration shows bearing clearance being checked. Identify the items indicated.

   (A) _____

   (B) _____

   (C) _____

(Acura)

Oil Pumps

53. Technician A says that gear-type pumps are commonly used as engine oil pumps. Technician B says that rotor-type pumps are commonly used as engine oil pumps. Who is right?

   (A) A only.
   (B) B only.
   (C) Both A & B.
   (D) Neither A nor B.

53. _____

54. When servicing rotor-type oil pumps, replace rotors in _____.

54. _____

55. Removing and replacing some oil pumps may alter the ignition _____.

55. _____

56. A pressure relief valve may be located in the _____ or the _____.

56. _____
_____

57. A pressure regulator can be cleaned with _____ cloth.

57. _____

58. The following illustration shows rotor end clearance being checked. Identify the parts indicated.

    (A) _____

    (B) _____

    (C) _____

    (D) _____

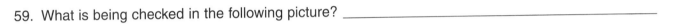

(Chrysler)

59. What is being checked in the following picture? _____
_____

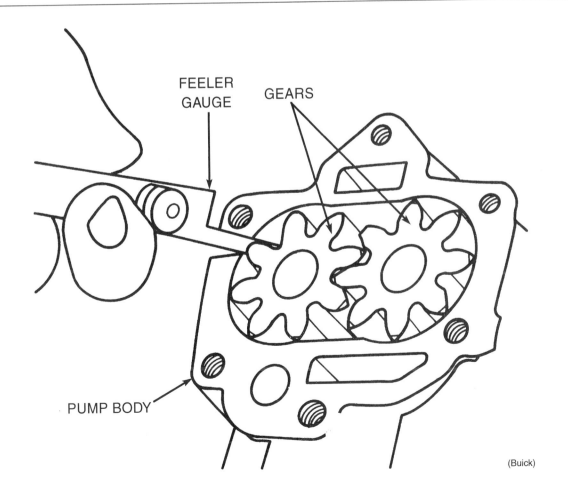

FEELER GAUGE

GEARS

PUMP BODY

(Buick)

60. Identify the parts of the pickup assembly shown in the following illustration.

    (A) _____

    (B) _____

    (C) _____

    (D) _____

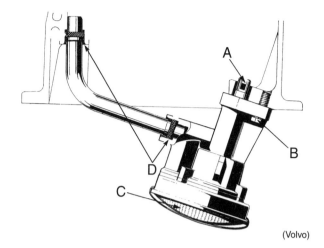

(Volvo)

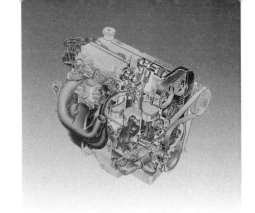

Name _____

Date _____ Period _____

Instructor _____

Score_____

Text pages 273-288

15

Crankshaft Service

Objectives: After studying Chapter 15 in the textbook and completing this section of the workbook, you will be able to:

- Remove and install a crankshaft.
- Check crankshaft and main bearing bores for problems.
- Install new main bearing inserts and rear seal.
- Measure main bearing clearance and crankshaft end play.

Tech Talk: The crankshaft changes the up-and-down motion of the pistons into the rotary motion that is sent to the transmission. At high engine speeds, each piston and rod assembly can exert over a ton of force on the crankshaft. Therefore, all crankshaft-related parts must be within specifications. If the crankshaft and bearings are not correctly installed, or if the bearing caps are not properly torqued, serious engine damage will occur almost immediately.

Instructions: Study Chapter 15 of the text; then answer the following questions in the spaces provided.

Removing the Crankshaft

1. The crankshaft main bearing caps should be removed only after they are _____.

1. _____

2. Technician A says that main bearing cap cross bolts should be removed before the standard cap bolts are removed. Technician B says that a special puller is needed to remove some bearing caps. Who is right?
   (A) A only.
   (B) B only.
   (C) Both A & B.
   (D) Neither A nor B.

2. _____

3. A study of the _____ will help indicate bore alignment problems.

3. _____

4. If a .0015″ feeler gauge can be slid between the _____ and bore, bore alignment must be corrected.

4. _____

5. When checking the main and rod journals, turn the shaft slowly and visually check each journal for signs of _____.

5. _____

6. If the journal surface finish is good, each journal must be checked for:

(A) _____.

(B) _____.

(C) _____.

7. Journal out-of-roundness must not exceed _____.

7. _____

8. Technician A says that journal taper is calculated by computing the difference between diameter readings for both ends of the journal. Technician B says that connecting rod journals are more prone to taper than the main bearing journals. Who is right?
(A) A only.
(B) B only.
(C) Both A & B.
(D) Neither A nor B.

8. _____

9. If the crankshaft is only slightly out of alignment, it may be _____.

9. _____

10. When crankshaft journal damage is present, material can be removed in multiples of _____.

10. _____

11. When installing bearing inserts, the bearing _____ and the insert backs must be clean and dry.

11. _____

12. Check each insert to be sure that the oil holes _____ with the oil passageways.

12. _____

13. To check bearing clearance, place a length of Plastigage on the _____, about 1/4″ (6.35 mm) from top center.

13. _____

14. This illustration shows a crankshaft being checked for _____.

14. _____

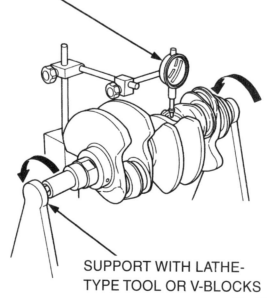

DIAL INDICATOR

SUPPORT WITH LATHE-
TYPE TOOL OR V-BLOCKS

(Honda)

15. Label the parts of the engine shown in the following illustration.

(A) _____

(B) _____

(C) _____

(D) _____

(E) _____

(F) _____

(G) _____

(H) _____

(I) _____

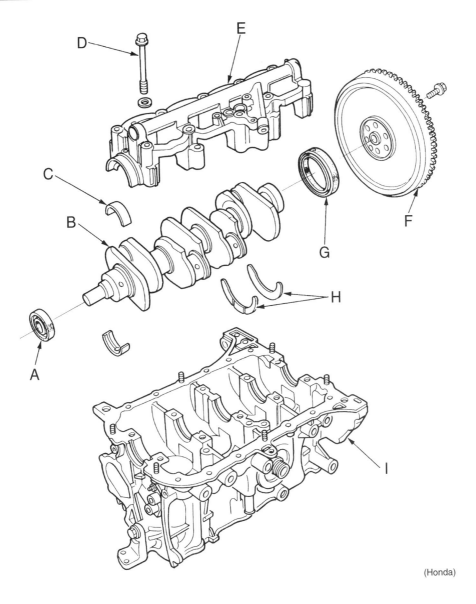

(Honda)

16. The illustration below shows a technician checking bearing clearance. Identify the parts indicated.

(A) _____

(B) _____

(Honda)

Rear Main Bearing Oil Seals

17. It is good practice to soak a wick seal in _____ prior to installation.

17. _____

18. When installing a synthetic crankshaft rear main seal, make sure that the seal lip faces _____.

18. _____

19. In the following illustration, the technician is installing a(n) _____. Label the parts indicated.

19. _____

(A) _____

(B) _____

(C) _____

(Dodge)

Installing the Crankshaft

20. When installing a crankshaft, wipe a heavy _____ on all bearing surfaces.

20. _____

21. Technician A says that a dial indicator can be used to check crankshaft end play. Technician B says that a feeler gauge can be used to check crankshaft end play. Who is right?
(A) A only.
(B) B only.
(C) Both A & B.
(D) Neither A nor B.

21. _____

22. Average crankshaft end play ranges from _____ to _____.

22. _____

_____

23. To remove bearing inserts in an emergency, a plug can be made from a(n) _____ _____ to push the bearing from the engine.

23. _____

24. Make certain the insert _____ _____ engages the recess in the bore.

24. _____

25. It is possible to install a new rear main oil seal without removing the _____.
    (A) rear main cap
    (B) oil pan
    (C) old seal
    (D) crankshaft

25. _____

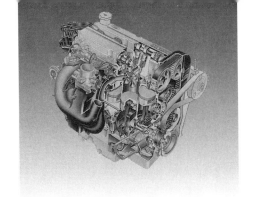

16

Camshaft and Valve Train Service

Objectives: After studying Chapter 16 in the textbook and completing this section of the workbook, you will be able to:

- Remove, check, and install a block-mounted camshaft.
- Remove, check, and install a cylinder-head-mounted camshaft.
- Remove and install camshaft bearings.
- Properly remove and install a vibration damper.
- Measure timing gear and chain wear.
- Remove and install camshaft gears and sprockets.
- Inspect a camshaft and its drive mechanism for problems.
- Service a front cover oil seal.
- Remove and install a timing belt.
- Service camshaft bearings.
- Test and service mechanical lifters.
- Test and service hydraulic lifters.

Tech Talk: The importance of an engine's camshaft and valve train is often overlooked. Since the valves are directly involved in the entry of the air-fuel mixture into the cylinder, the development of compression, and the exhaust of burned gases, minor valve system defects can have a great effect on engine performance. Worn camshaft drive components can alter the valve timing (when valves open and close) and reduce engine performance. A jumped timing belt or chain (slips on drive sprockets) will cause the valves to hit the pistons, damaging both the pistons and the valves. A worn camshaft will reduce the amount and duration of valve opening, lowering engine power. Worn cam bearings will leak and reduce engine oil pressure. Wear or careless repair of almost any part of the valve train will cause valve noise.

Instructions: Study Chapter 16 of the text; then answer the following questions in the spaces provided.

Servicing the Camshaft Drive Components

1. Technician A says that a worn timing chain can alter valve timing. Technician B says that worn timing gears or sprockets can cause camshaft torsional vibration. Who is right?
   - (A) A only.
   - (B) B only.
   - (C) Both A & B.
   - (D) Neither A nor B.

   1. _____

2. Define *gear backlash*. _____

_____

_____

3. Timing gear backlash can be checked with all of the follow-   3. _____
   ing, EXCEPT:
   (A) feel gauge.
   (B) micrometer.
   (C) dial indicator.
   (D) None of the above.

4. Some camshaft gears are _____ in place, while others are   4. _____
   force fit on the shaft and must be pressed off.

5. When installing a camshaft, turn the crankshaft so the tim-   5. _____
   ing mark faces the _____ of the front cam bearing.

6. The camshaft gear timing mark should be aligned with the   6. _____
   _____ _____ timing mark.

Servicing the Timing Chain and Sprockets

7. Technician A says that when removing the timing chain   7. _____
   setup, the engine should be cranked until the timing marks
   on both sprockets face each other. Technician B says that
   when removing the timing chain setup, the engine should be
   cranked until the timing marks on both sprockets are aligned
   with a line between the center of the crankshaft and the center of the camshaft. Who is right?
   (A) A only.
   (B) B only.
   (C) Both A & B.
   (D) Neither A nor B.

8. When installing a new timing chain, the best practice is to   8. _____
   use new _____.

9. After installing the timing chain and oil slinger, check   9. _____
   sprocket _____, chain slack, and camshaft end play.

10. The following illustration shows three methods of _____.   10. _____

These three methods are:

    (A)_____.

    (B)_____.

    (C) _____.

(Jeep)

Removing and Replacing Front Cover Oil Seal

11. When the chain or gear front cover is removed, the front seal and the cover-to-block _____ should be replaced to prevent possible oil leakage.

11. _____

12. Always install the timing cover seals so the seal lip faces _____.

12. _____

13. If the front cover is not positioned by dowel pins, a suitable _____ _____ should be used to prevent oil seal leakage.

13. _____

Servicing the Timing Belt and Sprocket

14. Before removing the timing belt, the technician will usually have to loosen the belt _____.

14. _____

15. Many camshaft belt drive assemblies have more than one _____ _____.

15. _____

16. Identify the timing belt problems shown in the following illustration.

(A) _____

(B) _____

(C) _____

(D) _____

(E) _____

(F) _____

(G) _____

(H) _____

(I) _____

(J) _____

(Chrysler)

Checking the Camshaft

17. Worn camshaft bearings can seriously lower _____ pressure and produce excessive throw off.

17. _____

18. Maximum camshaft-journal-to-bearing clearance will be around _____ (_____).

18. _____

19. To check a camshaft for wear, _____ each journal in several spots to determine the amount of wear.

19. _____

20. Technician A says that camshaft lobes are usually tapered to assist with lifter rotation. Technician B says that the bottom of each lifter is ground to a taper to promote lifter rotation. Who is right?
(A) A only.
(B) B only.
(C) Both A & B.
(D) Neither A nor B.

20. _____

21. A chipped and badly worn camshaft can be built up by _____, and then reground to original specifications.

21. _____

22. One-piece cam bearings are removed by _____ or _____.

22. _____
_____

23. When installing cam bearings, make sure they are _____ properly.

23. _____

24. Cam bearing and block _____ holes must be aligned.

24. _____

25. When cam lobes wear, they may not raise the _____ to the specified height.

25. _____

26. Cam lobe lift is checked using a(n) _____ _____.

26. _____

Lifter Service

27. The lower portion of a used lifter body is often coated with gum or varnish, which makes _____ difficult.

27. _____

28. The lifter-to-camshaft surface should be _____ and free of cam wear, grooving, chipping, and galling.

28. _____

29. Due to the close _____, hydraulic lifters must be thoroughly cleaned and assembled in a spotless condition.

29. _____

30. Each lifter must have the correct _____ rate characteristic.

30. _____

31. When lifters have been installed without filling them with oil, do not exceed a(n) _____ _____ after starting the engine.

31. _____

32. The advantage of a roller lifter is that it reduces _____ to reduce wear of the lifter and camshaft lobes.

32. _____

33. Technician A says that excessive rocker arm-to-shaft clearance will restrict the flow of oil to the valve stems. Technician B says that excessive rocker-arm-to-shaft clearance will cause increased oil consumption. Who is right?
(A) A only.
(B) B only.
(C) Both A & B.
(D) Neither A nor B.

33. _____

34. Push rods should be _____ and both ends must be smooth.

34. _____

35. If a push rod carries oil, the _____ should be thoroughly cleaned.

35. _____

36. Push rod straightness can be checked with V-blocks and a(n) _____ _____.

36. _____

37. The individual rocker shaft oil passages are generally posi-
tioned so they face the _____.
(A) rocker arms
(B) head
(C) valve cover
(D) None of the above.

38. Hydraulic lifters are used primarily to eliminate the need for
_____ between the end of the valve stem and the rocker
arm.

39. The object in adjusting hydraulic lifters is placing the lifter
plunger somewhere near the _____.

40. With mechanical lifters, a certain amount of _____ is
needed.

41. Excessive mechanical tappet clearance will cause all of the
following, EXCEPT:
(A) early valve closing.
(B) increased lift.
(C) noisy operation.
(D) late valve opening.

42. List three problems caused by insufficient mechanical lifter clearance.

(A) _____

(B) _____

(C) _____

43. The rocker arm is adjusted so that the correct clearance
exists between the _____ _____ and the _____ _____.

44. Label the valve train parts shown in the following illustration.

(A) _____

(B) _____

(C) _____

(D) _____

(E) _____

(F) _____

(G) _____

(H) _____

(I) _____

(J) _____

(K) _____

(L) _____

(M) _____

(N) _____

45. Identify the parts of the camshaft setup shown in the following illustration.

(A) _____

(B) _____

(C) _____

(D) _____

(E) _____

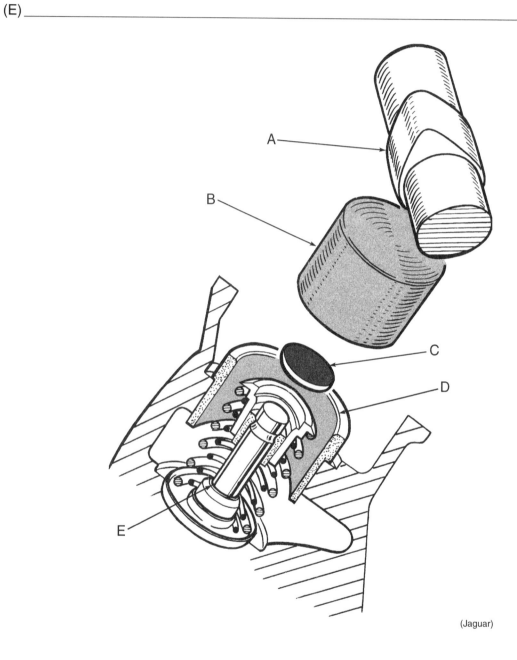

(Jaguar)

Name _____

Date _____ Period _____

Instructor _____

Score_____

Text pages 321-329

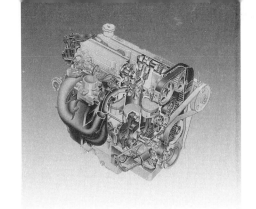

17

Engine Assembly, Installation, and Break-In

Objectives: After studying Chapter 17 in the textbook and completing this section of the workbook, you will be able to:

- Summarize a typical sequence for assembling an engine.
- Describe how to install an engine in a car.
- Pressurize the engine lubrication system with oil.
- Make final checks before starting the engine.
- Operate an engine properly for safe break-in.

Tech Talk: Rebuilding an engine is a time-consuming and unforgiving job. A complete engine overhaul will take several hours and will require hundreds of different assembly operations. Only one small mistake, however, will cause all of that time to be wasted. You may have to rebuild the engine over again. For this reason, you must use extreme care when assembling and installing an engine.

Instructions: Study Chapter 17 of the text; then answer the following questions in the spaces provided.

Typical Engine Assembly Sequence

1. As a general rule, engine parts should be installed in a specific order. Place the following engine parts in the order that they should be installed. **Note:** Not all parts are listed.

<table>
<tr><td>(A) Camshaft</td><td>1. _____</td></tr>
<tr><td>(B) Crankshaft</td><td>2. _____</td></tr>
<tr><td>(C) Cylinder heads</td><td>3. _____</td></tr>
<tr><td>(D) Distributor</td><td>4. _____</td></tr>
<tr><td>(E) Exhaust manifold</td><td>5. _____</td></tr>
<tr><td>(F) Flywheel</td><td>6. _____</td></tr>
<tr><td>(G) Front cover</td><td>7. _____</td></tr>
<tr><td>(H) Oil pan</td><td>8. _____</td></tr>
<tr><td>(I) Piston/rod assemblies</td><td>9. _____</td></tr>
<tr><td>(J) Timing gears</td><td>10. _____</td></tr>
<tr><td>(K) Valve lifters</td><td>11. _____</td></tr>
<tr><td>(L) Wiring connectors</td><td>12. _____</td></tr>
</table>

2. Many overhaul jobs are ruined at the last minute by _____.

2. _____

3. When not actively working on an engine, the technician should keep it _____.

3. _____

Engine Installation

4. When installing an engine with the transmission in the car, the engine crankshaft and transmission input shaft center-lines must be _____.

4. _____

5. All wires, lines, and hoses should have been _____ so they can be reinstalled correctly.

5. _____

6. Remember that during the initial starting after a rebuild, the engine is operating without _____.

6. _____

7. Technician A says that an oil pressurizer can be used to prime the oil pump and fill the filter, galleries, lifters, and bearings. Technician B says that an oil pressurizer can be used to check bearing clearance. Who is right?
   (A) A only.
   (B) B only.
   (C) Both A & B.
   (D) Neither A nor B.

7. _____

8. An overhauled engine that has been in _____ should be repressurized before starting.

8. _____

9. List the checks you should make before starting an overhauled engine for the first time.

   (A) _____

   (B) _____

   (C) _____

   (D) _____

   (E) _____

   (F) _____

   (G) _____

Starting the Engine

10. Technician A says that an engine that has been properly overhauled will start readily when cranked by the starter. Technician B says that vehicles with electric fuel pumps may have to be cranked for about 60 seconds to allow the pump to fill the system. Who is right?
    (A) A only.
    (B) B only.
    (C) Both A & B.
    (D) Neither A nor B.

10. _____

11. A booster battery should always be connected in _____ with the vehicle battery.

11. _____

12. The first _____ of operation of an overhauled engine is critical.

12. _____

13. As soon as the engine is started, set the idle to produce an engine speed of around _____ rpm.
    (A) 600
    (B) 800
    (C) 1200
    (D) 2500

13. _____

14. Check for signs of fuel, oil, or coolant _____ as the engine warms up.

14. _____

15. When normal engine operation has been reached for the first time, turn off the engine and _____ the head and manifold bolts.

15. _____

16. Alternating accelerating and coasting during the first few miles of operation will help to seat the _____.

16. _____

17. The technician can break in the engine and make a road test in the shop using a(n) _____.

17. _____

18. All of the statements about the procedure shown in the following illustration are true, EXCEPT:
    (A) the procedure should be performed before the engine is started after an overhaul.
    (B) the procedure should be performed after the engine has warmed up as part of break-in.
    (C) the procedure is not necessary on engines with mechanical lifters.
    (D) the procedure is not necessary on vehicles with self-adjusting valve trains.

18. _____

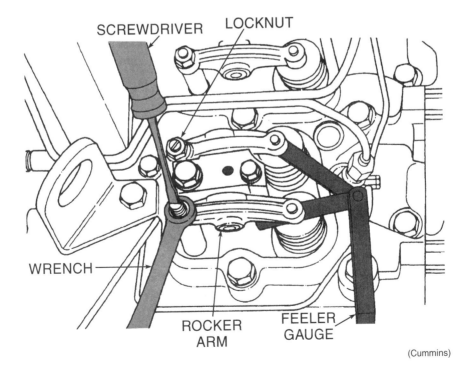

SCREWDRIVER   LOCKNUT

WRENCH

ROCKER
ARM

FEELER
GAUGE

(Cummins)

Deliver the Vehicle to the Owner

19. Be sure to caution the owner to avoid sustained high _____ and heavy _____ during the first critical _____ of driving to provide proper break-in.

19. _____

_____

20. Engine oil consumption should drop to one quart every _____ miles or less after _____ miles of break-in.

20. _____

_____

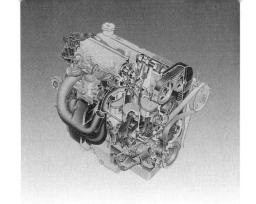

18

Ignition System Service

Objectives: After studying Chapter 18 in the textbook and completing this section of the workbook, you will be able to:

- Inspect, test, and repair electronic ignition systems.
- Explain the difference between electronic ignition systems and computerized ignition systems.
- Inspect, test, and repair contact point ignition systems.
- Describe the purpose of firing order information.
- Remove, test, and replace a distributor assembly.
- Adjust ignition timing.
- Clean, inspect, test, and replace spark plugs.
- Explain the use of an ignition oscilloscope.

Tech Talk: Servicing modern electronic and computer-controlled ignition systems is in some ways simpler than servicing older systems. For example, modern systems do not contain contact points, which tend to require frequent adjustment or replacement. However, troubleshooting electronic and computer-controlled systems can be difficult since there is no way to detect problems in the electronic components by looking at them. Also, because electronic systems produce higher voltages at the spark plugs, worn or defective plugs may be overlooked until they fail completely. Studying this chapter will enable you to take a logical approach to diagnosing and repairing ignition problems.

Instructions: Study Chapter 18 of the text; then answer the following questions in the spaces provided.

Ignition System Problem Diagnosis

1. Technician A says that the first step in ignition system problem diagnosis is to perform a spark test. Technician B says that the first step in ignition system diagnosis is to visually inspect the ignition components. Who is right?
   (A) A only.
   (B) B only.
   (C) Both A & B.
   (D) Neither A nor B.

1. _____

2. Primary wiring should be checked for:

(A) _Signs of cracking Burning and corrosion_.

(B) _____.

(C) _____.

3. Problems in the _____ circuit can affect the voltage output of the _____ circuit.

3. _Primary_
Secondary

4. Check the coil and distributor cap for:

(A) _Flashover_.

(B) _Burning and_.

(C) _Corrosion_.

5. Electronic and computerized ignition systems produce between _____ volts.
(A) 3000 and 5000
(B) 5000 and 15,000
(C) 15,000 and 20,000
(D) 30,000 and 100,000

5. _D_

6. If an engine cranks but will not start, what should be done *first*? _Better conect_ _spark test - wire from distrib_ _coil ignswtch eletsonice_ _contiole units point \ condasor_

7. The following illustration shows a spark test being performed. Label the items indicated.

(A) _Spark_

(B) _Grce_

(C) _Coil_

(Chrysler)

Testing, Replacing, and Adjusting Ignition System Components

8. If the engine starts but immediately dies when the ignition switch is released, the ignition switch _____ terminal is defective.

8. _____

9. An ignition resistor can be a calibrated resistance _____ or a separate ballast resistor.

9. _____

10. Technician A says that if a vehicle has an electrical system in which the battery negative is grounded, the coil positive is grounded through the ignition module. Technician B says that if the coil is not connected to obtain the correct polarity, up to 40% more voltage will be needed to fire the plugs. Who is right?
(A) A only.
(B) B only.
(C) Both A & B.
(D) Neither A nor B.

10. _____A_____

11. Secondary plug wires can be checked with a(n) _____ to determine their condition.

11. ___Oscillosc___

12. Remember that resistance wire is easily damaged. Grasp the _____, not the wire.

12. ___Boot___

13. All of the following should be observed when arranging spark plug wires in their holders, EXCEPT:
(A) avoid running wires perpendicular to each other.
(B) separate wires going to adjacent cylinders that fire in succession.
(C) route wires to prevent pinching and fraying by other engine parts.
(D) keep wires away from heat and oil.

13. ___B___

14. If the engine is positioned to fire the #1 _____, the rotor (chalk mark) will be aligned with the #1_____ in the cap.

14. _____
_____

15. During a distributor cap inspection, check inside the cap for signs of _____.

15. _____

16. The tips of some replacement rotors should be coated with _____ _____ before they are installed.

16. _____

17. In the figure below, illustration A shows the coil being checked for _____ resistance. Illustration B shows the coil being checked for _____ resistance.

17. _____
_____

POSITIVE AND NEGATIVE TERMINALS

OHMMETER LEADS

COIL

A

HIGH TENSION TERMINAL (TOWER)

B

(Toyota)

18. Label the defects in the distributor cap shown below.

(A) _____

(B) _____

(C) _____

(D) _____

(Jeep)

19. Label the defects in the distributor rotor shown below.

(A) _____

(B) _____

(C) _____

(D) _____

(Chrysler)

Electronic Ignition Distributor Service

20. Most electronic ignition systems use a distributor-mounted _____ mechanism.

20. _____

21. Technician A says that periodic maintenance on an electronic ignition system consists of checking timing and replacing the plugs and rotor. Technician B says that the secondary components of an electronic ignition system can develop the same types of problems as those on an older point-type system. Who is right?
    (A) A only.
    (B) B only.
    (C) Both A & B.
    (D) Neither A nor B.

21. _____

22. Explain how distributor air gap is adjusted. _____

_____

_____

_____

_____

23. If the engine dies or begins running when the ignition module is _____ or _____, the module is defective.

23. _____
_____

24. A distributorless ignition system contains at least two _____.

24. _____

Contact Point Service

25. On older point-type systems, the breaker points should be _____ when the ignition system is serviced, especially if the points are burned or pitted.

25. _____

26. A defective condenser will cause point arcing or _____ transfer.

26. _____

27. If new contact points cannot be obtained, the old points can be reused after they are _____.

27. _____

28. Technician A says that dwell increases when point gap decreases. Technician B says that excessive point gap will cause missing at low speeds. Who is right?
(A) A only.
(B) B only.
(C) Both A & B.
(D) Neither A nor B.

28. _____

29. When point gap is too small, the points will _____

_____.

30. A(n) _____ or, better yet, a(n) _____ should be used to set worn or used points.

30. _____
_____

31. When new points are installed, the distributor cam should be _____

_____

_____.

Setting Ignition Timing

32. Before setting ignition timing, check for preliminary steps listed on the _____ _____ located under the hood.

32. _____

33. If the distributor has a vacuum advance unit, the _____ to the unit is usually disconnected and plugged before checking initial timing.

33. _____

34. On many vehicles with engine computers, the _____ must be disconnected from the computer before the timing is set.
(A) coil
(B) ignition module
(C) distributor
(D) None of the above.

34. _____

35. The distributor body must be _____ to set timing.

35. _____

36. If a vehicle has provisions for a magnetic probe, a(n) _____ timing light can be used.

36. _____

37. The timing scale and pointer should be _____ before setting timing.

37. _____

38. Technician A says that the engine should be run at idle to set timing because higher speeds would cause the automatic advance mechanisms to operate. Technician B says that the engine should be run at idle to set timing because the timing mark is difficult to see at higher speeds. Who is right?
    (A) A only.
    (B) B only.
    (C) Both A & B.
    (D) Neither A nor B.

38. _____

Spark Advance Mechanisms

39. To quickly test the centrifugal advance in the distributor, run the engine slowly from _____. Using a timing light, watch the timing mark. It should advance _____ of engine rotation.

39. _____
    _____

40. As a quick test of the distributor vacuum advance, run the engine at a steady 1200 rpm. Note the position of the timing mark with a timing light. When the vacuum line is connected to the distributor diaphragm, the timing mark should immediately _____.

40. _____

41. Computer-controlled ignition makes use of which of the following to adjust timing?
    (A) Vacuum advance.
    (B) Centrifugal advance.
    (C) Input sensors.
    (D) Both B and C.

41. _____

42. Many computerized ignition systems have _____ diagnostic capabilities.

42. _____

Overhauling Distributors

43. Technician A says that distributors must be overhauled when bushing, shaft, gear, or cam wear becomes excessive. Technician B says that some new distributors are not repairable and must be replaced when defective. Who is right?
    (A) A only.
    (B) B only.
    (C) Both A & B.
    (D) Neither A nor B.

43. _____

44. Before removing the distributor, mark the relative positions of the _____ and the _____ to simplify reinstallation.

44. _____
    _____

45. If a distributor will not bottom during installation, the distributor shaft is probably not aligned with the _____.

45. _____

46. Identify the parts of the electronic ignition distributor shown in the following illustration.

(A) _____

(B) _____

(C) _____

(D) _____

(E) _____

(F) _____

(G) _____

(H) _____

(I) _____

(J) _____

(K) _____

(Chrysler)

Servicing Spark Plugs

47. Technician A says that a frequently recommended replacement interval for spark plugs is every 15,000 to 30,000 miles. Technician B says that in some late-model engines, the plugs can be used for up to 100,000 miles. Who is right?
(A) A only.
(B) B only.
(C) Both A & B.
(D) Neither A nor B.

47. _____

48. If the cylinder head is made of _____, allow it to cool thoroughly before removing the spark plugs.

48. _____

49. A careful study of used spark plugs is helpful in determining _____

_____

_____

_____.

50. A spark plug operating in a sound engine, at the correct temperature, will have a deposit color ranging from _____ to _____.

50. _____

51. Fuel fouling may be caused by all of the following, EXCEPT:
    (A) clogged air cleaner.
    (B) sticking valves.
    (C) plugs that are too hot for the engine.
    (D) excessive choking.

51. _____

52. Plug oil fouling is caused by an excessive amount of _____.

52. _____

53. When gapping plugs bend only the _____ electrode.

53. _____

54. Plug gap should be checked using a(n) _____.

54. _____

55. If torque specs are not available, tighten a gasket-equipped plug finger tight. Then, give it about _____ turn more.

55. _____

56. Technician A says that a spark plug that is too cold will quickly foul out. Technician B says that a spark plug that is too hot will suffer from burning and preignition. Who is right?
    (A) A only.
    (B) B only.
    (C) Both A & B.
    (D) Neither A nor B.

56. _____

57. The heat range of a plug is controlled by the _____ of the insulator.

57. _____

58. Spark plug size is determined by the _____ of the threaded section.

58. _____

59. Spark plug reach is determined by the _____ of the threaded section.

59. _____

60. List five common spark plug types.

    (A) _____

    (B) _____

    (C) _____

    (D) _____

    (E) _____

61. Identify the spark plug conditions shown in the following illustrations.

    (A) _____

    (B) _____

    (C) _____

    (D) _____

    (E) _____

    (F) _____

    (G) _____

62. The technician in the following illustration is _____

_____.

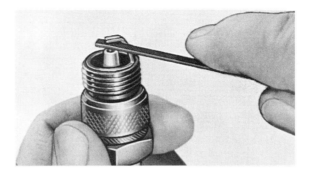

63. Identify the parts of the spark plug in the following illustration.

(A) _____

(B) _____

(C) _____

(D) _____

(E) _____

(F) _____

(G) _____

(H) _____

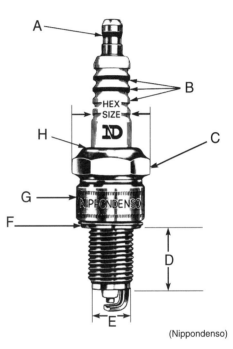

(Nippondenso)

Checking the Ignition System with an Oscilloscope

64. An oscilloscope can be used to obtain accurate information about all parts of the _____ system.

64. _____

65. On a scope, the amount of voltage required to "fire" a spark plug is indicated by the _____ of the firing line.

65. _____

66. When using an oscilloscope, follow the manufacturer's directions and pattern evaluation _____.

66. _____

67. What do oscilloscope pattern irregularities tell you? _____

_____

_____

_____

68. Special adapters are required to allow a(n) _____ ignition system to be checked with an oscilloscope.

68. _____

69. Label the scope pattern sections in the following illustration.

(A) _____

(B) _____

(C) _____

(D) _____

(E) _____

(F) _____

(G) _____

(H) _____

(I) _____

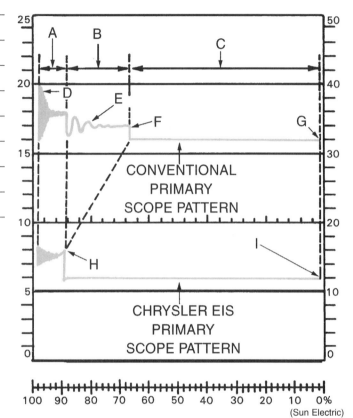

(Sun Electric)

70. Identify the pattern irregularities in the following illustration.

(A) _____

(B) _____

(C) _____

(D) _____

(E) _____

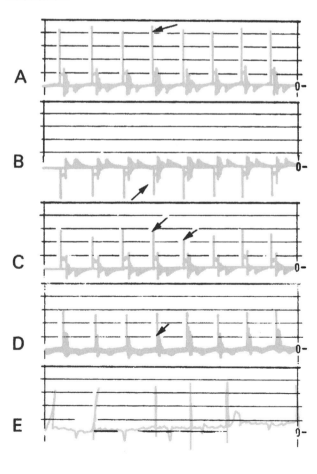

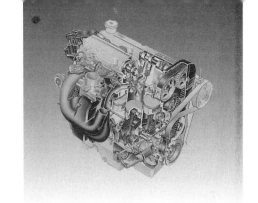

Name _____

Date _____ Period _____

Instructor _____

Score_____

Text pages 359-373

19

Fuel Delivery

Objectives: After studying Chapter 19 in the textbook and completing this section of the workbook, you will be able to:

- Describe the cleaning, removal, repair, and replacement of fuel tanks.
- Clean, repair, and install fuel lines.
- Test, remove, repair, and replace mechanical fuel pumps.
- Test, remove, repair, and replace electric fuel pumps.
- Service fuel filters.
- Explain vapor lock.
- List the safety rules involved in fuel delivery system service.

Tech Talk: A fuel delivery system must provide a sufficient quantity of clean, filtered fuel to the engine to supply the carburetor, fuel injectors, or diesel injection pump. The fuel delivery system consists of the fuel tank, mechanical or electric pump, filter, and lines. The fuel delivery system affects the performance and dependability of the engine. Defects in the fuel supply system can leave the vehicle stranded. Study this system carefully, so that you will be prepared to work on automotive fuel delivery systems.

Instructions: Study Chapter 19 of the text; then answer the following questions in the spaces provided.

Fuel Tanks and Lines

1. Technician A says that the negative battery terminal should be removed before servicing a fuel tank. Technician B says that residual fuel system pressure should be released before servicing a fuel tank. Who is right?
   (A) A only.
   (B) B only.
   (C) Both A & B.
   (D) Neither A nor B.

1. _____

2. Even an empty fuel tank will contain _____ that, if ignited, will produce an explosion.

2. _____

3. A leaking metal fuel tank may be repaired by _____

_____

_____.

4. A dent in a fuel tank can be removed by the use of air pressure with the tank filled with _____.

4. _____

5. To clean a fuel line, direct an air blast from the _____ toward the fuel tank.

5. _____

6. Identify the parts of the fuel delivery system shown in the illustration below.

(A) _____

(B) _____

(C) _____

(D) _____

(E) _____

(F) _____

(G) _____

(H) _____

(I) _____

(J) _____

(K) _____

(L) _____

(M) _____

(N) _____

(O) _____

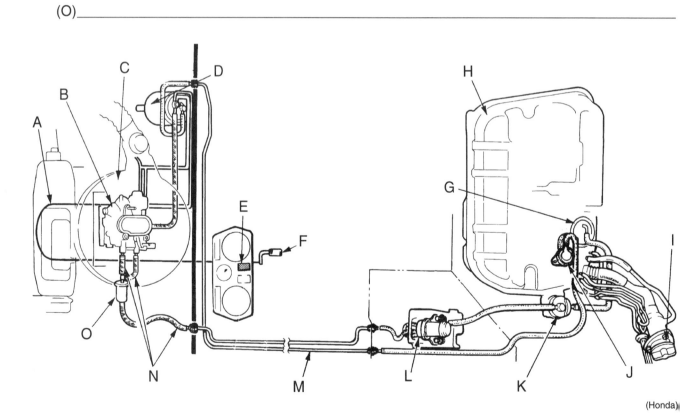

(Honda)

Mechanical Fuel Pump Repair

7. Before testing a mechanical fuel pump, inspect lines for damage and clean or replace all _____.

7. _____

8. When testing a mechanical fuel pump, it should be checked for _____ pressure and _____ pressure.

8. _____
   _____

9. Average mechanical fuel pump pressure will be from _____ (_____) and will be constant.

9. _____

10. During mechanical fuel pump volume testing, manufacturer's specifications will generally call for a flow of around _____ in one minute at 500 rpm.
    (A) one pint
    (B) one quart
    (C) one gallon
    (D) None of the above.

10. _____

11. When volume or pressure does not meet specifications, the pump _____ should be determined before condemning the pump.

11. _____

12. In general, fuel pump vacuum should read _____ (_____) minimum.

12. _____

13. When installing a mechanical fuel pump, make certain the rocker arm bears against the _____.

13. _____

14. Technician A says that most mechanical fuel pumps are rebuilt when problems are encountered. Technician B says that when rebuilding fuel pumps, the metal parts should be soaked in carburetor cleaner for at least 30 minutes. Who is right?
    (A) A only.
    (B) B only.
    (C) Both A & B.
    (D) Neither A nor B.

14. _____

15. The following illustration shows the setup used to check fuel pump pressure and volume. Identify the parts indicated.

(A) _____

(B) _____

(C) _____

(D) _____

(E) _____

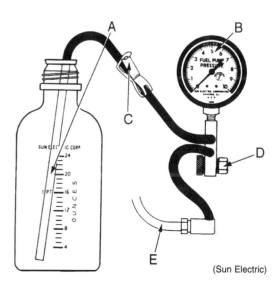

(Sun Electric)

Electric Fuel Pumps

16. All of the following are common electric fuel pump types,
    EXCEPT:
    (A) centrifugal.
    (B) diaphragm.
    (C) roller vane.
    (D) impeller.

16. _____

17. Electric fuel pump pressures are _____ than those of
    mechanical pumps.

17. _____

18. Tapping a fuel pump that is _____ may get it working again.

18. _____

19. Most electric fuel pumps cannot be repaired and are _____
    as a unit.

19. _____

20. Before replacing a(n) _____ fuel pump, bleed off the fuel
    pressure.

20. _____

21. What is the purpose of the inertia switch? _____

_____

22. Identify the parts of the inertia switch shown in the following illustration.

    (A) _____

    (B) _____

    (C) _____

    (D) _____

    (E) _____

(Ford)

Fuel Filter Service

23. Most modern fuel filters are _____ instead of being cleaned
    and reinstalled.

23. _____

24. Some diesel engine filters contain a(n) _____ trap in
    addition to the filtering element.

24. _____

25. Define *vapor lock*. _____

_____

_____

Name _____

Date _____ Period _____

Instructor _____

Score_____

Text pages 375-407

20

Fuel Injection

Objectives: After studying Chapter 20 in the textbook and completing this section of the workbook, you will be able to:

- Explain mechanical fuel injection construction, operation, and service.
- Describe the construction, operation, and service of pulsed and continuous electronic fuel injection.
- Explain diesel injection construction, operation, and service.
- Describe the construction, operation, and service of turbochargers.
- Service different types of air cleaners.
- Perform a fuel mileage test.

Tech Talk: Fuel injection systems have replaced carburetors on all new vehicles. A gasoline fuel injection system can more closely control the amount of fuel entering each engine cylinder. Diesel engines must use high-pressure injection systems to inject fuel directly into the combustion chamber. To be prepared to service today's cars and trucks, you must know how to work on fuel injection systems. Study this chapter carefully!

Instructions: Study Chapter 20 of the text; then answer the following questions in the spaces provided.

Why Fuel Injection Is Needed

1. To burn, fuel must be _____.

2. The proportion of air and fuel in a mixture is known as the air-fuel _____.

3. What are the two reasons that fuel injection has replaced carburetors on all late-model vehicles?

   (A) _____

   (B) _____

4. By administering a closely controlled fuel mixture, fuel injection systems produce two distinct benefits. Name them.

   (A) _____

   _____

   (B) _____

   _____

1. _____

2. _____

5. Fuel injection is a system that supplies a metered amount of fuel into the _____.
   (A) cylinder
   (B) intake manifold
   (C) valve port
   (D) Any of the above, depending on the system.

5. _____

Electronic Fuel Injection

6. The two basic types of electronic fuel injection systems are _____ and _____.

6. _____
   _____

7. Technician A says that the injectors used in the pulsed injection system always contain an internal electrical solenoid. Technician B says that on pulsed injection systems, the amount of time that the injector is open is controlled by varying the strength of the electrical signal from the computer. Who is right?
   (A) A only.
   (B) B only.
   (C) Both A & B.
   (D) Neither A nor B.

7. _____

8. Central fuel injection assemblies are installed in the spot formerly occupied by the _____.

8. _____

9. A multiport injection system uses one injector per _____.

9. _____

10. The typical multiport injection system injects fuel just ahead of the _____.

10. _____

11. The air induction system consists of three major parts. Name them.

   (A) _____

   (B) _____

   (C) _____

12. The fuel pressure regulator controls pressure by bleeding fuel back into the _____ or the _____.

12. _____
    _____

13. Changes in engine load affect intake manifold _____, which assists a spring inside the pressure regulator to control fuel pressure.

13. _____

14. Fuel injectors installed in the intake manifold are usually connected to the fuel supply through a fuel _____.

14. _____

15. A cold start valve adds extra _____ to the mixture when the engine is cold.

15. _____

16. On some vehicles with electronic fuel injection, the pulse _____ is increased when the engine is cold.

16. _____

17. The amount of fuel injected is controlled by the vehicle computer based on the input from various _____.

17. _____

18. Technician A says that the two types of mass airflow (MAF) sensors are the heated wire sensor and the air valve sensor. Technician B says that some manufacturers are replacing the MAF sensor with the speed density system. Who is right?
    (A) A only.
    (B) B only.
    (C) Both A & B.
    (D) Neither A nor B.

18. _____

19. Identify the parts of the injector illustrated below.

    (A) _____

    (B) _____

    (C) _____

    (D) _____

    (E) _____

    (F) _____

(Volvo)

Electronic Fuel Injection System Service

20. All of the following statements about fuel injection system service are true, EXCEPT:
    (A) some manufacturers recommend removing fuel pressure by disconnecting a fuel line and operating the engine until it stops.
    (B) the spray pattern of a central fuel injection system can be made more visible by using a timing light.
    (C) it is sometimes necessary to remove the intake manifold or plenum to gain access to the fuel injectors.
    (D) fuel injectors can be cleaned on the engine.

20. _____

21. Some fuel injection systems have a(n) _____ valve for bleeding fuel pressure.

21. _____

22. Technician A says that if an injector makes a clicking noise as the engine operates, it is defective. Technician B says that most fuel injector tubing has an internal coating. Who is right?
    (A) A only.
    (B) B only.
    (C) Both A & B.
    (D) Neither A nor B.

22. _____

23. Fuel injectors should never be soaked in _____.

23. _____

24. Lubricate the injector _____ before reinstalling them.

24. _____

25. After fuel injectors are serviced, it is important that the engine be started and checked carefully for _____.

25. _____

26. Most fuel pressure regulators cannot be _____ and must be replaced if they will not properly control fuel pressure.

26. _____

Mechanical Fuel Injection

27. The mechanical fuel injection system uses an engine-driven _____.

27. _____

28. The mechanical fuel injector is held closed by spring pressure and opened by _____ pressure.

28. _____

29. Some injection systems have two idle speed adjustments—one on the _____ and another in the _____.

29. _____
_____

Diesel Fuel Injection

30. List the three ways that the diesel injection system differs from the mechanical gasoline injection system.

(A) _____

_____

(B) _____

_____

(C) _____

_____

31. Name four problems caused by dirty, damaged, or sticking injectors.

(A) _____

_____

(B) _____

_____

(C) _____

_____

(D) _____

_____

32. The diesel injector can be tested for _____.
    (A) chatter
    (B) opening pressure
    (C) spray pressure
    (D) All of the above.

32. _____

33. When a diesel engine is cold, there is not enough _____ heat to start the engine.

33. _____

34. A glow plug is a low-voltage _____ element.

34. _____

35. Technician A says that the glow plug wires can become very hot. Technician B says that current can flow to the glow plugs for up to 10 minutes after the control light goes out. Who is right?
(A) A only.
(B) B only.
(C) Both A & B.
(D) Neither A nor B.

35. _____

36. A defective glow plug or glow plug control system can cause hard starting when the diesel engine is _____.

36. _____

37. Label the parts of the diesel injection system illustrated below.

(A) _____

(B) _____

(C) _____

(D) _____

(E) _____

(F) _____

(G) _____

(H) _____

(I) _____

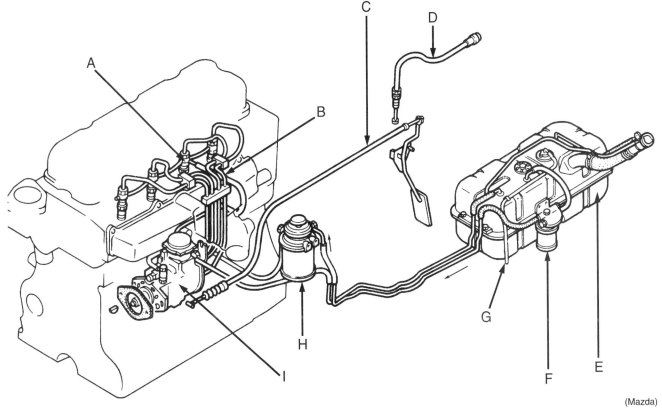

(Mazda)

38. Label the parts of the diesel injection pump illustrated below.

(A) _____

(B) _____

(C) _____

(D) _____

(E) _____

(F) _____

(G) _____

(H) _____

(I) _____

(J) _____

(K) _____

(L) _____

(M) _____

(N) _____

(O) _____

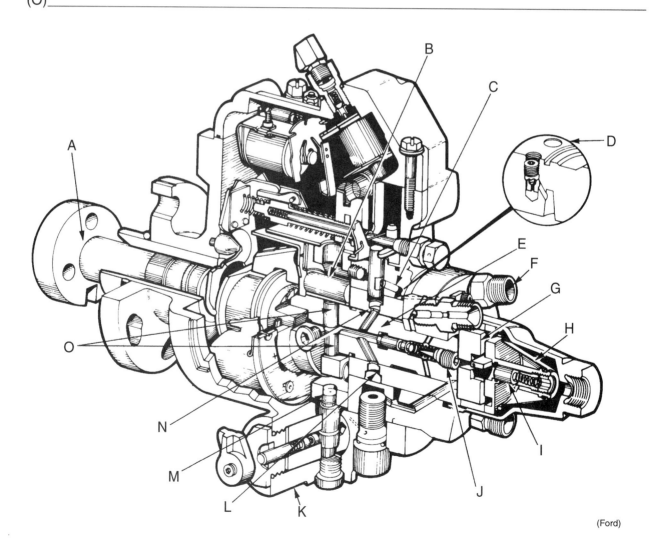

(Ford)

Superchargers and Turbochargers

39. A supercharger is driven from the engine by one of three methods. Name them.

    (A) _____

    (B) _____

    (C) _____

40. A turbocharger is driven by _____ _____.

40. _____

41. The intercooler is used to cool the incoming air to reduce engine _____.

41. _____

42. What is the purpose of the turbocharger waste gate? _____

    _____

43. Turbocharger bearings are lubricated by _____.
    (A) a grease fitting
    (B) two grease fittings
    (C) engine oil
    (D) None of the above.

43. _____

44. Label the parts of the supercharger system in the following illustration.

    (A) _____

    (B) _____

    (C) _____

    (D) _____

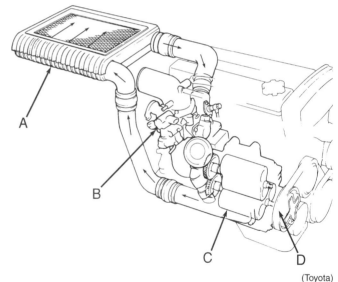

(Toyota)

45. Label the parts of the turbocharger system in the following illustration.

    (A) _____

    (B) _____

    (C) _____

    (D) _____

    (E) _____

    (F) _____

    (G) _____

    (H) _____

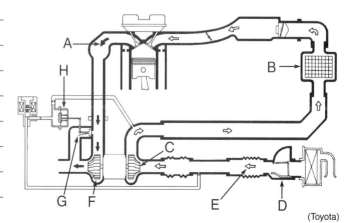

(Toyota)

Air Cleaners Service

46. All modern air cleaner elements are made of _____.

46. _____

47. Although air cleaner elements are usually replaced, they can be cleaned with _____ air directed in the opposite direction of normal airflow.

47. _____

48. When replacing an air filter housing, be sure to clean the housing and check the condition of all related _____.

48. _____

Fuel Mileage Check

49. Fuel mileage suffers when there is a lot of _____.
    (A) highway driving
    (B) hot starts
    (C) idling
    (D) All of the above.

49. _____

50. Technician A says that using a measured amount of fuel and driving the vehicle at normal speeds on a level road allows the technician to accurately check fuel mileage. Technician B says the fuel mileage tests should cover the road in both directions to allow for any wind or downgrade. Who is right?
    (A) A only.
    (B) B only.
    (C) Both A & B.
    (D) Neither A nor B.

50. _____

Name _____

Date _____ Period _____

Instructor _____

Score_____

Text pages 409–427

21

Carburetor Service

Objectives: After studying Chapter 21 in the textbook and completing this section of the workbook, you will be able to:

- Detect intake manifold air leakage.
- Adjust carburetor idle speed and idle mixture.
- Adjust a manual and automatic choke.
- Adjust throttle linkage.
- Service a manifold heat control valve.
- Adjust a fuel bowl vent.
- Set float level and float drop.
- Adjust an accelerator pump.
- Disassemble, clean, inspect, and reassemble a carburetor.

Tech Talk: Although fuel injection has replaced the carburetor on new vehicles, there are millions of carburetors still in use. Late-model carburetors use engine sensors and a computer to control the carburetor fuel mixture. The computer operates a mixture solenoid on the carburetor. The solenoid can allow more or less fuel to enter the air stream, maintaining a precise air-fuel mixture under all operating conditions. Although this makes carburetor diagnosis and repair more difficult, it does not make it impossible. In many cases, the computer self-diagnostic system can help with carburetor troubleshooting. Study this chapter to increase your knowledge of carburetor systems and their service.

Instructions: Study Chapter 21 of the text; then answer the following questions in the spaces provided.

Carburetor Functions

1. All of the following are basic carburetor systems, EXCEPT:
   (A) main metering.
   (B) economizer.
   (C) float.
   (D) power.

1. _____

2. Venturi vacuum is developed in the carburetor _____.

2. _____

3. The choke operates when the engine is _____.

3. _____

4. Technician A says that newer carburetors often use motors or solenoids to control idle speed. Technician B says that newer carburetors often use motors or solenoids to control mixture. Who is right?
   (A) A only.
   (B) B only.
   (C) Both A & B.
   (D) Neither A nor B.

4. _____

Pre-Service Checks

5. Before servicing the carburetor, check for _____.
   (A) vacuum leaks
   (B) fouled spark plugs
   (C) low cylinder compression
   (D) All of the above.

5. _____

6. To check an intake manifold or carburetor base gasket for vacuum leaks, squirt _____ along the gasket. A leak will cause the idle speed to change.

6. _____

Carburetor Adjustments

7. When adjusting the fast idle (cold idle) speed, connect a(n) _____ to the engine. Turn the fast idle screw with it contacting the recommended _____ on the fast idle cam. Adjust until the prescribed rpm reading is obtained.

7. _____
   _____

8. Fast idle specifications average about _____ when the screw is resting on the first or lowest step on the cam.

8. _____

9. To adjust hot idle speed, check specifications to see if the automatic transmission should be in _____ or _____. Then, adjust the idle speed screw.

9. _____

10. Idle speed control devices are used to change idle speed when the idle _____ changes.

10. _____

11. An anti-stall dashpot prevents stalling when the throttle is _____ suddenly at low speeds.

11. _____

12. Engine missing as the idle mixture screw is turned in is a normal result of a(n) _____ mixture.

12. _____

13. The idle drop method is a way of adjusting the idle _____ screws to get the proper air-fuel ratio.

13. _____

14. During the propane enrichment adjustment procedure, the idle speed will drop when the propane feed is _____.

14. _____

15. Most newer chokes are heated by _____.
    (A) the cooling system
    (B) electric current
    (C) exhaust heat
    (D) friction

15. _____

16. The choke valve should be closed when the engine is _____ and open when the engine is _____.

16. _____
    _____

17. If the cover of an automatic choke is held in place with rivets, they can be _____ out to adjust the choke.

17. _____

18. Technician A says that the need for a richer choke setting may be indicated by black exhaust smoke. Technician B says that the need for a leaner choke setting may be indicated by sputtering during warm up. Who is right?
(A) A only.
(B) B only.
(C) Both A & B.
(D) Neither A nor B.

18. _____

19. When cleaning and reassembling an automatic choke, align the _____ and _____ index marks. Tighten the cover fasteners securely.

19. _____
_____

20. A defective accelerator pump will cause a(n) _____ when accelerating.

20. _____

21. A quick accelerator pump check involves opening and closing the throttle. Watch to see if one or more _____ of gas are evident in the throat of the carburetor.

21. _____

22. Float level setting is critical. A higher than specified fuel level will result in all of the following, EXCEPT:
(A) poor gas mileage.
(B) plug fouling.
(C) backfiring.
(D) crankcase dilution.

22. _____

23. A float drop setting may be checked with a _____ or by measuring between two specified points.

23. _____

24. Label the parts of the carburetor shown in the following illustration.

(A) _____

(B) _____

(C) _____

(D) _____

(E) _____

(F) _____

(G) _____

(Chrysler)

25. Label the parts of the anti-dieseling solenoid shown in the following illustration.

(A) _____

(B) _____

(C) _____

(D) _____

(E) _____

(Motorcraft)

26. Identify the parts and actions pertaining to choke adjustment in the illustration below.

(A) _____

(B) _____

(C) _____

(D) _____

(Ford)

Carburetor Service

27. None of the following parts should be soaked in carburetor cleaner, EXCEPT:
(A) anti-stall dashpot.
(B) fuel enrichment valve.
(C) accelerator pump lever.
(D) power valve.

27. _____

28. To thoroughly clean a carburetor during a rebuild, compressed air is commonly used to blow out all internal _____.

28. _____

29. To obtain the proper carburetor overhaul kit, you will need the carburetor _____, which may be located on the carburetor body or a separate tag.

29. _____

30. Identify the parts of the carburetor shown in the following illustration.

(A) _____

(B) _____

(C) _____

(D) _____

(E) _____

(F) _____

(G) _____

(H) _____

(I) _____

(J) _____

(K) _____

(L) _____

(M)_____

(N) _____

(O) _____

(P) _____

(Q) _____

(R) _____

(S) _____

(T) _____

(U) _____

(V) _____

(W)_____

(X) _____

(Y) _____

(Z) _____

(AA) _____

(AB) _____

(AC) _____

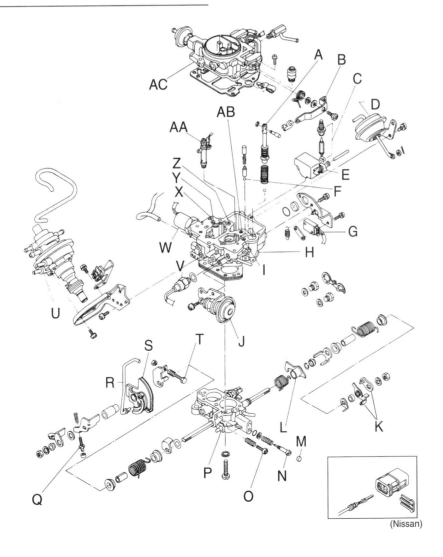

(Nissan)

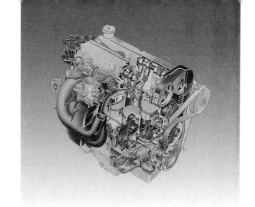

Name _____

Date _____ Period _____

Instructor _____

Score _____

Text pages 429-451

22

Cooling System Service

Objectives: After studying Chapter 22 in the textbook and completing this section of the workbook, you will be able to:

- Explain the role of antifreeze in an engine cooling system.
- Properly clean a cooling system.
- Detect leaks in a cooling system.
- Test a radiator pressure cap.
- List the safety rules dealing with cooling systems.
- Inspect and replace cooling system hoses.
- Inspect, replace, and adjust drive belts.
- Test and replace a thermostat.
- Inspect, repair, and replace a coolant pump.

Tech Talk: Without a properly functioning cooling system, a car's engine may overheat in a matter of minutes. Overheating may cause serious damage to the engine. Engine parts can get hot enough to score, crack, or warp. Thousands of people have made the mistake of trying to "make it home" with an overheated engine. Many ended up paying hundreds of dollars to repair blown head gaskets, burned valves, warped cylinder heads, cracked blocks, and other major problems. Study this chapter to learn how to service a cooling system and prevent engine damage.

Instructions: Study Chapter 22 of the text; then answer the following questions in the spaces provided.

Cooling System Service

1. About _____ of the heat produced by combustion is absorbed by the metal parts of an engine and must be disposed of by the cooling system.

1. _____

2. Antifreeze should be used in all areas where the temperature will drop below _____°F (_____°C).

2. _____

3. _____ antifreeze is widely used today to protect against freezing and to inhibit rust.
   (A) Ethyl alcohol
   (B) Methanol
   (C) Ethylene glycol
   (D) None of the above.

3. _____

4. Common coolant ratios are around _____ water and _____ ethylene glycol.

4. _____
   _____

5. Unless leaks develop and dilution is a problem, antifreeze can normally be left in the system for _____ months.

5. _____

6. A(n) _____ is used to test coolant protection at engine operating temperature.

6. _____

7. Technician A says a mild rust and scale condition can be corrected by cleaning with a chemical cleaner. Technician B says that after using some chemical cleaners, a neutralizer must be used before refilling the system with antifreeze and water. Who is right?
   (A) A only.
   (B) B only.
   (C) Both A & B.
   (D) Neither A nor B.

7. _____

8. A cooling system in bad condition (rust) may be cleaned by _____ flushing with power equipment.

8. _____

9. Any time the cooling system slowly loses water, the system should be _____ _____.

9. _____

10. When pressure testing, check the pressure marking on the _____ or check the _____ for system limits.

10. _____
    _____

11. If the pressure tester shows an increase in pressure when the engine is running, a(n) _____ is indicated.

11. _____

12. When testing for combustion (internal) leaks with test chemicals, the test fluid will change _____ if leakage is present.

12. _____

13. If you suspect a combustion leak, always watch for _____.

13. _____

14. Label the potential cooling system problem areas in the illustration at the top of the following page.

(A) _____   (J) _____

(B) _____   (K) _____

(C) _____   (L) _____

(D) _____   (M) _____

(E) _____   (N) _____

(F) _____   (O) _____

(G) _____   (P) _____

(H) _____   (Q) _____

(I) _____

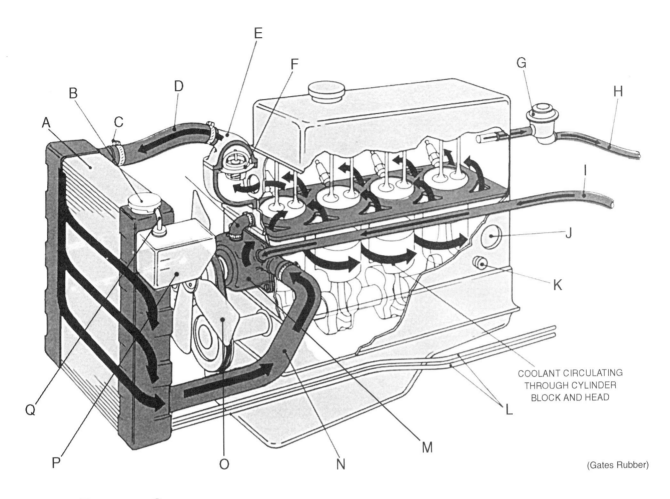

(Gates Rubber)

Radiator Pressure Caps

15. Technician A says that with a pressurized cooling system, an engine can operate at higher temperatures without causing the coolant to boil. Technician B says that higher operating temperatures increase combustion efficiency. Who is right?
    (A) A only.
    (B) B only.
    (C) Both A & B.
    (D) Neither A nor B.

15. _____

16. The operation of a pressure cap can be tested with a(n) _____.

16. _____

17. The cap should retain a pressure within _____ (_____) of its rating.

17. _____

18. Check the condition of the _____ _____ inside of the filler neck.

18. _____

Hose Inspection

19. All hoses should be visually inspected for signs of _____.

19. _____

20. Pay particular attention to the bottom radiator hose. It is under suction and, if soft, will _____.

20. _____

Drive Belt Inspection

21. When inspecting belts for signs of failure, look for _____.
    (A) cracking
    (B) oil soaking
    (C) glazing
    (D) All of the above.

21. _____

22. Some belts are automatically tightened by an engine-mounted _____.

22. _____

23. Technician A says that a loose belt will squeal or flap. Technician B says that a loose belt will place a heavy strain on the bearings of the driven unit. Who is right?
    (A) A only.
    (B) B only.
    (C) Both A & B.
    (D) Neither A nor B.

23. _____

24. Identify the belts in the following illustrations.

    (A) _____

    (B) _____

    (C) _____

(Ford)

Fan Service

25. Never attempt to repair a fan by straightening the _____.

25. _____

26. If a warmed up fluid clutch fan turns more than _____ revolution(s) before stopping, it is defective.

26. _____

27. Technician A says that many electric radiator cooling fans are turned on and off by a thermoswitch. Technician B says that on late-model vehicles, the fan is often controlled by the computer. Who is right?
    (A) A only.
    (B) B only.
    (C) Both A & B.
    (D) Neither A nor B.

27. _____

28. A cracked plastic fan should be _____.

28. _____

Thermostat Service

29. A thermostat can cause overheating by _____

    _____.

30. A thermostat that is stuck open or removed can cause all of   30. _____
    the following, EXCEPT:
    (A) overcooling.
    (B) oil dilution.
    (C) increased fuel vaporization.
    (D) crankcase sludging.

31. Always install a thermostat so that the thermostatic element   31. _____
    will be in contact with the _____ in the block.

32. Identify the parts of the thermostat setup shown in the following illustration.

    (A) _____

    (B) _____

    (C) _____

    (D) _____

    (E) _____

    (F) _____

(Geo)

Coolant Pumps

33. Coolant pump problems include _____.   33. _____
    (A) worn bearings
    (B) leaking seals
    (C) worn impeller blades
    (D) All of the above.

34. Inspect the water pump for signs of leakage at the seal drain   34. _____
    hole and the _____ area.

35. When mounting the water pump, use a new _____.   35. _____

36. To prevent cracking of the pump, fasteners must be tight-   36. _____
    ened to the proper _____.

37. When removing core hole plugs (freeze plugs), drive a   37. _____
    sharp-nosed _____ through the plug and pry to remove the
    plug.

38. Some replacement freeze plugs are made of _____ for easy   38. _____
    installation.

39. When servicing air-cooled engines, always check blower fan   39. _____
    _____ condition and tension.

40. Identify the indicated parts of the coolant pump shown in the following illustration.

(A) _____

(B) _____

(C) _____

(D) _____

(E) _____

(F) _____

(G) _____

(H) _____

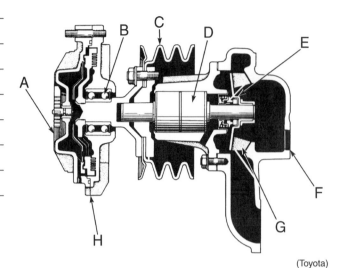

(Toyota)

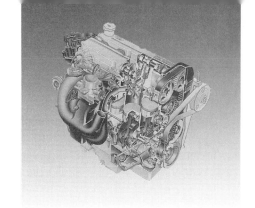

Name _____

Date _____ Period _____

Instructor _____

Score_____

Text pages 453-463

23

Exhaust System Service

Objectives: After studying Chapter 23 in the textbook and completing this section of the workbook, you will be able to:

* Explain heat control valve operation, service, and repair.
* Describe exhaust manifold removal and installation.
* Summarize muffler design and operation.
* Remove and install a muffler.
* Describe exhaust and tailpipe removal and installation.
* Use special exhaust system service tools.

Tech Talk: While the job of the exhaust system is relatively simple—to remove engine exhaust gases—improper service procedures can cause engine damage, objectionable noise, or even death from carbon monoxide poisoning. Some parts of the exhaust system also help with engine warm-up and air pollution reduction. This chapter will cover the ways that the technician can prevent poor engine operation, part damage, and personal injury by properly servicing the exhaust system components.

Instructions: Study Chapter 23 of the text; then answer the following questions in the spaces provided.

Exhaust System Service

1. Technician A says that as the burned gases leave the engine cylinders, they pass into the exhaust manifold. Technician B says that once the exhaust manifold is affixed to the cylinder head, periodic service is not necessary. Who is right?
   (A) A only.
   (B) B only.
   (C) Both A & B.
   (D) Neither A nor B.

1. _____

2. To provide heat to help vaporization of the fuel charge during engine warm-up, a(n) _____ is usually installed in the _____.

2. _____
   _____

3. Vacuum-operated heat control valves are supplied with vacuum through a(n) _____ _____ switch.

3. _____

4. Define *exhaust back pressure*. _____

_____

5. Technician A says that a power chisel, with suitable cutter heads, is useful for removing exhaust pipes and tailpipes. Technician B says that pipes must often be expanded to provide a proper joint fit. Who is right?
   (A) A only.
   (B) B only.
   (C) Both A & B.
   (D) Neither A nor B.

5. _____

6. A straightening cone is used to bring a pipe end that has been crimped or dented _____ shape.

6. _____

7. If one exhaust pipe nipple (pipe) enters its mating nipple too deeply, the _____ _____ may be too high.

7. _____

8. If one exhaust pipe nipple does not enter its mating nipple deeply enough, the joint may _____ or _____.

8. _____

9. Exhaust alignment is important. Make a careful check of the entire system to make certain that all exhaust system parts have sufficient operating _____.

9. _____

10. As a final step in exhaust system testing, always operate the engine and check each _____ for any signs of _____.

10. _____
    _____

11. Technician A says that the exhaust-pipe-to-manifold gasket can be reused if it is not damaged. Technician B says that when the exhaust pipe is part of the muffler, it should never be cut off during service. Who is right?
    (A) A only.
    (B) B only.
    (C) Both A & B.
    (D) Neither A nor B.

11. _____

12. Identify the parts of the intake and exhaust manifold assembly illustrated below.
    (A) _____
    (B) _____
    (C) _____
    (D) _____
    (E) _____
    (F) _____
    (G) _____
    (H) _____
    (I) _____

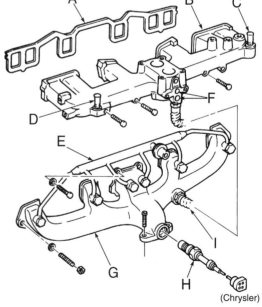

(Chrysler)

13. Label the parts of the heat control valve shown in the following illustration.

(A) _____

(B) _____

(C) _____

(D) _____

(E) _____

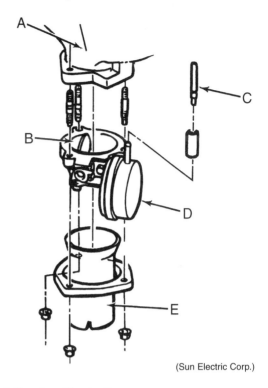

(Sun Electric Corp.)

14. Label the parts of the exhaust system shown in the following illustration.

(A) _____

(B) _____

(C) _____

(D) _____

(E) _____

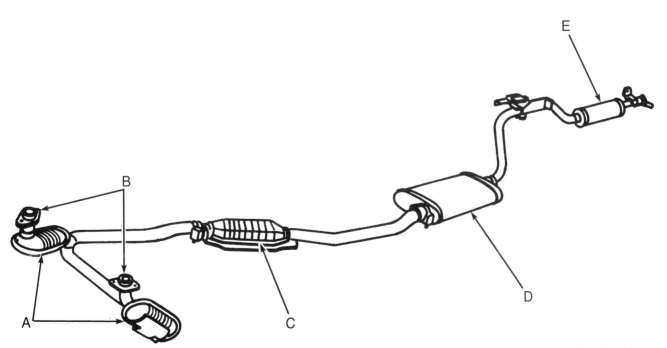

(Sun Electric Corp.)

15. Write down the basic service procedures shown in the following illustration.

(A) _____

_____

(B) _____

_____

(C) _____

_____

(D) _____

_____

(E) _____

_____

(F) _____

_____

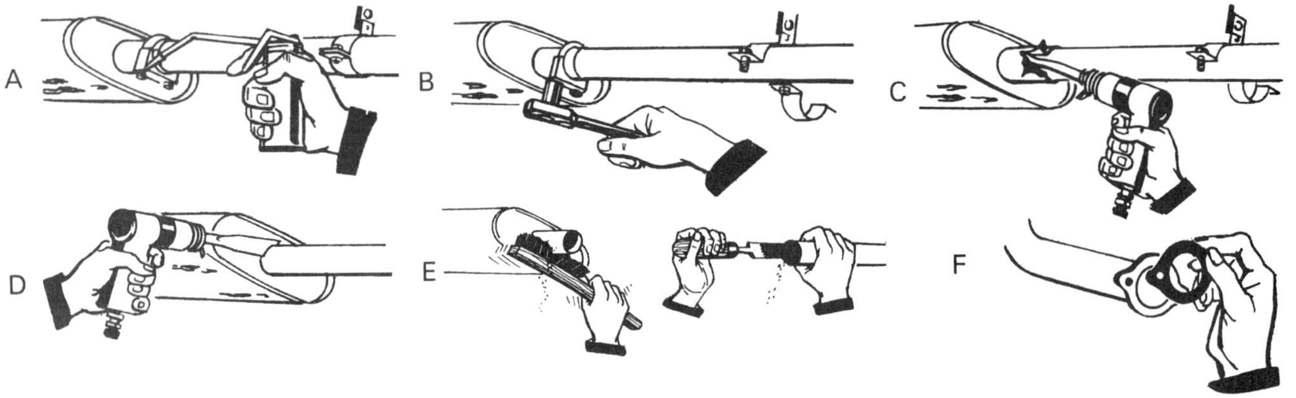

(A. P. Parts)

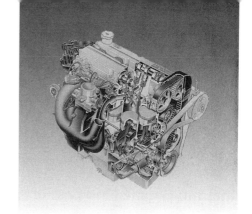

Name _____

Date _____ Period _____

Instructor _____

Score_____

Text pages 465-491

24

Emission System Service

Objectives: After studying Chapter 24 in the textbook and completing this section of the workbook, you will be able to:

- Describe internal engine modifications for reduced emissions.
- Describe fuel system modifications for reduced emissions.
- Describe thermostatic air cleaner operation, service, and repair.
- Explain early fuel evaporation system operation, service, and repair.
- Explain exhaust gas recirculation system operation, service, and repair.
- Explain catalytic converter construction and operation.
- Remove, install, and service a catalytic converter.
- Describe air injection system operation, service, and repair.
- Explain positive crankcase ventilation system operation, service, and repair.
- Explain evaporative control system operation, service, and repair.
- Diagnose exhaust system and emission control problems.

Tech Talk: Automotive emission control systems are designed to eliminate the pollutants that enter the atmosphere from a motor vehicle. They do this in two ways: by reducing the amount of pollutants produced by the internal combustion process and by changing engine pollutants into harmless substances. This helps keep the air we breathe clean. By maintaining emission control systems, the automotive technician protects an extremely vital resource—the air that supports life on earth.

Instructions: Study Chapter 24 of the text; then answer the following questions in the spaces provided.

Emission Control System Service

1. Hydrocarbons and carbon monoxide form when fuel burning is _____.

1. _____

2. Oxides of nitrogen are formed when the combustion chamber is _____.
   (A) too hot
   (B) too cold
   (C) under high vacuum
   (D) None of the above.

2. _____

3. All of the following are basic classifications of emission con-   3. _____
   trols, EXCEPT:
   (A) internal engine modifications.
   (B) fuel vapor controls.
   (C) internal cleaning systems.
   (D) external cleaning systems.

Internal Engine Modifications and Controls

4. Modern combustion chambers are shaped to reduce the   4. _____
   formation of _____.

5. Modern camshafts have reduced _____ to reduce   5. _____
   emissions.

6. A hotter thermostat reduces the formation of _____.   6. _____

7. All of the following statements about lowering compression   7. _____
   are true, EXCEPT:
   (A) lowering compression reduces detonation.
   (B) lowering compression reduces dieseling.
   (C) lower compression increases formation of NO_x.
   (D) lower compression allows the use of unleaded gas.

8. Replacing the cylinder heads on a late-model vehicle with   8. _____
   an older set of heads is _____.

9. A thermostatic air cleaner will lower emissions and help to   9. _____
   prevent carburetor _____ when the engine is cold.

10. The air control door of a thermostatic air cleaner is operat-   10. _____
    ed by _____.

11. A(n) _____ _____ is used to check the operation of a   11. _____
    thermostatic air cleaner.

12. The early fuel evaporation (EFE) system transfers heat from   12. _____
    the _____ system to the intake manifold.

13. Older spark timing controls reduced emissions by reducing   13. _____
    the amount of distributor _____ advance.

14. Recycling some of the engine exhaust gases reduces the   14. _____
    formation of _____.
    (A) oxides of nitrogen
    (B) hydrocarbons
    (C) carbon monoxide
    (D) None of the above.

15. The amount of exhaust gases fed into the intake manifold is automatically controlled by the _____

    _____

    _____.

16. During idle and wide open throttle, the EGR valve remains   16. _____
    _____.

17. Name the five basic types of EGR valves.

(A) _____

(B) _____

(C) _____

(D) _____

(E) _____

18. To test a vacuum-operated EGR valve, depress the EGR valve diaphragm with your finger. If the engine was idling smoothly, it should _____

_____.

19. Closed loop emission control systems use a(n) _____ sensor located in the exhaust stream to monitor emissions.

19. _____

20. Extremely low voltages require that all closed loop emission control system wire splices be _____.

20. _____

21. Label the parts of the thermostatic air cleaner assembly illustrated below.

(A) _____

(B) _____

(C) _____

(D) _____

(E) _____

(F) _____

(Toyota)

22. Label the parts of the EGR valve shown in the following illustration.

(A) _____

(B) _____

(C) _____

(D) _____

(E) _____

(F) _____

(G) _____

(H) _____

(Chevrolet)

23. Label the parts of the digital EGR valve shown in the following illustration.

(A) _____

(B) _____

(C) _____

(D) _____

(E) _____

(F) _____

(G) _____

(H) _____

(Sun Electric)

External Engine Controls

24. Technician A says that the air injection system attacks the emissions problem by prolonging the combustion process inside the cylinder. Technician B says that the air injection system uses a belt-driven air pump and a series of tubes or passages to route fresh air into the exhaust gases. Who is right?

(A) A only.

(B) B only.

(C) Both A & B.

(D) Neither A nor B.

24. _____

25. The diverter valve prevents backfiring by momentarily diverting the _____

_____

_____

_____.

26. Normal air pump pressure will be about _____(_____).

26. _____

27. A catalytic converter can significantly lower the amount of

_____.

(A) oxides of nitrogen

(B) carbon monoxide

(C) hydrocarbons

(D) All of the above, depending on the catalyst agents.

27. _____

28. The converter core can be made in two ways. One employs a great number of _____, and the other uses a(n) _____.

28. _____

_____

29. Technician A says that catalytic converters can be damaged by using leaded fuel. Technician B says that catalytic converters can be damaged by shorting out plugs during engine tests. Who is right?

(A) A only.

(B) B only.

(C) Both A & B.

(D) Neither A nor B.

29. _____

30. A honeycomb-type converter can be repaired by replacing the _____.
    (A) internal pellets
    (B) internal honeycomb
    (C) converter cover
    (D) None of the above.

30. _____

31. The term PCV stands for _____ _____ _____.

31. _____

32. A defective PCV system can cause _____.
    (A) rough idle
    (B) blown engine gaskets
    (C) increased emissions
    (D) All of the above.

32. _____

33. The PCV system should be checked at every _____.

33. _____

34. Most evaporation control systems (ECS) use a gas tank filler cap that is not vented to the _____.

34. _____

35. Label the parts of the air injection system illustrated below.

(A) _____   (G) _____

(B) _____   (H) _____

(C) _____   (I) _____

(D) _____   (J) _____

(E) _____   (K) _____

(F) _____   (L) _____

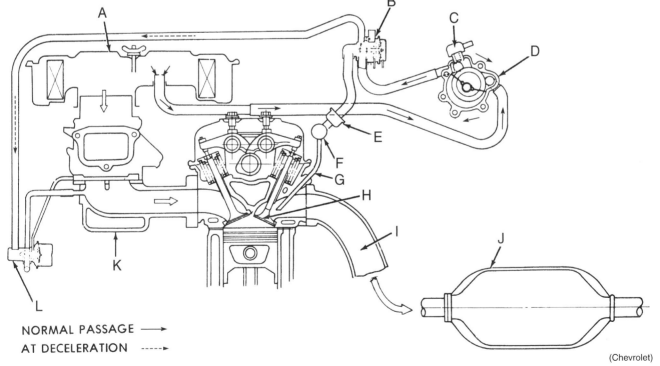

NORMAL PASSAGE ⟶
AT DECELERATION ----▸

(Chevrolet)

36. Label the parts of the diverter valve illustrated below.

(A) _____

(B) _____

(C) _____

(D) _____

(E) _____

(F) _____

(G) _____

(H) _____

(I) _____

(J) _____

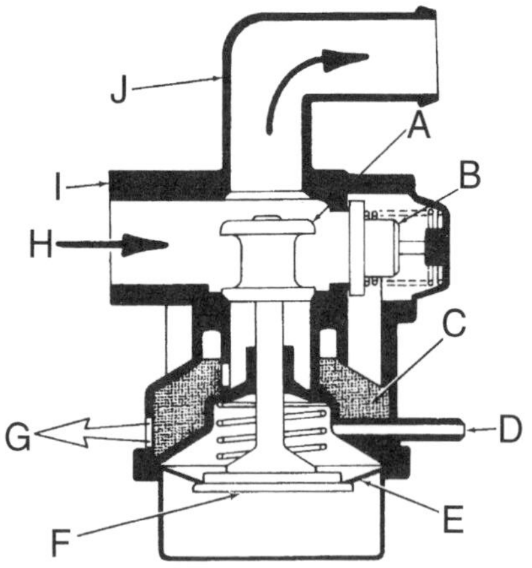

(Cadillac)

37. The system illustrated below uses the pulse effect of the engine _____ to draw air into the exhaust manifold.

37. _____

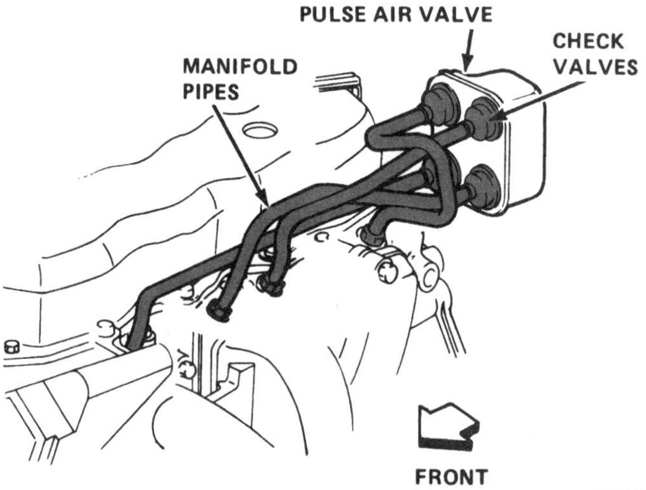

PULSE AIR VALVE

CHECK VALVES

MANIFOLD PIPES

FRONT

(GMC)

38. Label the parts of the catalytic converter illustrated below.

(A) _____

(B) _____

(C) _____

(D) _____

(E) _____

(F) _____

(G) _____

(H) _____

(I) _____

(J) _____

(K) _____

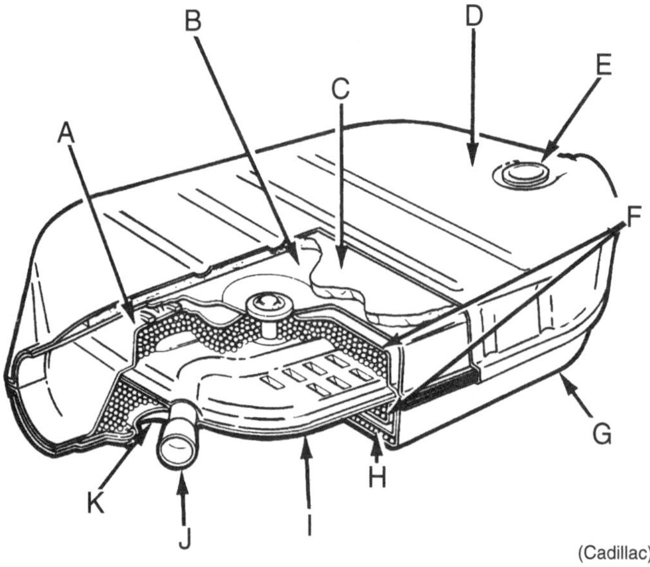

(Cadillac)

Preventive Maintenance

39. An exhaust gas analyzer is used to check the _____ _____ ratio and is the only sure way of telling whether the emissions equipment is functioning.

39. _____

40. Technician A says that the simplest analyzer will measure hydrocarbons only. Technician B says that more advanced analyzers will measure carbon monoxide, hydrocarbons, oxides of nitrogen, and free oxygen. Who is right?
    (A) A only.
    (B) B only.
    (C) Both A & B.
    (D) Neither A nor B.

40. _____

41. Before recording exhaust gas analyzer readings, allow the engine to run at _____ for a few minutes to _____ the readings.

41. _____
    _____

42. If the oxygen sensor and computer control system are operating properly, what will happen to the exhaust gas analyzer readings when the airflow through the intake manifold is restricted?_____

_____

_____

43. If the computer control system does not appear to be operating properly, what is the *first* thing the technician should do? _____

_____.

44. What is the purpose of the emission information label? _____

_____

45. Forcing a hose over a fitting that is too large can cause it to _____.

45. _____

Name _____

Date _____ Period _____

Instructor _____

Score_____

Text pages 493-515

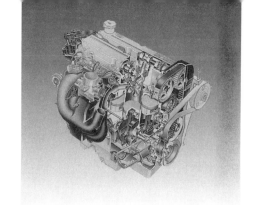

25

Computer System Service

Objectives: After studying Chapter 25 in the textbook and completing this section of the workbook, you will be able to:

- Explain engine computer control system operation.
- Define control loops.
- Explain the function and operation of input sensors.
- Explain the function and operation of output actuators.
- Access computer control system self-diagnostic systems.
- Troubleshoot electronic control system problems.
- Troubleshoot and service sensors, actuators, and electronic control units.

Tech Talk: The untrained mechanic can no longer hope to fix today's "electronic cars." The term "mechanic" implies that someone is competent at servicing only mechanical components: pistons, rods, control arms, clutches and drive shafts. The term "technician" is more appropriate for those who must diagnose and repair today's cars, which are equipped with computers, sensors, and actuators.

Instructions: Study Chapter 25 of the text; then answer the following questions in the spaces provided.

The Need for Computers

1. Technician A says that computerized engine controls accurately and instantaneously control the fuel, ignition, and emission control systems on late-model vehicles. Technician B says that most components in a computerized system do not require periodic replacement or adjustment. Who is right?
   (A) A only.
   (B) B only.
   (C) Both A & B.
   (D) Neither A nor B.

1. _____

2. In addition to controlling engine operating conditions, computers are used to govern various systems, such as the _____ system.
   (A) brake
   (B) suspension
   (C) occupant restraint
   (D) All of the above.

2. _____

3. List and describe the three basic components of a computer system.

(A) _____

_____

_____

(B) _____

_____

_____

(C) _____

_____

_____

4. All of the following are stages of computer operation, EXCEPT:
   (A) input.
   (B) conversion.
   (C) output.
   (D) processing.

4. _____

5. Technician A says that closed control loop can occur with no inputs. Technician B says that an open loop operates the engine on preset information. Who is right?
   (A) A only.
   (B) B only.
   (C) Both A & B.
   (D) Neither A nor B.

5. _____

6. When a computer system component fails, the system automatically goes into _____ loop.

6. _____

7. Identify the computer control system components shown in the illustration on the following page.

(A) _____

(B) _____

(C) _____

(D) _____

(E) _____

(F) _____

(G) _____

(H) _____

(I) _____

(J) _____

(K) _____

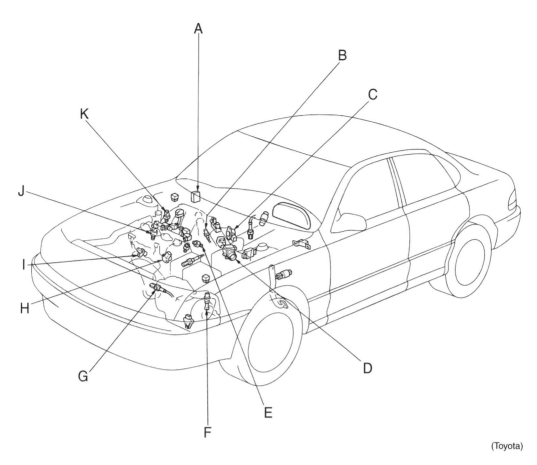

(Toyota)

Computerized Engine Control Components

8. A signal-producing sensor generates its own _____ signal.

8. _____

9. Technician A says that an oxygen sensor works like a small, variable battery. Technician B says that the oxygen sensor is generally located in the intake manifold. Who is right?
   (A) A only.
   (B) B only.
   (C) Both A & B.
   (D) Neither A nor B.

9. _____

10. With most speed sensors, _____ action generates a signal voltage.

10. _____

11. A signal-modifying sensor depends on _____ voltage to operate.
    (A) a self-generated
    (B) full battery
    (C) a reference
    (D) None of the above.

11. _____

12. What is a MAT sensor? _____

_____

_____

_____

13. How does a throttle position sensor work? _____

_____

_____

14. Technician A says that the two major types of airflow sensors are the flap airflow sensor and the heated wire airflow
sensor. Technician B says that some airflow sensors measure airflow from the vibration of a small mirror. Who is
right?
(A) A only.
(B) B only.
(C) Both A & B.
(D) Neither A nor B.

14. _____

15. A switching sensor has two positions. They are _____.
(A) low and high frequency
(B) low and high temperature
(C) low and high rotational speed
(D) on and off

15. _____

16. The system operating instructions are stored in _____.
(A) ROM
(B) RAM
(C) the input section
(D) the arithmetic-logic section

16. _____

17. Technician A says that ROM is serviceable in the field.
Technician B says that RAM is a temporary storage place
for sensor inputs. Who is right?
(A) A only.
(B) B only.
(C) Both A & B.
(D) Neither A nor B.

17. _____

18. _____ memory will be lost if the battery is disconnected for
any time.

18. _____

19. All of the following are common actuators, EXCEPT:
(A) fuel injectors.
(B) ignition module.
(C) distributor.
(D) electric fan relay.

19. _____

20. A mixture control solenoid is found only on vehicles with
a(n) _____.

20. _____

21. A electric fan relay turns the fan on when the _____
reaches a certain temperature.

21. _____

Troubleshooting—A Logical Approach

22. Define computer *self-diagnosis.* _____

_____

_____

23. Trouble codes are retrieved by _____.
    (A) grounding a terminal on the diagnostic test link
    (B) connecting a voltmeter to a terminal of the diagnostic link
    (C) connecting two diagnostic link terminals
    (D) All of the above, depending on the manufacturer.

23. _____

24. Some vehicles have the capability of displaying trouble codes directly onto a screen on the _____.

24. _____

25. A(n) _____ tool converts trouble codes into a digital or alpha-numeric display.

25. _____

26. Technician A says that in many cases, a computer system problem can be detected by a visual inspection. Technician B says that most computer system problems are caused by loose connections, leaking hoses, or physical damage. Who is right?
    (A) A only.
    (B) B only.
    (C) Both A & B.
    (D) Neither A nor B.

26. _____

Servicing Electronic Engine Control System Components

27. If an oxygen sensor has a defect, it must be _____.

27. _____

28. A detonation sensor and its related circuitry can be checked by using a(n) _____ light.

28. _____

29. How do you replace a PROM? _____

    _____

30. Identify parts of the mass airflow sensor shown in the following illustration.

    (A) _____
    (B) _____
    (C) _____
    (D) _____
    (E) _____
    (F) _____
    (G) _____
    (H) _____

(Bosch)

Name _____

Date _____ Period _____

Instructor _____

Score_____

Text pages 517-544

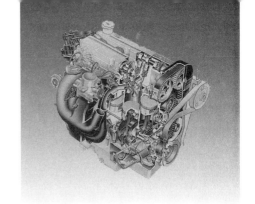

26

Charging and Starting Systems Service

Objectives: After studying Chapter 26 in the textbook and completing this section of the workbook, you will be able to:

- Install, test, and service a battery.
- Use jumper cables correctly.
- Test, service, and repair a charging system.
- Service an alternator and a voltage regulator.
- Test, service, and repair a starting system.
- Service a starter and starter solenoid.

Tech Talk: Batteries, starters, and alternators have not changed as much as other automotive electrical equipment. With the exception of electronic voltage regulators, the starting and charging system is largely unchanged over the last 30 years. However, their effect on the operation of the vehicle is as important as ever. The alternator and battery must handle the increased electrical load caused by optional equipment and electronic control systems that are almost universal. Modern starters must be lighter and more heat resistant than older models, but they still must produce enough torque to start the engine. Studying this chapter will prepare you for starting and charging system service.

Instructions: Study Chapter 26 of the text; then answer the following questions in the spaces provided.

Battery Service

1. A visual inspection of the battery will help determine service needs, which might include _____.
   (A) cleaning the cable terminals
   (B) replacing the battery
   (C) charging the battery
   (D) All of the above.

1. _____

2. Battery electrolyte contains _____ acid, which can cause serious _____.

2. _____
   _____

3. Technician A says that skin should be flushed with cold water if it comes in contact with electrolyte. Technician B says that acid can be neutralized with baking soda and water. Who is right?
   (A) A only.
   (B) B only.
   (C) Both A & B.
   (D) Neither A nor B.

3. _____

4. Technician A says that dirt on the top of the battery can cause it to slowly discharge. Technician B says that corrosion on the battery terminals makes them more conductive. Who is right?
   (A) A only.
   (B) B only.
   (C) Both A & B.
   (D) Neither A nor B.

4. _____

5. A battery that requires the frequent addition of water may indicate _____.

5. _____

6. While tap water can be used in most batteries, _____ water is preferred.

6. _____

7. Technician A says that the condition of a battery is determined by its state of charge. Technician B says that cold weather increases the efficiency of a battery. Who is right?
   (A) A only.
   (B) B only.
   (C) Both A & B.
   (D) Neither A nor B.

7. _____

8. When the temperature drops, battery capacity _____.

8. _____

9. All of the following statements about a frozen battery are true, EXCEPT:
   (A) a frozen battery cannot be tested.
   (B) only badly discharged batteries will freeze.
   (C) a frozen battery can be thawed and will be usable.
   (D) a frozen battery must be thawed out before it can be recharged.

9. _____

10. When a battery has an open circuit voltage of 12.0V, it is about _____% charged.

10. _____

11. A charging battery gives off _____ and _____ gases, which are flammable.

11. _____
    _____

12. Specific gravity testing is a handy method of determining _____.

12. _____

13. If water is added to a battery, it cannot be immediately tested with a(n) _____.

13. _____

14. A difference of more than _____ points (specific gravity) between cells indicates that the battery is _____.

14. _____
    _____

15. The preferred method of battery charging is the _____ charge.

15. _____

16. Battery groups are based on all of the following, EXCEPT: 16. _____
    (A) size.
    (B) weight.
    (C) terminal type.
    (D) voltage.

17. The standard battery rating measurement for modern   17. _____
    batteries is _____ _____ _____.

18. Reserve capacity is a measure of how long the battery can   18. _____
    operate the vehicle's electrical system if the _____ system
    fails.

19. If battery polarity is not observed, what could happen? _____

    _____

20. Label the battery parts in the following illustration.

    (A) _____
    (B) _____
    (C) _____
    (D) _____
    (E) _____
    (F) _____
    (G) _____
    (H) _____
    (I) _____
    (J) _____
    (K) _____

(General Motors)

Charging System Service

21. Overcharging may be the cause of short _____ life.   21. _____

22. A light _____ noise when the alternator is charging is   22. _____
    normal.

23. The two electrical properties that must be checked to deter-   23. _____
    mine alternator condition are output _____ and _____.   _____

24. If the alternator does not charge when the _____ is   24. _____
    bypassed, the alternator is defective.

25. Most _____ voltage regulators cannot be serviced and must   25. _____
    be replaced.

26. Some regulators are installed _____.   26. _____
    (A) on the engine firewall
    (B) on the alternator
    (C) in the alternator
    (D) All of the above.

27. Most _____ charging systems have self-diagnostic capabilities.

27. _____

28. Technician A says that high resistance in the charging circuit can be cured only by replacing wires. Technician B says that high resistance in the charging circuit can be cured by cleaning connections. Who is right?
    (A) A only.
    (B) B only.
    (C) Both A & B.
    (D) Neither A nor B.

28. _____

29. Brushes should be replaced if they show any _____.

29. _____

30. An ohmmeter is used to test the rotor for _____, _____, and _____.

30. _____

31. Technician A says that dirty slip rings can be cleaned with 400 grit emery cloth. Technician B says that diodes can best be tested with a 120 volt test lamp. Who is right?
    (A) A only.
    (B) B only.
    (C) Both A & B.
    (D) Neither A nor B.

31. _____

32. A(n) _____ diode will cause the test lamp to light in both directions.

32. _____

33. Alternator brushes are often held in place with a pin until the _____ is installed.

33. _____

34. The following illustration shows an alternator regulator being _____.

34. _____

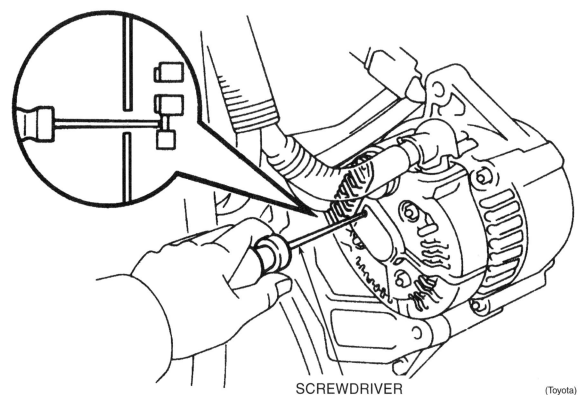

SCREWDRIVER   (Toyota)

Starting System Service

35. The starting system consists of all of the following, EXCEPT:
    (A) neutral safety switch.
    (B) battery.
    (C) ignition switch.
    (D) regulator.

35. _____

36. Many complaints of poor starter performance are traced to the _____.

36. _____

37. If the starter solenoid clicks but does not operate the starter, the problem may be in the solenoid internal _____.

37. _____

38. If the starter spins but does not engage the flywheel, the solenoid may not be operating the _____ mechanism.

38. _____

39. The neutral safety switch will not allow the engine to start in

    _____.
    (A) neutral
    (B) drive
    (C) park
    (D) None of the above.

39. _____

40. Define *starter load test.* _____

_____

_____

41. Technician A says that starters can often be repaired. Technician B says that it is often cheaper to install a new starter than fix the old one. Who is right?
    (A) A only.
    (B) B only.
    (C) Both A & B.
    (D) Neither A nor B.

41. _____

42. Which starter parts *cannot* be cleaned in solvent? _____

_____

43. To test a starter armature for short circuits, place the armature in a(n) _____. If a short circuit exists, the thin strip of metal will _____.

43. _____
    _____

44. Prolonged cranking of the starter will often overheat the starter and cause _____

_____.

45. Recommended practice calls for replacing brushes in a starter when _____

_____.

46. Always inspect the pinion (Bendix) gear teeth for signs of _____. This is a frequent cause of "starter disengage" during cranking and flywheel teeth damage.

46. _____

47. The starter mounting pad should be cleaned to ensure good _____ and _____.

47. _____
    _____

48. If the flywheel-to-pinion clearance is incorrect, it is often possible to adjust it by using _____.

48. _____

49. Draw the missing wires and identify the parts indicated in the basic starting circuit illustrated below.

(A) _____

(B) _____

(C) _____

(D) _____

(E) _____

(F) _____

(G) _____

(Ignition Mfg's Inst.)

50. Identify the parts of the starter illustrated below.

(A) _____   (I) _____

(B) _____   (J) _____

(C) _____   (K) _____

(D) _____   (L) _____

(E) _____   (M) _____

(F) _____   (N) _____

(G) _____   (O) _____

(H) _____

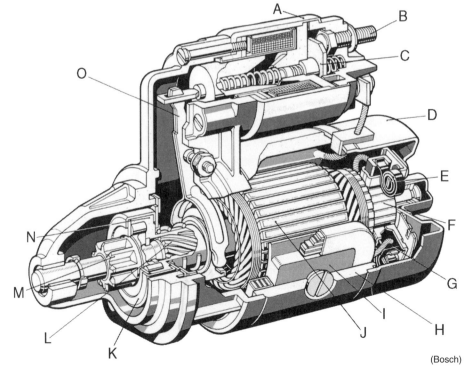

(Bosch)

Name _____

Date _____ Period _____

Instructor _____

Score_____

Text pages 545-566

27

Chassis Electrical Service

Objectives: After studying Chapter 27 in the textbook and completing this section of the workbook, you will be able to:

- Identify and define chassis wiring and related components.
- Explain the differences between chassis wiring and engine wiring.
- Identify chassis electrical components.
- Troubleshoot and replace chassis electrical components.
- Work safely on vehicles equipped with air bag systems.
- Troubleshoot and service air bag systems.

Tech Talk: Chassis electrical equipment includes many vehicle systems that are not related to the ignition starting, or charging systems. However, these systems are important to overall operation of the vehicle and the safety of the passengers. In addition to lighting, windshield wipers, and horns, chassis electrical equipment includes the radios and CD players, electric windows and seats, door locks, rear window defrosters, cruise control systems, and air bag systems. Studying this chapter will prepare you to service chassis electrical components and systems.

Instructions: Study Chapter 27 of the text; then answer the following questions in the spaces provided.

Chassis Wiring

1. Technician A says that a wiring harness is a group of wires wrapped together for ease of installation. Technician B says that wiring harnesses have molded connectors that plug into other harnesses or electrical components. Who is right?
   (A) A only.
   (B) B only.
   (C) Both A & B.
   (D) Neither A nor B.

1. _____

2. Define *printed circuit.* _____

_____

_____

3. Chassis wires are _____ _____ to make identification easier.

3. _____

4. Almost all factory installed fuses are installed in a(n) _____ _____.

4. _____

5. What is the difference between a fusible link and a fuse? _____
_____

6. What is the advantage of a circuit breaker over a fuse? _____
_____

7. The most common causes of a blown fuse include _____.
(A) shorted wires
(B) shorts in electrical devices
(C) motor overload
(D) All of the above.

7. _____

8. Wires may short inside the _____ if they are pinched between body parts.

8. _____

Vehicle Lights and Switches

9. The two main classes of lights are _____ and _____.

9. _____
_____

10. The headlight switch contains a(n) _____ for adjusting the brightness of the dashboard lights.

10. _____

11. All of the following statements about sealed beam headlights are true, EXCEPT:
(A) sealed beams can be round or square.
(B) the outer sealed beams on a four headlight system contain one filament.
(C) the sealed beams on a two headlight system have two filaments.
(D) the filaments, lens, and mirrored inner surface are enclosed in one unit.

11. _____

12. Technician A says that halogen headlights are brighter than older sealed beams. Technician B says that halogen headlights generally cannot be changed without removing the headlight assembly. Who is right?
(A) A only.
(B) B only.
(C) Both A & B.
(D) Neither A nor B.

12. _____

13. Backup light bulbs contain _____ filament(s).

13. _____

14. Technician A says that the brake light switch is a pressure switch. Technician B says that the brake light switch is usually installed on the brake pedal. Who is right?
(A) A only.
(B) B only.
(C) Both A & B.
(D) Neither A nor B.

14. _____

15. The turn signal wiring is always routed through a(n) _____ unit.

15. _____

16. The two classes of dashboard lights are _____ and _____.

16. _____
_____

17. A fiber optic harness carries _____ instead of electricity.

17. _____

18. What is the most common light system problem?_____
_____

19. If the burned out element of a dual-filament bulb contacts the working filament, what can happen?
(A) A fuse can blow.
(B) A wire can melt.
(C) Electrical feedback.
(D) Alternator overloading.

19. _____

20. Some brake switches must be adjusted when they are _____.

20. _____

Chassis-Mounted Motors

21. The modern vehicle may have as many as _____ dc motors.

21. _____

22. Some older windshield wiper motors also operate the _____ _____.

22. _____

23. Technician A says that when a small electric motor is defective, it is usually repaired. Technician B says that an electric motor can be tested by bypassing the controls. Who is right?
(A) A only.
(B) B only.
(C) Both A & B.
(D) Neither A nor B.

23. _____

24. Some motors may require _____ when they are replaced in the vehicle.

24. _____

25. _____ straps can be in place when a motor is reinstalled.

25. _____

Chassis-Mounted Solenoids and Relays

26. Relays are a type of _____ that close electrical contacts.

26. _____

27. Technician A says that power door lock solenoids are four-position solenoids. Technician B says that power door lock solenoids have two windings, allowing them to move the control rod in four directions. Who is right?
(A) A only.
(B) B only.
(C) Both A & B.
(D) Neither A nor B.

27. _____

28. A solenoid can be tested by bypassing the solenoid _____.

28. _____

29. The remote keyless entry system relies on a(n) _____ transmitter to unlock the vehicle door.

29. _____

30. The transmitter used in remote keyless entry systems is _____ to the vehicle.

30. _____

31. Many relays used on late-model vehicles are _____ _____.

31. _____

32. Technician A says that solenoids cannot be repaired. Technician B says that relays use more current than running extra wires, but are more reliable. Who is right?
    (A) A only.
    (B) B only.
    (C) Both A & B.
    (D) Neither A nor B.

32. _____

33. If radio static is only present when the engine is running, it could be caused by the _____.
    (A) alternator
    (B) ground straps
    (C) ignition system
    (D) All of the above.

33. _____

34. Most horn problems are caused by defects in the _____ _____ contacts.

34. _____

35. Most rear window defroster service consists of finding breaks in the _____.

35. _____

Body Computer Systems

36. Technician A says that a body computer controls any function that does not affect the operation of the engine. Technician B says that the sensors, control units, and actuators used in body computer systems are similar to those found in computerized engine control systems. Who is right?
    (A) A only.
    (B) B only.
    (C) Both A & B.
    (D) Neither A nor B.

36. _____

37. The _____ sensor keeps the air bag system from being activated by a faulty impact sensor.

37. _____

38. The air bag is inflated by _____ generating material.

38. _____

39. Many air bag components are not _____.

39. _____

40. When an air bag is deployed, _____ _____ powder is released into the interior.

40. _____

41. This powder released during air bag deployment can cause skin _____.

41. _____

42. All of the following rules should be followed when servicing air bag systems, EXCEPT:
    (A) if any air bag system component is accidentally dropped, the component should be replaced.
    (B) when placing a live inflator module on a workbench, always face the bag and trim cover down.
    (C) always disable the air bag system before attempting to service any component on or near the system.
    (D) never subject the inflator module to temperatures greater than 175°F (79.4°C).

42. _____

43. The common cruise control components include:

(A) _____.

(B) _____.

(C) _____.

(D) _____.

44. The majority of cruise control problems involve the _____   44. _____
linkage or the _____ system.   _____

45. Identify the components of the air bag system shown in the following illustration.

(A) _____

(B) _____

(C) _____

(D) _____

(E) _____

(F) _____

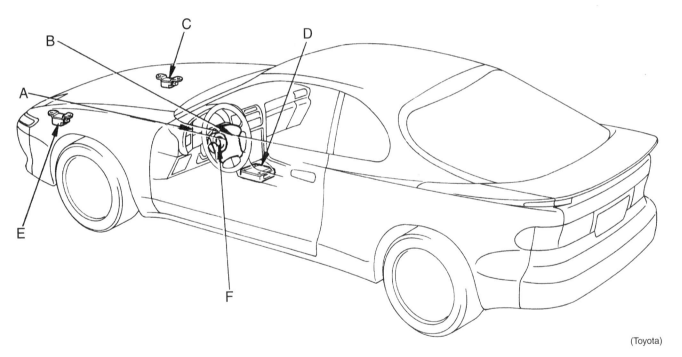

(Toyota)

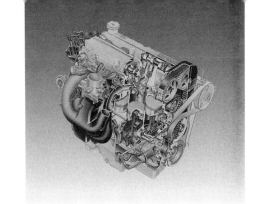

Name _____

Date _____ Period _____

Instructor _____

Score_____

Text pages 567-578

28

Driveability

Objectives: After studying Chapter 28 in the textbook and completing this section of the workbook, you will be able to:

- Identify driveability.
- Explain the differences between tune-ups and driveability diagnosis.
- Explain the modern use of the term tune-up.
- List the basic steps for a maintenance tune-up.
- Summarize important preliminary tests.
- Do road and dynamometer tests.
- Explain engine system problem diagnosis.

Tech Talk: One of the most important areas of modern automotive service is driveability diagnosis. The technician must learn what causes driveability problems and how to cure them. The technician must also discard the old notion of a tune-up as a cure for driveability problems. Tune-ups today are maintenance procedures, similar to an oil change. Study this chapter to become proficient at driveability diagnosis.

Instructions: Study Chapter 28 of the text; then answer the following questions in the spaces provided.

Maintenance Tune-Up

1. In the past, performance and smoothness were restored by the _____ _____. Today performance and smoothness are restored by _____ _____.

    1. _____
       _____

2. The maintenance tune-up is sometimes called a(n) _____ tune-up.

    2. _____

3. Parts that are replaced during a maintenance tune-up include _____ and _____.

    3. _____
       _____

4. Technician A says that before beginning a tune-up, you should have access to the proper engine specifications. Technician B says that the owner comments and service records should be studied to determine whether a maintenance tune-up will solve the problem. Who is right?
    (A) A only.
    (B) B only.
    (C) Both A & B.
    (D) Neither A nor B.

    4. _____

5. Before beginning a tune-up always check engine _____.

5. _____

6. If the distributor cap is replaced, the _____ should also be replaced.

6. _____

7. If the ignition timing is adjustable, it should be checked according to the procedure on the underhood _____ label.

7. _____

8. Before finishing the tune-up, check the _____ system voltage.

8. _____

9. Always conduct a(n) _____ test before returning the vehicle to the customer.

9. _____

Driveability Diagnosis

10. Technician A says that driveability diagnosis is a matter of changing defective parts. Technician B says that when diagnosing a problem, educated guesses should always be avoided. Who is right?
   (A) A only.
   (B) B only.
   (C) Both A & B.
   (D) Neither A nor B.

10. _____

11. Technician A says that knowing the exact problem is not as important as knowing what usually goes bad on a particular engine. Technician B says that it is just as important to correctly interpret test equipment readings as to have the right equipment. Who is right?
   (A) A only.
   (B) B only.
   (C) Both A & B.
   (D) Neither A nor B.

11. _____

12. When diagnosing a driveability problem, the technician should always check the _____ things first.

12. _____

13. Service _____ is vital to driveability diagnosis.

13. _____

14. Trouble codes indicate one of two things. Name them. _____

_____

_____

_____

15. Hard trouble codes are set _____ in the computer's memory.

15. _____

16. Intermittent trouble codes are set _____ in the computer's memory.

16. _____

17. Explain how to separate hard trouble codes and intermittent trouble codes. _____

_____

_____

_____

18. Technician A says that after clearing trouble codes, the vehicle should be operated for at least 10 minutes to check computer system operation. Technician B says that the vehicle should be operated for at least 10 minutes after clearing the trouble codes to see whether any codes reset. Who is right?
    (A) A only.
    (B) B only.
    (C) Both A & B.
    (D) Neither A nor B.

18. _____

- The following illustration should be used when answering questions 19 and 20.

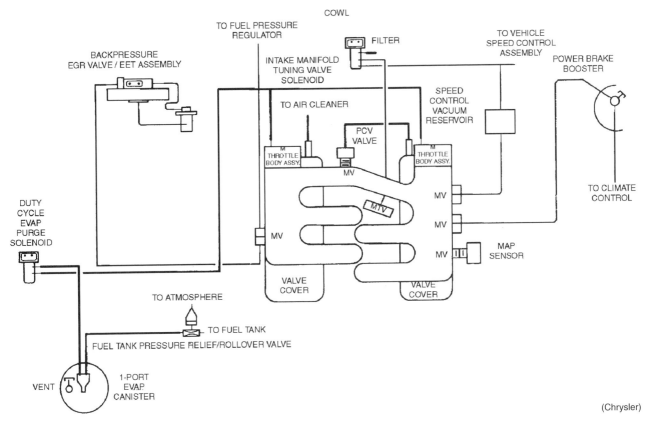

(Chrysler)

19. The schematic above would be useful for checking _____ problems.

19. _____

20. Tracing the connections in the above schematic would enable the technician to check for incorrect hose _____.

20. _____

Name _____

Date _____ Period _____

Instructor _____

Score_____

Text pages 579-597

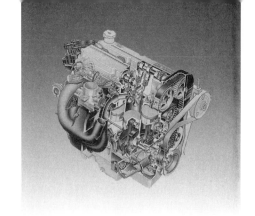

29

Clutch and Flywheel Service

Objectives: After studying Chapter 29 in the textbook and completing this section of the workbook, you will be able to:

- Explain the construction, operation, and service of diaphragm spring clutches.
- Describe the construction, operation, and service of coil spring clutches.
- Adjust different types of clutch linkages.
- Summarize clutch break-in procedures.
- Diagnose clutch problems and suggest possible corrections.

Tech Talk: Manual clutches have not changed much over the years and neither have the causes of clutch problems. Many clutch failures are caused by improper driving techniques. For example, "riding the clutch" (resting foot on clutch pedal while driving) may cause premature throw-out bearing wear. Another poor driving technique is "slipping the clutch" (allowing clutch to slip for extended period when accelerating). This will speed clutch disc wear. When drivers complain of repeated clutch failures, question them about their driving habits.

Instructions: Study Chapter 29 of the text; then answer the following questions in the spaces provided.

Clutch Service

1. Technician A says that the modern clutch consists of one friction disk installed between the flywheel and the pressure plate. Technician B says that the modern clutch consists of two friction disks located between the pressure plate and the bell housing. Who is right?
   (A) A only.
   (B) B only.
   (C) Both A & B.
   (D) Neither A nor B.

   1. _____

2. Clutches contain _____, which can cause cancer.

   2. _____

3. The pressure plate springs can be _____ springs or a(n) _____ spring.

   3. _____
      _____

4. Before condemning the clutch, check the pedal _____ _____.

   4. _____

5. Before removing the pressure plate, mark the pressure plate and _____. This will preserve the assembly _____ if the pressure plate is reused.

5. _____

_____

6. Checking flywheel runout requires a _____.
   (A) dial indicator
   (B) feeler gauge
   (C) micrometer
   (D) All of the above.

6. _____

7. If the flywheel clutch contact area is scored or wavy, the flywheel must be _____ or _____.

7. _____

_____

8. The purpose of the flywheel ring gear is to provide a contact with the _____.
   (A) pressure plate
   (B) friction disc
   (C) starter teeth
   (D) crankshaft

8. _____

9. The ring gear is installed on the flywheel by _____.
   (A) shrink fit
   (B) welds
   (C) bolts
   (D) All of the above, depending on the manufacturer.

9. _____

10. Technician A says that many pressure plates can be rebuilt. Technician B says that it is often cheaper to get a new pressure plate than to rebuild the old plate. Who is right?
    (A) A only.
    (B) B only.
    (C) Both A & B.
    (D) Neither A nor B.

10. _____

11. Rebuilding a pressure plate requires a special fixture or a(n) _____ press.

11. _____

12. Technician A says that pilot bushings should be replaced only if they are obviously bad. Technician B says that pilot bushings should be replaced whenever the clutch is serviced. Who is right?
    (A) A only.
    (B) B only.
    (C) Both A & B.
    (D) Neither A nor B.

12. _____

13. Pilot bushings can be removed using a special _____.

13. _____

14. Pilot bearings should be installed with the _____ side facing away from the transmission.

14. _____

15. Oil leaking from the _____ or from the _____ can quickly ruin a new clutch disc.

15. _____

_____

16. Technician A says that it is usually advisable to install a new clutch disc whenever the clutch has been disassembled. Technician B says that clutch discs are identical and can be installed in either direction. Who is right?
    (A) A only.
    (B) B only.
    (C) Both A & B.
    (D) Neither A nor B.

16. _____

17. The throw-out bearing should be replaced whenever the clutch is _____.

17. _____

18. Some throw-out bearings are one-piece _____ units.

18. _____

19. Do not press on the clutch pedal until _____ is complete.

19. _____

20. Clutch pedal height measurement is usually determined by _____

_____

_____.

21. If a clutch pedal sticks or catches, check for _____.

21. _____

22. When adjusting clutch pedal free travel, measure the distance the _____ moves from the _____ position to the point at which the release fingers are _____.

22. _____
    _____

23. A self-adjusting clutch should be checked for _____.
    (A) worn parts
    (B) kinked cable
    (C) adequate lubrication
    (D) All of the above.

23. _____

24. If the fluid level is low in a hydraulic clutch linkage assembly, check the _____ cylinder, slave cylinder, and connecting _____.

24. _____
    _____

25. Steam cleaning a clutch assembly may cause the parts to _____ together.

25. _____

26. The following illustration shows clutch housing _____ runout being checked.

26. _____

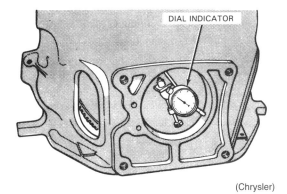

(Chrysler)

27. Label the parts of the clutch assembly shown in the following illustration.

(A) _____

(B) _____

(C) _____

(D) _____

(E) _____

(F) _____

(G) _____

(H) _____

(I) _____

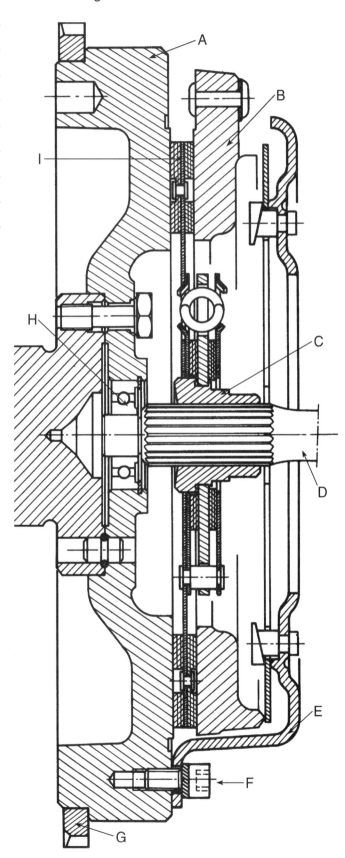

28. Label the parts of the clutch disc shown in the following illustration.

    (A) _____

    (B) _____

    (C) _____

    (D) _____

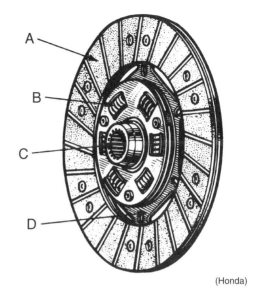

(Honda)

29. Label the parts in the following illustration.

    (A) _____

    (B) _____

    (C) _____

    (D) _____

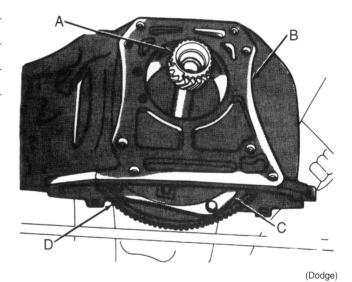

(Dodge)

30. Label the parts of the clutch setup shown in the following illustration.

(A) _____

(B) _____

(C) _____

(D) _____

(E) _____

(F) _____

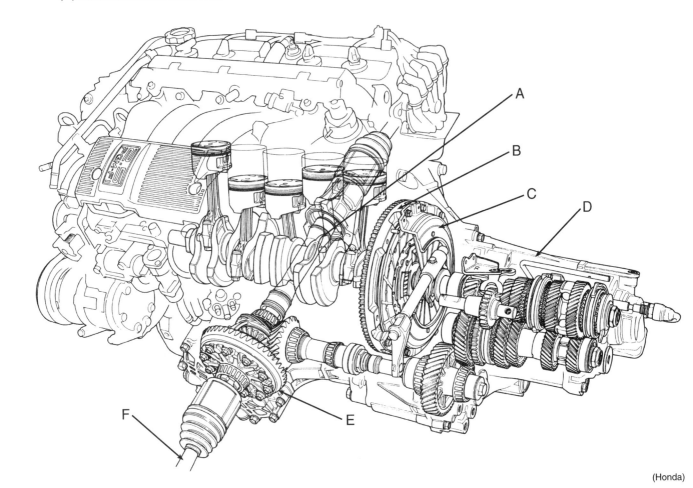

(Honda)

Name _____

Date _____ Period _____

Instructor _____

Score_____

Text pages 599-620

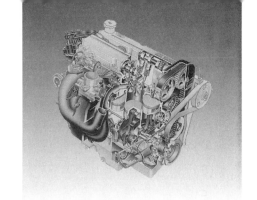

30

Manual Transmission and Transaxle Service

Objectives: After studying Chapter 30 in the textbook and completing this section of the workbook, you will be able to:

- Explain manual transmission construction and operation.
- Explain manual transaxle construction and operation.
- Disassemble, check parts, and reassemble a manual transmission.
- Disassemble, check parts, and reassemble a manual transaxle.
- Diagnose manual transmission and transaxle problems.

Tech Talk: Although most vehicles have automatic transmissions or transaxles, many vehicles—especially economy cars and pickup trucks—have manual transmissions. A renewed interest in fuel economy has made manual transmissions more popular in the last few years. Therefore, the technician must know how to service manual transmissions and transaxles.

Instructions: Study Chapter 30 of the text; then answer the following questions in the spaces provided.

Transmission and Transaxle Designs

1. The three speed transmission provides drive ratios of around _____ to _____ in first gear, 1.70 to 1 in second gear, and 1 to 1 in third gear.

   1. _____
   _____

2. On many four- and five-speed transmissions, the highest gear is a(n) _____.
   (A) planetary gear
   (B) overdrive
   (C) power drive
   (D) None of the above.

   2. _____

3. In a transaxle, the transmission and the _____ assemblies are installed in a single housing.

   3. _____

4. The major differences in the manual transmission and manual transaxle are the shape of the _____ and the placement of _____.

   4. _____
   _____

5. The most obvious external difference between the transmission and transaxle is the presence of two _____ _____ on a transaxle system.

   5. _____

6. Label the working parts of the four-speed synchronized transmission shown in the following illustration.

(A) _____

(B) _____

(C) _____

(D) _____

(E) _____

(F) _____

(G) _____

(H) _____

(I) _____

(J) _____

(Ford)

Servicing Transmissions and Transaxles

7. If the owner complains of hard shifting, gear clash, or jumping out of gear, check the _____ before road testing.

7. _____

8. Failure of the shift linkage to provide full engagement can result in _____.

8. _____

9. Technician A says that whenever possible, a vehicle should be road tested to help pinpoint transmission problems. Technician B says that road tests should never include heavy acceleration or deceleration. Who is right?
   (A) A only.
   (B) B only.
   (C) Both A & B.
   (D) Neither A nor B.

9. _____

10. Some of the repairs that can be performed with the transmission or transaxle in the car include ___

_____

_____.

11. If a U-joint is of the cross-and-roller design, _____ the loose roller bearings together during disassembly to prevent them from falling off.

11. _____

12. When inspecting the gears, shafts, and synchronizers in a manual transmission, turn the gears over slowly while carefully inspecting for _____.
    (A) chipping
    (B) galling
    (C) excessive wear
    (D) All of the above.

12. _____

13. Inspect the synchronizer units for _____.

13. _____

14. It is recommended that a service _____ covering the unit to be repaired be used during transmission service.

14. _____

15. The transmission input shaft can often be removed by lowering _____
_____.

16. Check the clutch pilot bearing end for _____ and _____.   16. _____
_____

17. When replacing a seal in an extension housing, drive the   17. _____
seal into the housing squarely to the proper _____.

18. When inspecting the output shaft bearing surfaces, they   18. _____
should be smooth, with no evidence of _____.

19. When an old part is unfit for service, check the new part   19. _____
against the old for _____.

20. Technician A says that any type of oil can be used as a lubri-   20. _____
cant in a manual transaxle. Technician B says that the dif-
ferential of some transaxles has a separate oil reservoir.
Who is right?
(A) A only.
(B) B only.
(C) Both A & B.
(D) Neither A nor B.

21. By looking at the transmission drawings below, identify the gear positions. Also, use a pencil to
shade the gears transmitting power.

(A) This transmission is in _____gear.

(B) This transmission is in _____gear.

(C) This transmission is in _____gear.

(D) This transmission is in _____gear.

(E) This transmission is in _____gear.

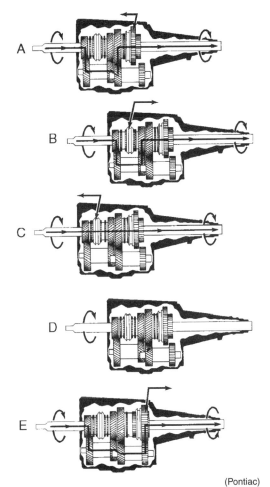

(Pontiac)

22. Label the parts of the manual transaxle in the following illustration.

(A) _____   (O) _____

(B) _____   (P) _____

(C) _____   (Q) _____

(D) _____   (R) _____

(E) _____   (S) _____

(F) _____   (T) _____

(G) _____   (U) _____

(H) _____   (V) _____

(I) _____   (W) _____

(J) _____   (X) _____

(K) _____   (Y) _____

(L) _____   (Z) _____

(M) _____   (AA) _____

(N) _____   (AB) _____

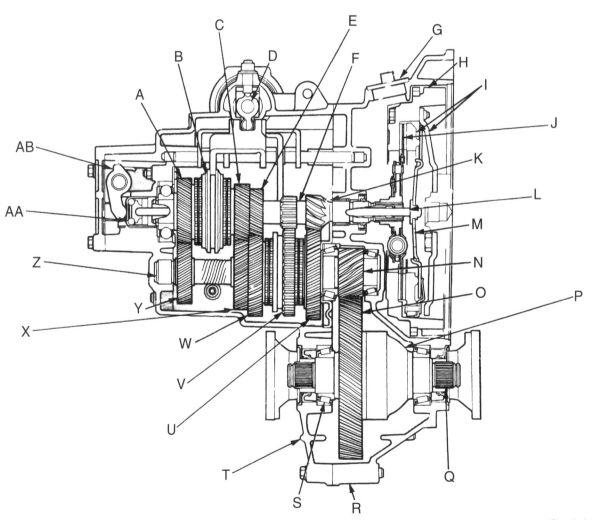

(Chrysler)

23. Label the parts of the synchronizer assembly in the following illustration.

(A) _____

(B) _____

(C) _____

(D) _____

(E) _____

(F) _____

(G) _____

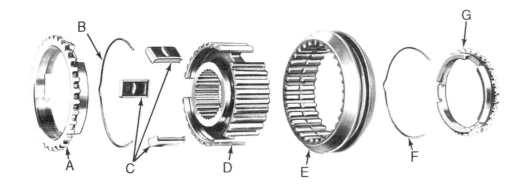

24. Label the parts of the shift mechanism illustrated below.

(A) _____

(B) _____

(C) _____

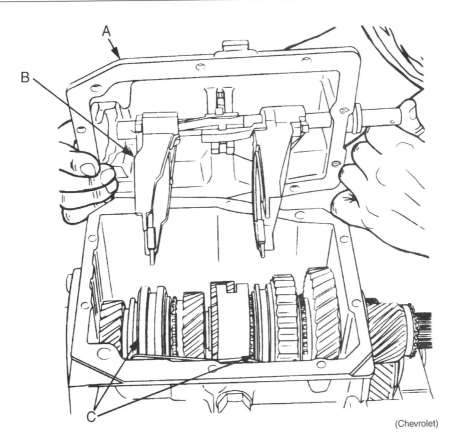

(Chevrolet)

25. Label the parts of the shift cable assembly shown in the following illustration.

(A) _____

(B) _____

(C) _____

(D) _____

(E) _____

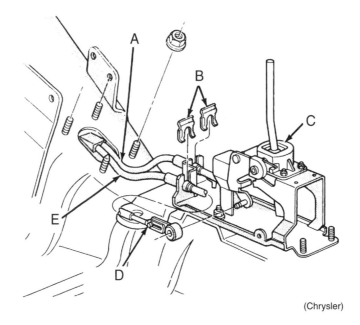

(Chrysler)

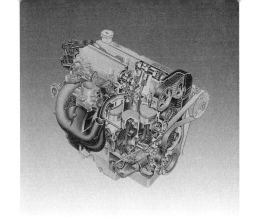

Name _____

Date _____ Period _____

Instructor _____

Score_____

Text pages 621-637

31

Four-Wheel Drive Service

Objectives: After studying Chapter 31 in the textbook and completing this section of the workbook, you will be able to:

- Explain four-wheel drive construction and operation.
- Define part-time and full-time four-wheel drive.
- Disassemble, check parts, and reassemble a transfer case.
- Disassemble, check parts, and reassemble a typical locking hub assembly.
- Diagnose four-wheel drive problems.

Tech Talk: Once only used by military personal, forest rangers, and hunters, four-wheel drive vehicles are now commonly used for commuting and shopping. The advantages of four-wheel drive vehicles on wet and icy roads have prompted their popularity. It is common to find four-wheel drive vehicles that have never been taken off the pavement. The automotive technician must know how to diagnose and repair these vehicles. This chapter will improve your knowledge of four-wheel drive service operations.

Instructions: Study Chapter 31 of the text; then answer the following questions in the spaces provided.

Four-Wheel Drive Components

1. All four-wheel drive vehicles incorporate a transfer case between the transmission _____ shaft and the system _____ shaft.

1. _____
   _____

Transfer Case

2. Technician A says that the transfer case is needed to supply output shaft torque to the front and rear drive shafts. Technician B says that all four-wheel drive vehicles have automatic transmissions. Who is right?
   (A) A only.
   (B) B only.
   (C) Both A & B.
   (D) Neither A nor B.

2. _____

3. If a part time four-wheel drive vehicle is operated on hard, dry surfaces, _____ will cause damage to the unit.

3. _____

4. Full-time four-wheel drive vehicles make use of a(n) _____ assembly or a(n) _____ clutch.

4. _____
   _____

5. Full-time four-wheel drive units often use a(n) _____ drive instead of gears.

5. _____

6. A full-time four-wheel drive _____ mechanism should never be engaged on dry pavement.

6. _____

7. Label the major parts of the four-wheel drive system illustrated below.

(A) _____

(B) _____

(C) _____

(D) _____

(Jeep)

8. Identify the parts of the transmission and transfer case assembly illustrated at the top of the following page.

(A) _____

(B) _____

(C) _____

(D) _____

(E) _____

(F) _____

(G) _____

(H) _____

(I) _____

(J) _____

(K) _____

(L) _____

(M) _____

(N) _____

(O) _____

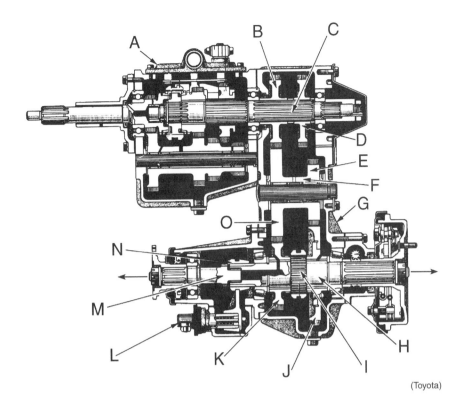

(Toyota)

Transfer Case Service

9. To begin diagnosis of a four-wheel drive mechanism, _____ _____ the vehicle after checking the lubricant level.

9. _____

10. Transfer case overhaul is similar to that of the _____. Use a(n) _____ for detailed instructions.

10. _____
_____

11. Technician A says that drive shafts should be marked before removal. Technician B says that pilot bolts can be used to facilitate transfer case removal. Who is right?
   (A) A only.
   (B) B only.
   (C) Both A & B.
   (D) Neither A nor B.

11. _____

12. If a transfer case support member must be removed, support the transfer case with a(n) _____.

12. _____

13. Technician A says that the outer surfaces of the transfer case should be cleaned thoroughly after disassembly. Technician B says that all transfer case designs are similar. Who is right?
   (A) A only.
   (B) B only.
   (C) Both A & B.
   (D) Neither A nor B.

13. _____

14. Use a(n) _____ hammer when parts must be hammered loose.

14. _____

15. A leaking viscous coupling will show up as globules of _____ in the transfer case lubricant.

15. _____

16. Any grease used to hold internal parts in place must _____   16. _____
in the lubricant used in the transfer case.

17. Label the parts of the transfer case lubrication pump shown in the following illustration.

(A) _____

(B) _____

(C) _____

(D) _____

(E) _____

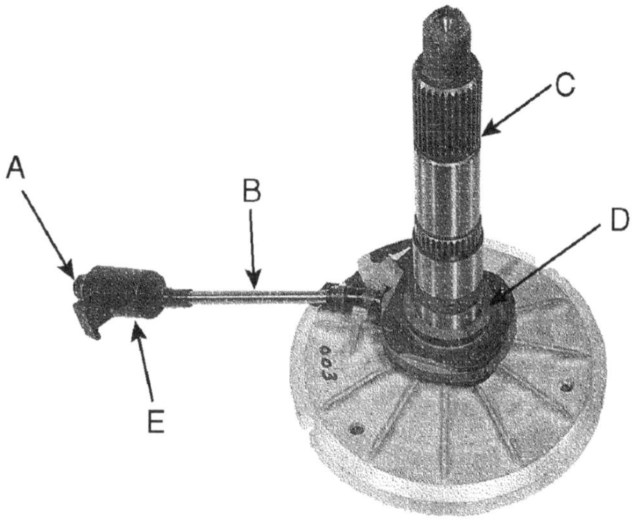

(Borg-Warner)

Locking Hubs

18. Locking hubs are much more likely than other parts to be   18. _____
damaged from the effects of _____.
    (A) dirt and water
    (B) low case oil level
    (C) maladjusted linkage
    (D) All of the above.

Vacuum Motor Service

19. A leaking _____ motor should be replaced.   19. _____

20. Label the parts of the vacuum motor and shift fork assembly shown in the following illustration.

(A) _____

(B) _____

(C) _____

(D) _____

(E) _____

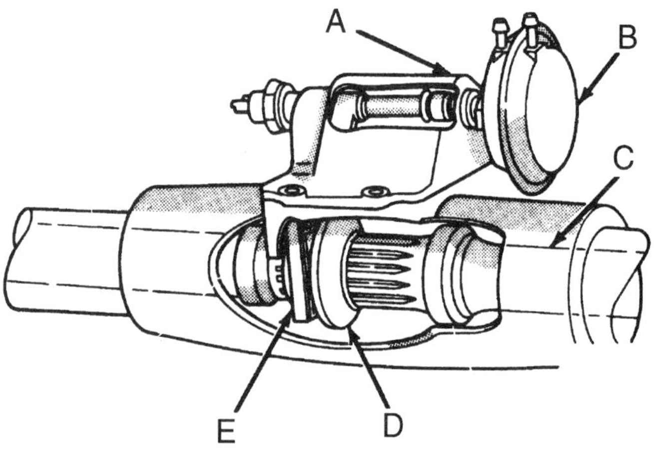

(Dodge)

Name _____

Date _____ Period _____

Instructor _____

Score_____

Text pages 639-667

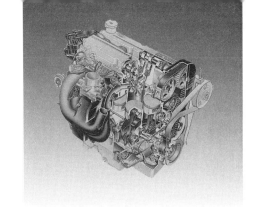

32

Automatic Transmission and Transaxle Service

Objectives: After studying Chapter 32 in the textbook and completing this section of the workbook, you will be able to:

- Explain automatic transmission and transaxle in-vehicle service and diagnosis.
- Explain towing procedures for vehicles with automatic transmissions and transaxles.
- Summarize the adjustment of automatic transmission and transaxle linkage.
- Explain automatic transmission and transaxle shift linkage and band adjustment.
- Describe common automatic transmission/transaxle testing tools and equipment.
- Summarize automatic transmission and transaxle removal and installation.
- List common automatic transmission and transaxle problems and corrections.
- Road test an automatic transmission or transaxle.

Tech Talk: Automatic transmissions and transaxles are complex devices that operate on various hydraulic and mechanical principles. Modern automatic transmissions are also partially or fully controlled by on-board computers. This means that the technician must have an understanding of mechanical, hydraulic, *and* electrical principles to properly service late-model automatic transmissions and transaxles. Nevertheless, many problems will have simple solutions, and like any part on the vehicle, the transmission/transaxle assembly can be diagnosed using logical troubleshooting techniques. Answer the following questions to increase your knowledge of automatic transmission and transaxle diagnosis and service.

Instructions: Study Chapter 32 of the text; then answer the following questions in the spaces provided.

Automatic Transmission/Transaxle

1. Technician A says that most torque converters have a lock-up clutch to increase fuel mileage. Technician B says that a lockup clutch can be applied in any gear except reverse and high. Who is right?
   (A) A only.
   (B) B only.
   (C) Both A & B.
   (D) Neither A nor B.

1. _____

2. Automatic transmission gear ratios are obtained by the use of _____ gearsets.

2. _____

3. The three main types of holding members are:

(A) _____

(B) _____

(C) _____

4. Match the component on the left with its description on the right.

<table>
<tr><td>___main pressure regulator</td><td>(A) driven by output shaft.</td></tr>
<tr><td>___manual valve</td><td>(B) redirect pressure to holding members.</td></tr>
<tr><td>___shift valves</td><td>(C) controls overall system pressure.</td></tr>
<tr><td>___throttle valve</td><td>(D) operated by driver.</td></tr>
<tr><td>___governor valve</td><td>(E) controls lockup clutch.</td></tr>
<tr><td>___filter</td><td>(F) operated by linkage or modulator.</td></tr>
<tr><td>___accumulator</td><td>(G) cushions shifts.</td></tr>
<tr><td>___servos</td><td>(H) removes dirt and metal.</td></tr>
<tr><td></td><td>(I) apply bands.</td></tr>
</table>

5. Transmissions are used on vehicles with _____ engines and _____ wheel drive.

5. _____

_____

6. A transverse transaxle mounting means that the transaxle is installed _____ in the vehicle.

6. _____

In-Vehicle Service and Problem Diagnosis

7. A large percentage of transmission problems can be solved by _____

_____.

8. Vehicles with automatic transmissions cannot be started by _____.

8. _____

9. Vehicles with automatic transmissions should be _____ for short distances if the drive shaft(s) are not removed.

9. _____

10. Always check transmission _____ before conducting any tests.

10. _____

11. Technician A says that a high fluid level (above the full mark) can cause aeration. Technician B says that a low transmission fluid level may cause overheating. Who is right?
(A) A only.
(B) B only.
(C) Both A & B.
(D) Neither A nor B.

11. _____

12. What four things should the technician be sure of when checking the automatic transmission fluid level?

(A) _____

(B) _____

(C) _____

(D) _____

13. When examining the fluid level on the dipstick, check the oil for _____

_____.

14. If any water is present in the transmission fluid, the fluid will look _____.

14. _____

15. _____ or _____ fluid is recommended for almost all modern automatic transmissions and transaxles.

15. _____
_____

16. Fluid and filter change cycles range from _____ to _____ miles (_____ to _____ km).

16. _____
_____

17. Most modern transmission and transaxle pans do not have a(n) _____ _____.

17. _____

18. Technician A says that the oil pan must be removed to change the transmission filter. Technician B says that the oil pan may require removal to make some band adjustments. Who is right?
(A) A only.
(B) B only.
(C) Both A & B.
(D) Neither A nor B.

18. _____

19. Adding _____ transmission fluid to a sludge-filled transmission or transaxle may cause quick failure.

19. _____

20. All of the following statements about band adjustment are true, EXCEPT:
(A) some bands are adjusted by adding or subtracting shims inside the servo.
(B) all bands can be adjusted without disassembling the transmission.
(C) some bands are adjusted by turning an adjusting screw.
(D) all bands should be adjusted to factory specifications.

20. _____

21. Following any type of band adjustment, the vehicle should be _____ tested.
(A) pressure
(B) leak
(C) road
(D) All of the above.

21. _____

22. After adjusting the shift linkage, make sure that the _____ pawl works correctly.

22. _____

23. Faulty throttle linkage adjustment will cause incorrect _____ points and may result in transmission/transaxle _____.

23. _____
_____

24. On some transmissions, a vacuum _____ is used in place of shift linkage.

24. _____

25. Forced downshifts can be accomplished mechanically by _____ or _____ or electrically by a switch and _____.

25. _____
_____
_____

26. If the neutral safety switch is operating correctly, the engine will crank with the shifter in _____ or _____ only.

26. _____
_____

27. Do not attempt to diagnose transmission/transaxle problems until you are sure that the _____ is in good condition.

27. _____

28. Technician A says that separating torque converter lockup from a gear change is sometimes difficult. Technician B says that a gear change will cause a smaller RPM drop than torque converter lockup. Who is right?
    (A) A only.
    (B) B only.
    (C) Both A & B.
    (D) Neither A nor B.

28. _____

29. A pressure test is used to test the condition of the _____ system.

29. _____

30. A stall test is useful for checking the condition of all the following, EXCEPT:
    (A) bands.
    (B) disc clutches.
    (C) one-way clutches.
    (D) pressure regulators.

30. _____

31. Cracks in the transmission case can often be fixed with _____.

31. _____

32. Sealing surfaces should be thoroughly _____.

32. _____

33. The lip of a transmission/transaxle seal should always face _____.

33. _____

34. To change solenoids or pressure sensors, the _____ must be removed.
    (A) oil pan
    (B) valve body
    (C) transmission
    (D) None of the above.

34. _____

35. The valve body assembly is removed by _____

_____.

36. If a valve is sticking in the valve body, it can be _____ and _____.

36. _____
    _____

37. The removal of the valve body makes it possible to apply _____ pressure to check clutch and band operation.

37. _____

38. The following illustration shows an automatic transmission and torque converter being drained. Identify the parts indicated.

    (A) _____

    (B) _____

    (C) _____

39. Identify the parts in the following illustration.

(A) _____

(B) _____

(C) _____

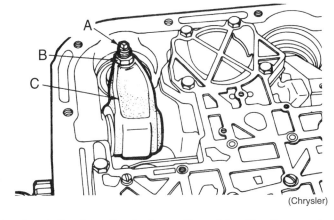

(Chrysler)

40. Draw the oil leaking from the transmission in the following illustration. Also, identify the parts indicated.

(A) _____

(B) _____

(C) _____

(D) _____

(E) _____

(F) _____

(G) _____

(H) _____

(I) _____

(J) _____

(K) _____

(L) _____

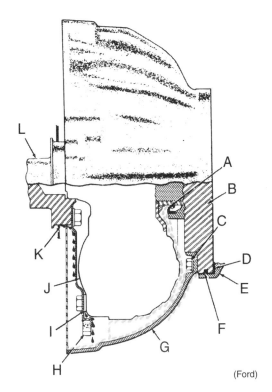

(Ford)

41. Air pressure is being applied in the illustration below to check _____ _____.

41. _____

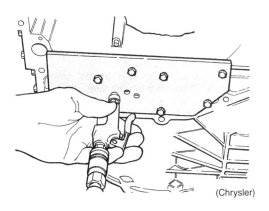

(Chrysler)

42. Identify the oil passages shown in the following illustration.

(A) _____

(B) _____

(C) _____

(D) _____

(E) _____

(F) _____

(G) _____

(H) _____

(I) _____

(J) _____

(K) _____

(L) _____

(M) _____

(N) _____

(O) _____

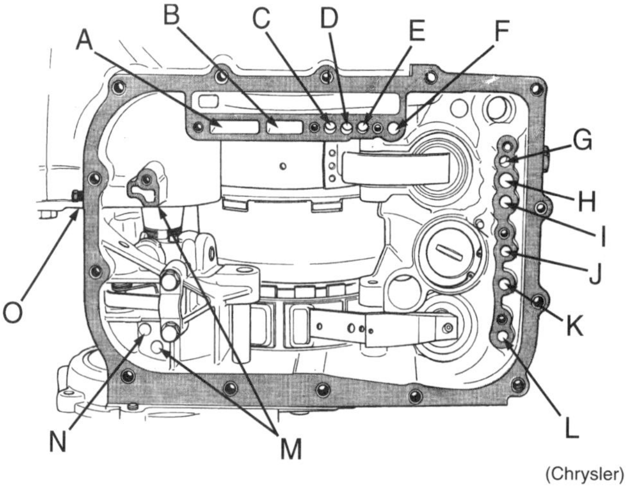

(Chrysler)

Transmission or Transaxle Removal

43. The transmission or transaxle and the _____ should always   43. _____
    be removed from the vehicle together.

44. To avoid the possibility of damage to a new or rebuilt transmission (contamination present in trans-
    mission before service), the oil cooler and lines should be _____

    _____ .

Transmission Installation

45. When installing a transmission, make sure the converter is   45. _____
    mounted in the transmission front _____ and to the full

    _____

    _____ .

Name _____

Date _____ Period _____

Instructor _____

Score_____

Text pages 669-711

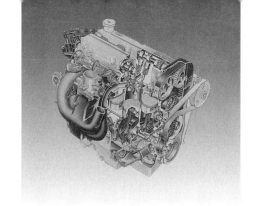

33

Axle and Driveline Service

Objectives: After studying Chapter 33 in the textbook and completing this section of the workbook, you will be able to:

- Explain the construction and operation of one- and two-piece Hotchkiss drive shafts.
- Service one- and two-piece drivelines.
- Describe cross-and-roller universal joints.
- Service cross-and-roller universal joints.
- Diagnose driveline and universal joint problems.
- Explain the construction and operation of front-wheel drive CV axles.
- Explain the construction and operation of CV joints.
- Service CV axles, joints, and boots.
- Explain the construction, operation, and service of axle housings.
- Compare drive axle types.
- Describe the construction, operation, and service of differentials.
- Diagnose differential and axle problems.

Tech Talk: Although many late-model cars are equipped with front-wheel drive systems, most new trucks and many older cars have rear-wheel drives. Therefore, the technician must know how to service both types of drivelines. Study this chapter carefully.

Instructions: Study Chapter 33 of the text; then answer the following questions in the spaces provided.

Rear Wheel Drive Shaft Service

1. The Hotchkiss drive consists of _____ or more pieces.

1. _____

2. Technician A says that the slip yoke allows lengthwise movement between the transmission and the rear axle housing. Technician B says that the slip yoke slides onto the splined transmission output shaft. Who is right?
   (A) A only.
   (B) B only.
   (C) Both A & B.
   (D) Neither A nor B.

2. _____

3. A two-piece propeller shaft requires the use of a(n) _____.

3. _____

4. The cross rollers can be retained by _____ _____ set into the yoke at the outer ends of the rollers.

4. _____

5. With a constant velocity universal joint, both the input and the output sides of the joint _____ at the same _____ throughout the full 360° of rotation.

5. _____
   _____

6. If the universal joint rollers are not retained with a thin strap, _____ them to prevent dropping the needle bearings.

6. _____

7. To remove a cross and roller U-joint, tap the _____ _____ inward a small amount to free the snap ring. Place the yoke between the jaws of a heavy _____ so that the yoke is just free to move. Strike the yoke sharply with a lead, brass, or plastic hammer.

7. _____
   _____

8. If the inside of the rollers and the trunnion bearing surfaces are free of _____ and _____, the parts may be reused.

8. _____
   _____

9. During inspection, try the rollers on the trunnions to check for evidence of _____.

9. _____

10. When assembling the universal joint, pack the bearing cap _____ with the recommended lubricant.

10. _____

11. The constant velocity universal joint is literally _____ cross and bearing cap joints attached to a center _____.

11. _____
    _____

12. During propeller shaft installation, make sure the bearing cap _____ are underneath the locating _____ on the differential yoke before tightening the U-bolts.

12. _____
    _____

13. Technician A says that the propeller shaft turns at high rpm when the vehicle is in high gear. Technician B says that the propeller shaft must be accurately balanced to prevent vibration. Who is right?
    (A) A only.
    (B) B only.
    (C) Both A & B.
    (D) Neither A nor B.

13. _____

14. If a car is being undercoated, keep the _____ _____ and _____ _____ covered.

14. _____
    _____

15. The drive shaft may be checked for runout by using a(n) _____ _____.

15. _____

16. Minor drive shaft unbalance can usually be corrected by using _____ _____.

16. _____

17. When universal joints are forced to operate at an angle other than specified, they may cause _____.

17. _____

18. Label the parts of the drive shaft shown in the following illustration.

(A) _____

(B) _____

(C) _____

(D) _____

(E) _____

(F) _____

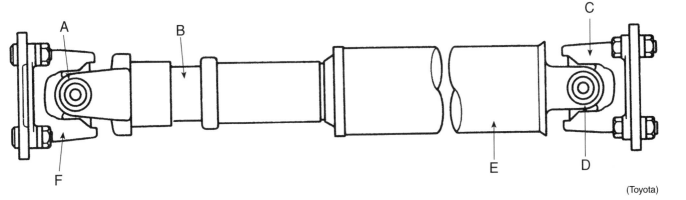

(Toyota)

19. Label the parts of the two-piece drive shaft shown in the following illustration.

(A) _____

(B) _____

(C) _____

(D) _____

(E) _____

(F) _____

(G) _____

(H) _____

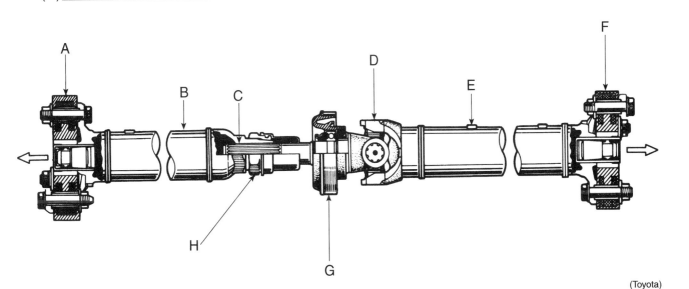

(Toyota)

20. Identify the parts of the universal joint shown in the following illustration.

(A) _____

(B) _____

(C) _____

(D) _____

(E) _____

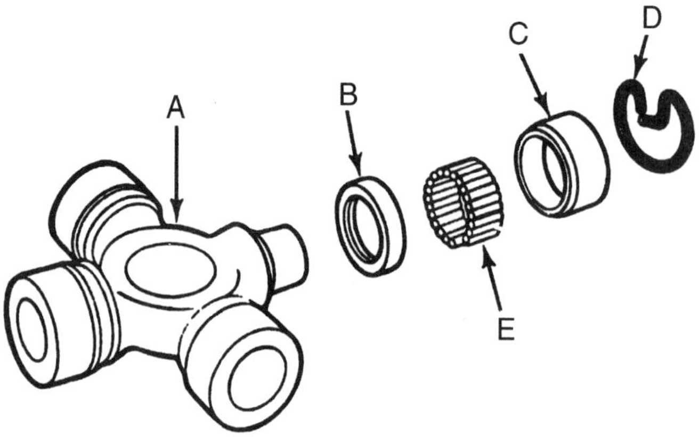

(Spicer)

Front-Wheel Drive CV Axle Service

21. The two main types of CV joint are the _____ joint and the _____ joint.

21. _____
    _____

22. On some vehicles, the steering _____ must be removed before the CV axle can be removed.

22. _____

23. The inner end of most CV axles is held to the transaxle by an internal _____.
    (A) bolt and nut
    (B) snap ring
    (C) c-lock
    (D) All of the above, depending on the manufacturer.

23. _____

24. All of the following statements about CV joint service are true, EXCEPT:
    (A) the boot straps should be removed after the CV joint is disassembled.
    (B) if a CV joint will not come apart, it can be tapped lightly with a hammer.
    (C) the Rzeppa joint cage must be tilted to remove the balls.
    (D) tripod joints will slide apart.

24. _____

25. Identify the parts of the front wheel axle illustrated at the top of the following page.

(A) _____   (L) _____

(B) _____   (M) _____

(C) _____   (N) _____

(D) _____   (O) _____

(E) _____   (P) _____

(F) _____   (Q) _____

(G) _____   (R) _____

(H) _____   (S) _____

(I) _____   (T) _____

(J) _____   (U) _____

(K) _____   (V) _____

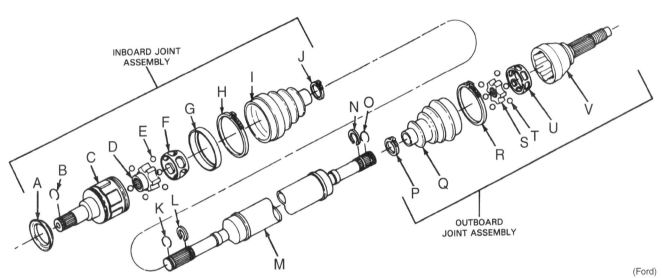

(Ford)

Servicing Axle Shafts

26. The typical automotive rear-wheel drive axle assembly is of the semifloating design in which the axle _____ the wheel.
    (A) retains
    (B) supports
    (C) drives
    (D) All of the above.

26. _____

27. Technician A says that an axle can be retained in the housing by a retainer plate. Technician B says that an axle can be retained in the housing by axle shaft locks on the inner ends of the axles. Who is right?
    (A) A only.
    (B) B only.
    (C) Both A & B.
    (D) Neither A nor B.

27. _____

28. The rear axles used with independent rear suspensions resemble small _____ _____.

28. _____

29. To pull an axle, remove the wheel and the _____ which may have retaining fasteners. Then, remove the nuts from the bearing retainer. Attach a slide-type puller to the axle _____. With a few sharp blows, remove the axle.

29. _____
    _____

30. On some rear axle applications, the axle is retained with a(n) _____.

30. _____

31. Technician A says that to remove an axle with a C-lock, the differential drive pinion should be removed. Technician B says that to remove an axle with a C-lock, the differential pinion shaft should be removed. Who is right?
    (A) A only.
    (B) B only.
    (C) Both A & B.
    (D) Neither A nor B.

31. _____

32. A section of broken axle may often be retrieved from the housing by using _____.

32. _____

33. Following axle removal, always install new _____ _____ to prevent oil leakage.

33. _____

34. When installing an axle, pass the splined end of the axle through the _____ _____ very carefully to avoid damage.

34. _____

35. Define *axle end play measurement*. _____

    _____

    _____

36. Label the parts of the rear drive axle assembly shown in the illustration at the top of the next page.

    (A) _____   (N) _____
    (B) _____   (O) _____
    (C) _____   (P) _____
    (D) _____   (Q) _____
    (E) _____   (R) _____
    (F) _____   (S) _____
    (G) _____   (T) _____
    (H) _____   (U) _____
    (I) _____   (V) _____
    (J) _____   (W) _____
    (K) _____   (X) _____
    (L) _____   (Y) _____
    (M) _____   (Z) _____

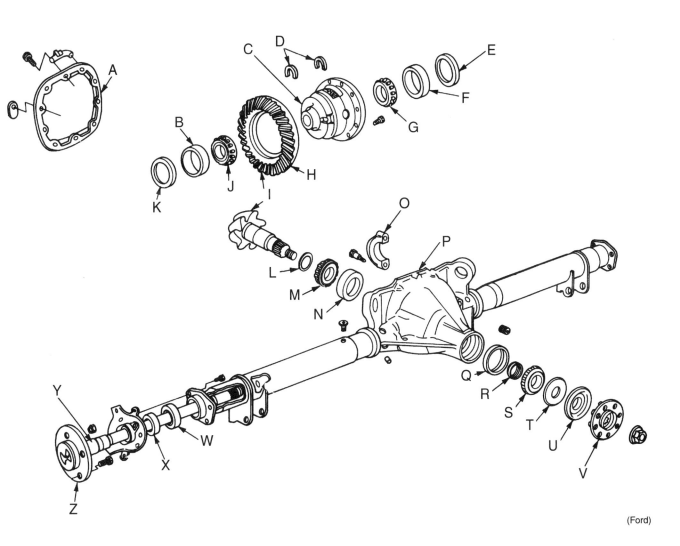

(Ford)

37. Identify the parts of the axle assembly illustrated below.

(A) _____

(B) _____

(C) _____

(D) _____

(E) _____

(F) _____

(G) _____

(H) _____

(I) _____

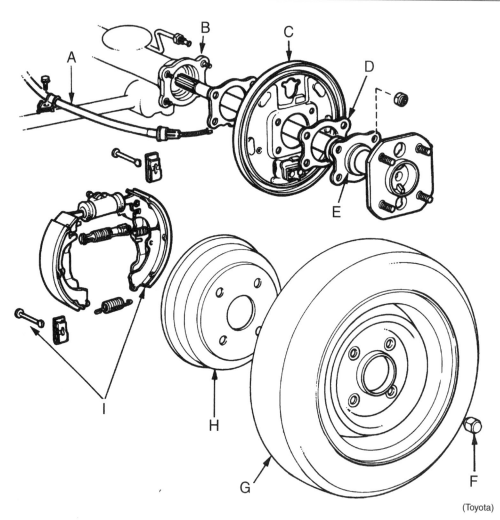

(Toyota)

Ring and Pinion, Differential Unit Service

38. The ring and pinion used on modern rear-wheel drive vehicles are _____ gears.

38. _____

39. When testing a drive axle, check the action during _____, _____, and _____ conditions.

39. _____

_____

_____

40. Various vehicle parts can cause noises that may be
mistaken for rear axle noises, including _____.
(A) tires
(B) front wheel bearings
(C) engine
(D) All of the above.

40. _____

41. What sounds do bearings tend to produce? _____

_____

42. Technician A says that sounds produced by gears are usu-
ally of variable pitch. Technician B says that gear noises will
sound the same under all pull conditions. Who is right?
(A) A only.
(B) B only.
(C) Both A & B.
(D) Neither A nor B.

42. _____

43. Defective _____ _____ bearings will produce a continuous
growl that is the same in all pull conditions.

43. _____

44. When will differential pinion and side gear noise be noticeable? _____

_____

45. A clanking sound during acceleration or deceleration may
be caused by all of the following, EXCEPT:
(A) worn universal joints.
(B) insufficient ring and pinion backlash.
(C) a worn transmission.
(D) a worn drive pinion shaft.

45. _____

46. Before removing the differential side bearing caps, make
certain each _____ and _____ is marked.

46. _____
      _____

47. When new side bearings are used, use new _____ also.

47. _____

48. When either a new ring gear or pinion drive is required, they
should be replaced as a(n) _____.

48. _____

49. Ring gear fasteners should be tightened _____, first on one
side and then on the other.

49. _____

50. Define *gear ratio.* _____

_____

_____

51. Define *pinion gear depth.*_____

_____

_____

52. If the original ring and pinion, inner bearing, and carrier will
be used, the original _____ will give the proper pinion depth.

52. _____

53. To prevent the pinion gear from moving away from the
_____ under load, the pinion bearings must be properly
_____.

53. _____
      _____

54. A(n) _____ is used to check gear backlash.   54. _____

55. Technician A says that differential gear pattern shape   55. _____
varies, depending on gear design, wear, and load.
Technician B says that in general, the differential gear pat-
tern should be uneven around the ring. Who is right?
(A) A only.
(B) B only.
(C) Both A & B.
(D) Neither A nor B.

56. The drive side of the ring gear is the _____ side. The coast   56. _____
side of the ring gear is the _____ side.   _____

57. Technician A says that a heel contact pattern is caused by   57. _____
excessive backlash. Technician B says that excessive back-
lash is corrected by moving the ring toward the pinion. Who
is right?
(A) A only.
(B) B only.
(C) Both A & B.
(D) Neither A nor B.

58. Define *limited slip differential.* _____

_____

_____

59. When checking the fluid level on a cold differential assem-   59. _____
bly, the level should be up to _____ below the filler hole.
(A) 1/2″
(B) 3/4″
(C) 1″
(D) None of the above.

60. What is being measured in the following illustration? _____

_____

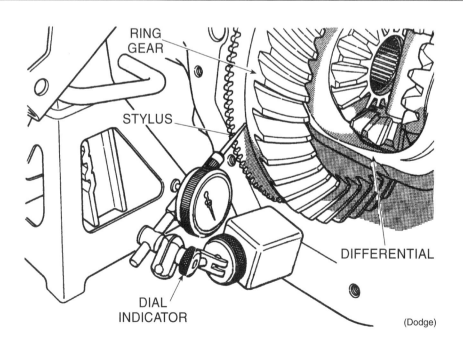

RING GEAR

STYLUS

DIFFERENTIAL

DIAL INDICATOR

(Dodge)

Name _____

Date _____ Period _____

Instructor _____

Score_____

Text pages 713-751

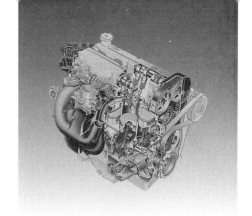

34

Brake Service

Objectives: After studying Chapter 34 in the textbook and completing this section of the workbook, you will be able to:

- Explain drum brake construction, operation, and service.
- Summarize disc brake construction, operation, and service.
- Explain the operation and service of power brakes.
- Explain the operation and service of anti-lock brake system.
- Describe master cylinder operation, construction, and service.
- Diagnose brake hydraulic system problems.
- Diagnose brake friction system problems.
- Diagnose power brake system problems.

Tech Talk: The principles of automotive brake system operation have not changed much over the years. The same basic parts are used to produce friction for slowing and stopping the car. Recent trends to increase fuel economy, however, have made auto manufacturers use lighter materials. Aluminum and plastic parts are now being used in the brake system. Keep this in mind during service. These parts may be damaged more easily than conventional cast iron components.

Instructions: Study Chapter 34 of the text; then answer the following questions in the spaces provided.

Brake Inspection

1. Brake friction materials may contain _____, which is a known carcinogen.

2. During system inspection, the pedal should be firm, with no _____ feel.

3. A periodic wheel cylinder and brake shoe inspection generally involves pulling a(n) _____ and _____.

4. Brake drums should be checked for _____.
   (A) out-of-round
   (B) taper
   (C) scoring
   (D) All of the above.

1. _____

2. _____

3. _____
   _____

4. _____

5. Technician A says that disc brake pads should be checked for taper. Technician B says that disc brake rotors should be checked for scoring and cracking. Who is right?
   (A) A only.
   (B) B only.
   (C) Both A & B.
   (D) Neither A nor B.

5. _____

6. Caliper pistons should show no signs of fluid _____.

6. _____

7. Technician A says that a brake inspection must include a check for loose wheel bearings. Technician B says that a brake inspection should include a check for worn steering parts. Who is right?
   (A) A only.
   (B) B only.
   (C) Both A & B.
   (D) Neither A nor B.

7. _____

8. Identify the brake system inspection points in the following illustration.

   (A) _____   (H) _____

   (B) _____   (I) _____

   (C) _____   (J) _____

   (D) _____   (K) _____

   (E) _____   (L) _____

   (F) _____   (M) _____

   (G) _____   (N) _____

(Bendix)

Brake Hydraulic System Operation

9. The brake hydraulic system uses a master cylinder to develop _____ _____.

9. _____

10. Never mix regular and _____ brake fluids.

10. _____

11. When the brake pedal is released, the brake shoe _____
force fluid to flow backward into the master cylinder _____.

11. _____

_____

12. For years, the hydraulic brake system had one serious flaw in that a system leak could cause ___

_____.

13. The double piston (also called the dual piston or split system) master cylinder was developed so that the _____
_____ for the front and rear wheels could be completely
separated.

13. _____

14. With the dual system, failure of either the front or rear system will be evident by a(n)_____

_____.

15. A quick-take-up master cylinder is used with _____ _____
disc brake calipers.

15. _____

16. Brake fluid level should be around _____" (_____mm) from
the top of the reservoir.

16. _____

17. If an aluminum master cylinder has any scratches or other
imperfections, it should be _____.

17. _____

18. The cylinder, cups, and pistons must be coated with _____
before assembly.

18. _____

19. Define *brake pedal free travel.* _____

_____

_____

_____

20. Technician A says that proper free travel for manual brakes
is around 1". Technician B says that for power-assisted
brakes, free travel ranges from 1/8" to 3/8". Who is right?
(A) A only.
(B) B only.
(C) Both A & B.
(D) Neither A nor B.

20. _____

21. If the wheel cylinder has a special glassy, rolled finish, it
should not be _____.

21. _____

22. Technician A says that rebuilt wheel cylinders generally last
longer than new cylinders. Technician B says that it is often
more expensive to rebuild a wheel cylinder than to replace
it. Who is right?
(A) A only.
(B) B only.
(C) Both A & B.
(D) Neither A nor B.

22. _____

23. Disc brakes, as the name implies, use a heavy _____
instead of a conventional brake drum.

23. _____

24. Disc brakes are highly resistant to _____.

24. _____

25. The floating caliper often uses only one _____.

25. _____

26. Caliper bore size must not be increased by more than
_____″ (_____mm).

26. _____

27. A caliper cylinder bore in good condition can often be
cleaned by _____.

27. _____

28. Technician A says that brake lines must be free of kinks,
dents, rust, and abraded areas. Technician B says that
brake hoses must be free of cracking, kinking, swelling, and
cuts. Who is right?
(A) A only.
(B) B only.
(C) Both A & B.
(D) Neither A nor B.

28. _____

29. Technician A says that double-wrapped steel tubing should
be used for brake lines. Technician B says that copper tub-
ing can be used for brake lines. Who is right?
(A) A only.
(B) B only.
(C) Both A & B.
(D) Neither A nor B.

29. _____

30. A proportioning valve is used in the brake system with
_____ brakes in the front and _____ brakes in the rear.

30. _____
_____

31. A proportioning valve controls (and finally limits) _____ to
the rear wheels. This reduces the possibility of rear-wheel
_____ during heavy braking.

31. _____
_____

32. A height-sensing proportioning valve compensates for
changes in vehicle _____.

32. _____

33. The metering valve closes off _____

_____

_____.

34. Define *pressure differential valve.* _____

_____

_____

35. Define *combination valve.* _____

_____

_____

36. Define *brake bleeding.* _____

_____

_____

37. Technician A says that pressure bleeding is slower than manual bleeding. Technician B says that when front disc brakes are used, the metering valve must be blocked open when bleeding. Who is right?

37. _____

   (A) A only.
   (B) B only.
   (C) Both A & B.
   (D) Neither A nor B.

38. In the following illustration, the distance that the master cylinder push rod protrudes from the vacuum booster is being checked. Label the parts indicated.

   (A) _____

   (B) _____

   (C) _____

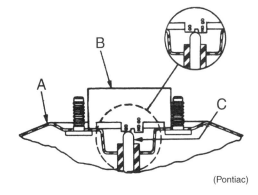

(Pontiac)

39. Identify the tools and parts in the following illustrations.

   (A) _____

   (B) _____

   (C) _____

   (D) _____

   (E) _____

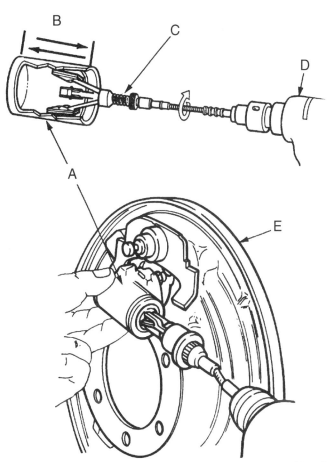

(Niehoff)

40. Label the parts of the pressure differential warning switch in the following illustration.

(A) _____

(B) _____

(C) _____

(D) _____

(E) _____

(Chevrolet)

41. Label the parts of the combination valve in the following illustration.

(A) _____

(B) _____

(C) _____

(D) _____

(E) _____

(Bendix)

Brake Friction Member Service

42. Define *servo brake*. _____

_____

43. The drum brake design in wide use today is the _____.

43. _____

44. Before attempting to remove the shoes, study the _____. This will help you during reassembly.

44. _____

45. Remember that even the slightest amount of oil or grease on the linings will _____.

45. _____

46. Technician A says that brakes with self-adjusting shoes need only an initial adjustment following installation of new shoes. Technician B says that a special gauge is used to adjust the self-adjusting shoes to the brake drum diameter. Who is right?
(A) A only.
(B) B only.
(C) Both A & B.
(D) Neither A nor B.

46. _____

47. Regardless of the wear determining service, pads should be
    changed when worn to within _____.

47. _____

48. Identify the parts in the following illustration.

    (A) _____

    (B) _____

    (C) _____

    (D) _____

    (E) _____

FRONT

(Bendix)

Drum and Disc Service

49. Inspect the brake drums for _____.
    (A) scoring
    (B) heat checking
    (C) cracking
    (D) All of the above.

49. _____

50. Drum scoring, bell-mouth and barrel wear may be removed
    by _____.

50. _____

51. Any drum measuring more than .010″ (0.254 mm) out-of-
    round or more than .005″ (0.217 mm) taper should be
    _____ by turning or grinding.

51. _____

52. Technician A says that drums that measure over .060″
    above standard must be trued. Technician B says that if the
    drum appears serviceable without turning, is should be
    polished with steel wool. Who is right?
    (A) A only.
    (B) B only.
    (C) Both A & B.
    (D) Neither A nor B.

52. _____

53. A turned brake drum finish can be slightly more resistant to
    _____ and _____ than a ground surface.

53. _____

    _____

54. New brake drums are usually given a protective coating to
    guard against rust, _____ and clean the braking surface
    with _____.

54. _____

    _____

55. Technician A says that when using a metallic lining, the
drum must be honed to a 50 micro-inch finish. Technician B
says that when using a metallic lining, special heat-resistant
springs must be used. Who is right?
(A) A only.
(B) B only.
(C) Both A & B.
(D) Neither A nor B.

55. _____

56. Rotor scoring up to around _____ (_____) deep, as long
as the disc is smooth, is permissible.

56. _____

57. Before checking a disc for lateral runout, set the _____
_____ _____ clearance to just remove any end play.

57. _____

58. Maximum rotor runout should not exceed _____ (_____).

58. _____

59. When wear has reduced disc thickness beyond recommended limits, the disc should be _____.

59. _____

Parking Brake Adjustments

60. To adjust a rear wheel type parking brake, apply the parking
brake about three notches (about 1 3/4″ or 44.5 mm) travel.
Adjust the equalizer _____ until a slight _____ is noticeable
at the rear wheels.

60. _____
_____

61. Technician A says that one type of rear wheel brake assembly contains a small drum brake inside of the main brake
rotor. Technician B says that a screw actuated rear disc
parking brake usually requires only cable adjustment. Who
is right?
(A) A only.
(B) B only.
(C) Both A & B.
(D) Neither A nor B.

61. _____

Power Brake Service

62. A power booster is used with a regular (standard) master cylinder to _____
_____
_____.

63. Technician A says that some power brakes are operated by
engine vacuum. Technician B says that some power brakes
are operated by hydraulic pressure. Who is right?
(A) A only.
(B) B only.
(C) Both A & B.
(D) Neither A nor B.

63. _____

64. If a vacuum booster has been exhausted (all vacuum used up) and the brake pedal is depressed,
what should happen when the engine is started? _____
_____

65. On a Hydroboost system, the _____ _____ pump is the   65. _____
source of power.
(A) power steering
(B) engine oil
(C) automatic transmission
(D) All of the above, depending on manufacturer.

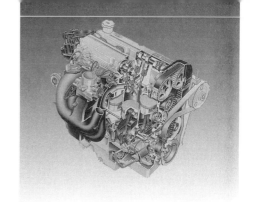

Name _____

Date _____ Period _____

Instructor _____

Score_____

Text pages 753-770

35

Anti-Lock Brake and Traction Control System Service

Objectives: After studying Chapter 35 in the textbook and completing this section of the workbook, you will be able to:

* Explain anti-lock brake system operation.
* Identify anti-lock brake system components.
* Diagnose anti-lock brake system problems.
* Explain traction control system operation.
* Identify traction control system components.
* Diagnose traction control system problems.

Tech Talk: Anti-lock brakes are becoming increasingly common on new vehicles. Anti-lock brakes reduce braking distances, decrease the chance of skidding on wet and icy surfaces, make the vehicle more controllable, and reduce tire flat spotting during hard braking. The basic principles of anti-lock brake system operation are essentially the same for all systems, but individual systems and components vary widely. The technician must carefully study this chapter to obtain the information needed to service anti-lock brake systems.

Instructions: Study Chapter 35 of the text; then answer the following questions in the spaces provided.

Anti-Lock Brake Systems

1. Some anti-lock brake systems control only two wheels. Two-wheel ABS systems are found on _____.
   (A) pickup trucks
   (B) large rear-wheel drive cars
   (C) small cars
   (D) Both A & C.

1. _____

2. Skidding tires cannot contribute to _____ the vehicle.

2. _____

3. A skidding tire on a dry road will begin to _____.

3. _____

4. The ABS system can alternately apply and release the brakes much _____ than any driver.

4. _____

5. The standard brake system friction and hydraulic components are called the _____ brakes.

5. _____

6. Speed sensor units determine the rate of _____.   6. _____
   (A) vehicle acceleration
   (B) vehicle deceleration
   (C) wheel rotation
   (D) wheel stopping power

7. Wheel speed sensors can be mounted in all of the following   7. _____
   places, EXCEPT:
   (A) brake rotor.
   (B) rear axle.
   (C) transmission input shaft.
   (D) transmission output shaft.

8. How does a G-force sensor measure deceleration? _____
   _____

9. The control module receives inputs from the _____ _____   9. _____
   sensors.

10. The hydraulic actuator consists of a pump, which supplies   10. _____
    pressure to _____ valves, and a(n) _____, which stores   _____
    extra pressure.

11. When the lockup condition is slight, what do the solenoids in the hydraulic actuator do? _____
    _____
    _____

12. When the lockup condition is severe, what do the solenoids in the hydraulic actuator do? _____
    _____
    _____

13. In the piston-operated hydraulic actuator, there is no   13. _____
    hydraulic _____.

14. Pressure in the piston-operated hydraulic actuator is pro-   14. _____
    duced by pistons operated by small _____ motors through   _____
    _____ gears.

15. The pedal travel switch is used to alert the control module 15. _____
    that pedal _____ is becoming excessive.
    (A) travel
    (B) pulsation
    (C) pressure
    (D) drop rate

16. Identify the ABS system components shown in the illustration on the following page.

    (A)_____

    (B)_____

    (C)_____

    (D)_____

    (E)_____

    (F)_____

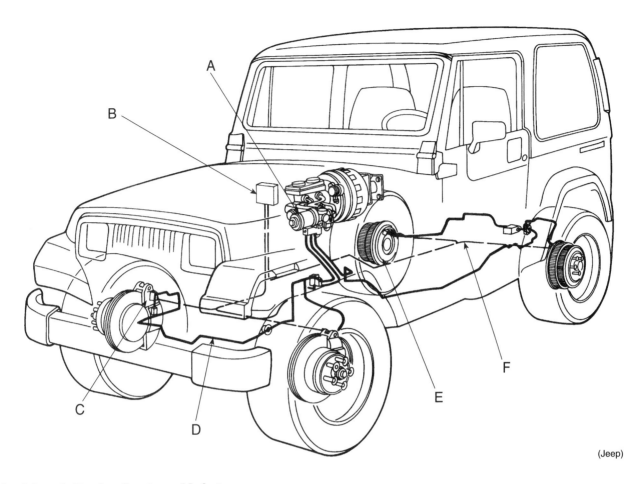

(Jeep)

Anti-Lock Brake System Maintenance

17. Maintenance of the ABS system consists of checking the wheel speed sensors and rotors for _____ and _____.

17. _____
    _____

18. Technician A says that checking the fluid level in an ABS system master cylinder is the same as checking the fluid level in a non-ABS system. Technician B says that some ABS systems will not accept silicone brake fluid. Who is right?
    (A) A only.
    (B) B only.
    (C) Both A & B.
    (D) Neither A nor B.

18. _____

Troubleshooting Anti-Lock Brake Systems

19. All of the following statements about ABS troubleshooting are true, EXCEPT:
    (A) pulsation of the brake pedal under hard braking is a sign of an ABS problem.
    (B) low brake fluid levels in the master cylinder can turn on the ABS warning light.
    (C) worn foundation brakes can cause ABS pressure problems.
    (D) mismatched tires will not affect ABS operation.

19. _____

20. Technician A says that the ABS electrical system operates directly from the battery, with no fuse protection. Technician B says that problems with the charging system can affect ABS operation. Who is right?
   (A) A only.
   (B) B only.
   (C) Both A & B.
   (D) Neither A nor B.

20. _____

21. A(n) _____ tool can be used to retrieve ABS trouble codes.

21. _____

22. Some scan tools can operate the control module by inputting _____ signals.

22. _____

23. Before replacing any ABS electrical connector, be sure that the ignition is in the _____ position or the battery is _____.

23. _____
    _____

24. Before repairing any part of the hydraulic system, the system should be _____.

24. _____

25. A standard (non-ABS) brake hose may _____ if it is used on an ABS system.

25. _____

26. If a G-force sensor is not mounted in exactly the same position as the old sensor, what will happen?

_____

_____

27. After an ABS system has been repaired, the light may remain on for a few minutes until the system has _____.

27. _____

28. Identify the following ABS system tools and components.

   (A) _____

   (B) _____

   (C) _____

(Nissan)

29. The illustration above shows sensor _____ _____ being checked.

29. _____

Traction Control Systems

30. Traction control systems improve _____ and _____ on low friction road surfaces.

30. _____
    _____

31. Technician A says that traction control systems operate by increasing engine power. Technician B says that traction control systems share some parts with the ABS system. Who is right?
    (A) A only.
    (B) B only.
    (C) Both A & B.
    (D) Neither A nor B.

31. _____

32. When it is operating, the traction control will apply the _____ on a wheel that is spinning at a faster rate than the others.

32. _____

33. How does the traction control system modify engine performance?
    (A) Moves the throttle plate.
    (B) Modifies spark advance.
    (C) Opens and closes the EGR valve.
    (D) Both A & B.

33. _____

34. A traction control light is used to tell the operator when the traction control system is _____.

34. _____

35. Some common brake service operations are not affected by the presence of ABS, including _____

_____

_____

Name _____

Date _____ Period _____

Instructor _____

Score_____

Text pages 771-796

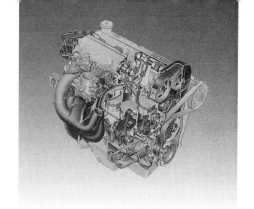

36

Suspension System Service

Objectives: After studying Chapter 36 in the textbook and completing this section of the workbook, you will be able to:

- Explain the construction, operation, and service of conventional front suspensions.
- Explain the construction, operation, and service of conventional rear suspensions.
- Describe the function of coil springs, torsion bars, and leaf springs.
- Describe the function of load-carrying and following ball joints.
- Explain the construction, operation, and service of MacPherson strut suspensions.
- Describe the function of control arms, strut rods, and sway bars.
- Describe the function of shock absorbers and MacPherson strut dampers.
- Summarize the operating principles and service of front and rear suspensions.
- Diagnose problems in suspension systems.

Tech Talk: There have been many suspension system design advances in the last 20 years. Most late-model cars use MacPherson strut front suspension systems—many variations of which are on the market. However, many cars and most pickup trucks have conventional suspension systems, with upper and lower control arms and either coil springs or torsion bars. It is important that you understand modern suspension technology. Study this chapter thoroughly!

Instructions: Study Chapter 36 of the text; then answer the following questions in the spaces provided.

Front Suspension Systems

1. Modern conventional front suspension systems use _____ springs or _____ bars between the suspension and frame.

1. _____
   _____

2. Technician A says that most coil springs are mounted between the vehicle frame and the lower control arm. Technician B says that in a few cases, the coil spring is mounted between the vehicle body and the upper control arm. Who is right?
   (A) A only.
   (B) B only.
   (C) Both A & B.
   (D) Neither A nor B.

2. _____

3. To remove the coil spring, a spring _____ may be necessary.

3. _____

4. When a shock absorber is operating properly, it will perform all of the following, EXCEPT:
   (A) control spring rebound.
   (B) support the weight of the vehicle.
   (C) limit spring oscillation.
   (D) control the rate of spring compression.

4. _____

5. Inspect each shock absorber for signs of _____.

5. _____

6. Shocks in good condition will allow about one free _____.

6. _____

7. Technician A says that the load-carrying ball joints carry the majority of a vehicle's weight. Technician B says that pre-loading keeps joint bearing surfaces in constant contact. Who is right?
   (A) A only.
   (B) B only.
   (C) Both A & B.
   (D) Neither A nor B.

7. _____

8. Excessive ball joint wear will _____

_____

_____.

9. The most rapid wearing ball joint is the _____.

9. _____

10. To check ball joints for wear, they must be properly _____.

10. _____

11. Some manufacturers recommend checking ball joint play by measuring axial play, which is the ___

_____

_____.

12. Place the following ball joint removal steps in the proper order. (NOTE: not all steps are given).

_____(A)   Loosen the stud nut several turns.

_____(B)   Remove the stud nut cotter key.

_____(C)   Place a jack under the lower control arm.

_____(D)   Strike the steering spindle sharply with a hammer to break the taper.

_____(E)   Remove the stud nut and lower the control arm.

_____(F)   Remove rivets or bolts holding the ball joint to the control arm.

_____(G)   Use a special tool to apply pressure to the ball joint stud.

13. The _____ _____ must be removed to replace the control arm bushings.

13. _____

14. When one control arm bushing is worn, always replace _____.

14. _____

15. The control arm bushings are usually _____ out.

15. _____

16. Strut rods may be threaded for _____ adjustment.

16. _____

17. Identify the parts of the suspension system illustrated below.

(A) _____

(B) _____

(C) _____

(D) _____

(E) _____

(F) _____

(G) _____

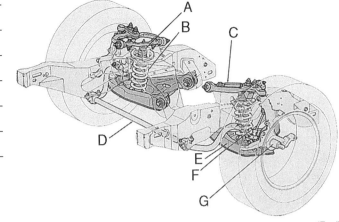

(Ford)

18. Identify the parts of the torsion bar rear support illustrated below.

(A) _____

(B) _____

(C) _____

(D) _____

(E) _____

(F) _____

(G) _____

(H) _____

(I) _____

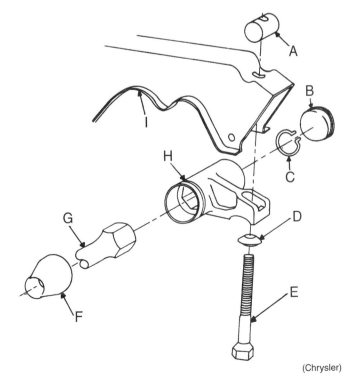

(Chrysler)

19. Identify the parts of the front suspension system illustrated below.

(A) _____

(B) _____

(C) _____

(D) _____

(E) _____

(F) _____

(G) _____

(H) _____

(I) _____

(J) _____

(K) _____

(L) _____

(M) _____

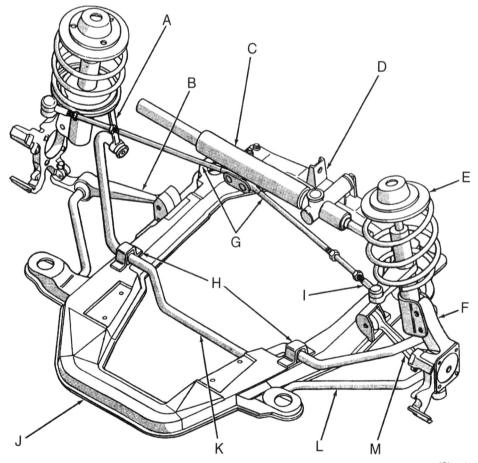

(Chrysler)

20. The illustration above shows a(n) _____ being disassembled.

20. _____

21. To perform the operation shown above, all _____ tension must be removed using a special spring _____.

21. _____

    _____

Rear Suspension Systems

22. Modern vehicles use all the following rear suspension systems, EXCEPT:
    (A) coil spring.
    (B) leaf spring.
    (C) torsion bar.
    (D) MacPherson strut.

    22. _____

23. When coil springs are used, _____ _____ must be used to provide proper rear axle housing alignment.

    23. _____

24. Some independent rear suspensions make use of a single leaf spring mounted in a(n) _____ position.

    24. _____

25. The most common leaf spring failure is defective _____.

    25. _____

26. When working with leaf springs, always allow the _____ of the vehicle to rest on bushings before torquing the shackle bolts.

    26. _____

27. Identify the parts of the rear suspension system illustrated below.

    (A) _____

    (B) _____

    (C) _____

    (D) _____

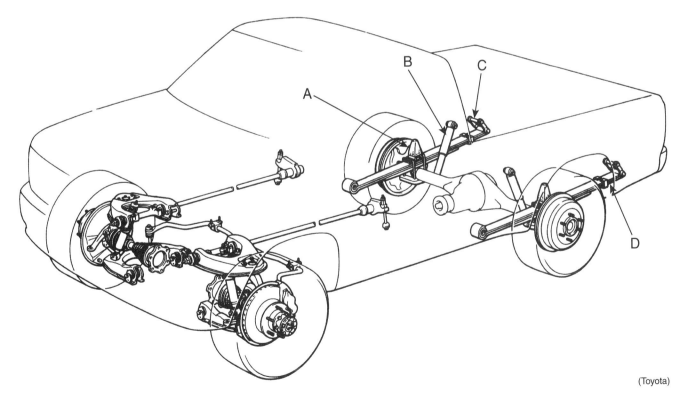

(Toyota)

28. What is the purpose of the spring shackle shown in the above illustration?_____

_____

Automatic Level Control

29. Most automatic level control systems are operated by _____ pressure.

29. _____

30. An automatic level control system contains all of the following components, EXCEPT:
    (A) compressor.
    (B) height control sensor.
    (C) control module.
    (D) air struts or air shock absorbers.

30. _____

31. Identify the automatic level control system parts illustrated below.

(A) _____   (H) _____

(B) _____   (I) _____

(C) _____   (J) _____

(D) _____   (K) _____

(E) _____   (L) _____

(F) _____   (M) _____

(G) _____

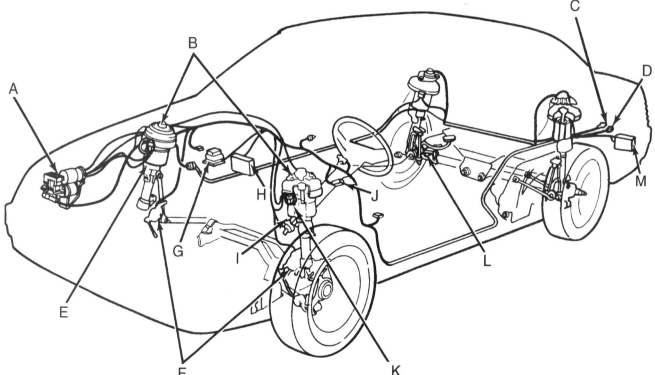

(Ford)

Computerized Ride Control Systems

32. The ride control system may override the driver settings dur-
    ing hard _____.

32. _____

33. Ride control input sensors include all of the following,
    EXCEPT:
    (A) steering.
    (B) transmission gear.
    (C) brake.
    (D) acceleration.

33. _____

34. The ride control module is generally located in the vehicle's
    _____ _____.

34. _____

35. The ride control system is similar to other computer control
    systems in that it can _____.
    (A) process inputs
    (B) store trouble codes
    (C) illuminate a dashboard warning light
    (D) All of the above.

35. _____

Name _____

Date _____ Period _____

Instructor _____

Score_____

Text pages 797-825

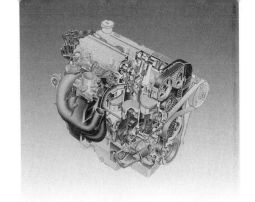

37

Steering System Service

Objectives: After studying Chapter 37 in the textbook and completing this section of the workbook, you will be able to:

- Explain the differences between conventional and rack and pinion steering systems.
- Identify the components of conventional steering systems.
- Identify the components of rack and pinion steering systems.
- Diagnose problems in conventional and rack and pinion steering systems.
- Summarize the construction, operation, and service of steering linkage components.

Tech Talk: Among the design advances in steering systems in the last 20 years was the introduction of the rack and pinion steering system. Although rack and pinion steering systems are used in most late-model vehicles, many large cars and light trucks continue to use the conventional parallelogram linkage steering system. The technician must, therefore, be familiar with the service procedures for both types of systems. To gain this knowledge, study this chapter thoroughly and apply the information to your work.

Instructions: Study Chapter 37 of the text; then answer the following questions in the spaces provided.

Steering Column and Steering Wheel

1. Worn or dry steering shaft bearings can cause _____.
   (A) roughness
   (B) binding
   (C) squeaking
   (D) All of the above.

1. _____

2. Technician A says that before servicing the steering wheel, the air bag (if used) must be disconnected. Technician B says that most steering wheels can be removed by prying gently around the hub. Who is right?
   (A) A only.
   (B) B only.
   (C) Both A & B.
   (D) Neither A nor B.

2. _____

3. The manual steering gear must turn the _____ of the steering wheel into side-to-side motion at the steering linkage.

3. _____

4. The gearbox is attached to the frame and is usually connected to the steering shaft by a shock-absorbing _____
   joint.

4. _____

5. Name the two adjustments found on most steering gears. _____

   _____

6. Label the parts of the rack and pinion steering assembly illustrated below.

   (A) _____

   (B) _____

   (C) _____

   (D) _____

   (E) _____

   (F) _____

   (Hyundai)

7. Label the parts of the steering gear shown in the following illustration.

   (A) _____

   (B) _____

   (C) _____

   (D) _____

   (E) _____

   (F) _____

   (G) _____

   (H) _____

   (I) _____

   (Plymouth)

Conventional Power Steering Service

8. Define *integral power cylinder.* _____

   _____

   _____

   _____

9. The basic inline power steering system adjustments include   9. _____
   _____.
   (A) worm to rack-piston preload
   (B) pitman shaft depth
   (C) thrust bearing alignment
   (D) All of the above.

10. The most critical inline power steering adjustment concerned with handling is the _____
    _____.

11. When reinstalling a steering gear, check for proper _____   11. _____
    with steering shaft. This will prevent binding and premature
    wear.

12. Label the leakage points on the power steering system shown in the following illustration.

   (A) _____   (K) _____

   (B) _____   (L) _____

   (C) _____   (M) _____

   (D) _____   (N) _____

   (E) _____   (O) _____

   (F) _____   (P) _____

   (G) _____   (Q) _____

   (H) _____   (R) _____

   (I) _____   (S) _____

   (J) _____

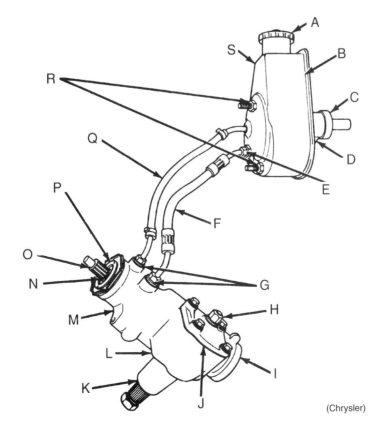

(Chrysler)

Rack and Pinion Steering Gears

13. On a rack and pinion steering system, the sector shaft, or pinion, is connected directly to the _____ _____.

13. _____

14. Technician A says that the rack and pinion steering system has more parts than the conventional steering system. Technician B says that the rack and pinion system is a more direct linkage arrangement than the conventional system. Who is right?
(A) A only.
(B) B only.
(C) Both A & B.
(D) Neither A nor B.

14. _____

15. Ideally, a rack and pinion gear should be _____ if it is defective.

15. _____

Rack and Pinion Power Steering

16. The power rack and pinion uses a(n) _____ valve to control hydraulic flow.

16. _____

17. Identify the parts of the power rack and pinion assembly illustrated below.

(A) _____

(B) _____

(C) _____

(D) _____

(E) _____

(F) _____

(G) _____

(Honda)

Power Steering Pumps and Hoses

18. The three main types of power steering pumps are the _____, _____, and _____.

18. _____
_____
_____

19. A loose or worn power steering pump belt will squeal when the wheels are _____.
(A) sharply turned
(B) in the straight ahead position
(C) returned from a turn
(D) All of the above.

19. _____

20. Never pry on the pump _____ or _____ when adjusting belt tension.

20. _____
_____

21. Modern power steering systems take special fluid, not _____ _____ fluid.

21. _____

22. When bleeding the power steering, which of the following steps should be done *first?* (Not all steps are listed.)
    (A) Shut off the engine and allow the vehicle to sit for two minutes.
    (B) Refill the reservoir if necessary.
    (C) Start the engine and allow it to run for one minute.
    (D) Road test the vehicle.

22. _____

23. When removing a pump pulley, always use a(n) _____.

23. _____

24. High-pressure hose should always be used between the pump _____ and the _____.

24. _____

_____

25. A power steering pressure sensing switch can be used to control the _____ _____ or turn the air conditioner on or off.

25. _____

Steering Linkage

26. When inspecting steering linkage, check the ball sockets for looseness by _____

_____.

27. All of the following statements are true, EXCEPT:
    (A) pitman arms are used on conventional steering systems only.
    (B) idler arms are used on conventional and rack and pinion steering systems.
    (C) tie rod ends are used on all steering systems.
    (D) adjuster sleeves on conventional linkage are threaded into the inner and outer tie rod ends.

27. _____

28. Technician A says that a special tool or hammer can be used to break a taper joint. Technician B says that cotter pins can be reused if they are in good shape. Who is right?
    (A) A only.
    (B) B only.
    (C) Both A & B.
    (D) Neither A nor B.

28. _____

29. Label the parts of the conventional linkage system illustrated below.

    (A) _____

    (B) _____

    (C) _____

    (D) _____

    (E) _____

    (F) _____

(Monroe Auto Equipment)

30. Technician A says that the following illustration shows a tie rod end being checked for looseness. Technician B says that the following illustration shows a tie rod end being replaced. Who is right?

    30. _____

(A) A only.
(B) B only.
(C) Both A & B.
(D) Neither A nor B.

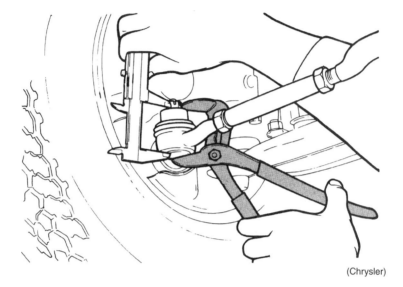

(Chrysler)

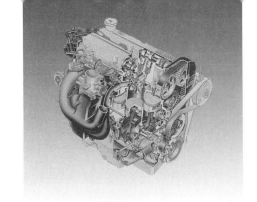

Name _____

Date _____ Period _____

Instructor _____

Score_____

Text pages 827-848

38

Wheel and Tire Service

Objectives: After studying Chapter 38 in the textbook and completing this section of the workbook, you will be able to:

- Describe the construction, operation, and service of wheel bearings.
- Explain tire and wheel construction and service.
- Summarize tire size, type, and quality ratings.
- Diagnose common wheel bearing and tire related problems.

Tech Talk: Have you ever tried to push a car with four flat tires? It would be almost impossible, and it should not be attempted. Nevertheless, this example illustrates how tire inflation pressure can affect tire rolling resistance and fuel consumption. Higher tire inflation pressure tends to decrease tire rolling resistance, improving fuel economy. Never, however, inflate a tire beyond the maximum inflation pressure printed on the sidewall, or tire damage can result. Keep tire pressure within specs.

Instructions: Study Chapter 38 of the text; then answer the following questions in the spaces provided.

Wheel Bearings

1. All of the following statements about bearings are true, EXCEPT:
   (A) tapered roller bearings can be cleaned and greased.
   (B) tapered roller bearings can be adjusted.
   (C) flat roller and ball bearings can be adjusted.
   (D) rear-wheel drive vehicles have tapered roller bearings on the front wheels.

1. _____

2. Technician A says that some older vehicles have greasable front ball bearings. Technician B says that front-wheel drive vehicles have tapered roller bearings on the front wheels. Who is right?
   (A) A only.
   (B) B only.
   (C) Both A & B.
   (D) Neither A nor B.

2. _____

3. The tapered roller bearing consists of the rollers and _____, and the _____.

3. _____
   _____

4. When removing a wheel _____, pry a little at a time, being careful to avoid bending it out of shape.

4. _____

5. Some wheel covers are held in place by _____.

5. _____

6. If the vehicle has disc brakes, the _____ must be removed to remove the bearings.

6. _____

7. Technician A says that a bearing showing the slightest sign of wear should be replaced. Technician B says that bearing rollers and races should always be replaced together. Who is right?
   (A) A only.
   (B) B only.
   (C) Both A & B.
   (D) Neither A nor B.

7. _____

8. Each wheel bearing must be filled with the specified wheel bearing grease by either using a(n) _____ or by packing by _____.

8. _____
   _____

9. Improper wheel bearing adjustment can cause _____.
   (A) wheel shake
   (B) poor steering
   (C) poor brake performance
   (D) All of the above.

9. _____

10. If the slot in the nut does not line up with the hole in the spindle, the nut should be _____ just enough to make the holes line up.

10. _____

11. Most sealed front bearings must be _____ out of the steering knuckle.

11. _____

12. Regardless of the technique used for bending, always use a(n) _____ cotter pin.

12. _____

13. If the steering knuckle is removed, the vehicle will need _____ after it is reinstalled.

13. _____

14. Identify the wheel bearing related parts in the illustration at the top of the following page.

   (A) _____   (I) _____

   (B) _____   (J) _____

   (C) _____   (K) _____

   (D) _____   (L) _____

   (E) _____   (M) _____

   (F) _____   (N) _____

   (G) _____   (O) _____

   (H) _____

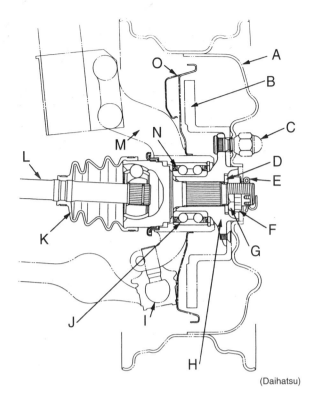

(Daihatsu)

15. Describe the spindle nut adjustment procedure shown in the following illustration.

(A) _____

(B) _____

(C) _____

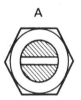  

(Ford)

16. Identify the bearing-related parts shown in the following illustration.

(A) _____

(B) _____

(C) _____

(D) _____

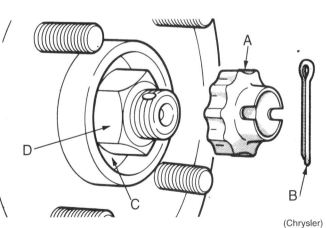

(Chrysler)

Vehicle Wheel Rims

17. Wheel rims are made of all of the following, EXCEPT: 17. _____
    (A) steel.
    (B) aluminum.
    (C) cast iron.
    (D) graphite.

18. Rim size is determined by the following three measurements:

    (A) _____

    (B) _____

    (C) _____

19. Technician A says that wheel lug nuts should tightened with   19. _____
    an impact wrench and torque sticks. Technician B says that
    if necessary, wheel lug nuts can be tightened with a torque
    wrench. Who is right?
    (A) A only.
    (B) B only.
    (C) Both A & B.
    (D) Neither A nor B.

20. Why is it important to tighten the lug nuts to the proper torque, even if the rim is steel? _____

    _____

21. Describe the process for installing a wheel lug shown in the following illustration. _____

    _____

    _____

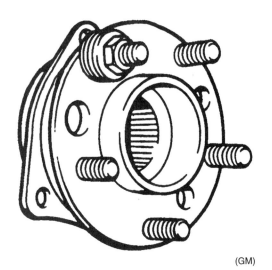

(GM)

Vehicle Tires

22. The type of tire that is commonly used today is the _____ design.
    (A) bias
    (B) radial
    (C) belted bias
    (D) None of the above.

22. _____

23. Tire cord materials include _____

    _____

    _____.

• Use the following tire rating information to answer questions 24 through 28.

P205/75HR15

24. The letter "P" indicates that the tire is designed for a(n) _____.

24. _____

25. The number "205" represents the tire's _____.

25. _____

26. The number "75" is the _____.

26. _____

27. The letter "H" is the tire's _____ rating.

27. _____

28. The number "15" is the _____ in _____.

28. _____

    _____

29. A tire with a DOT temperature resistance rating of B will resist heat generation better than one graded _____.

29. _____

30. A tire with a DOT traction grade of A has _____ traction than tires graded B or C.

30. _____

31. A tire with a DOT tread wear rating of 225 has approximately _____ percent more mileage than a tire with a rating of 100.

31. _____

32. A space saver tire is for _____ use only.

32. _____

33. What is the purpose of a tire interchange chart? _____

    _____

34. Technician A says that an underinflated tire will wear in the center. Technician B says that an underinflated tire will generate excessive heat. Who is right?
    (A) A only.
    (B) B only.
    (C) Both A & B.
    (D) Neither A nor B.

34. _____

35. When a vehicle is driven, the _____ of the tires increases.

35. _____

36. Tires should be rotated every _____ miles (_____km).

36. _____

37. To prevent tire bead damage, always use rubber _____ on the bead surfaces.

37. _____

38. If a rim has a dirty sealing area, it should be _____. If a rim has any splits or cracks, it should be _____.

38. _____
    _____

39. Do not repair a tire if it has _____.
    (A) tread separation
    (B) sidewall damage
    (C) a puncture larger than 1/2″ (13mm)
    (D) All of the above.

39. _____

40. Repairing a tire without _____ it is no longer recommended.

40. _____

41. Technician A says that feathered edges on front tires are caused by improper toe-in or toe-out. Technician B says that cupping of rear tires can be caused by improper toe-in or toe-out. Who is right?
    (A) A only.
    (B) B only.
    (C) Both A & B.
    (D) Neither A nor B.

41. _____

42. Technician A says that at today's highway speeds, even a slight tire unbalance can cause the tire and wheel to hop up and down. Technician B says that at highway speeds, a slight tire unbalance can cause the tire and wheel to shake from side to side. Who is right?
    (A) A only.
    (B) B only.
    (C) Both A & B.
    (D) Neither A nor B.

42. _____

43. To be in static balance, the tire's weight mass must be _____
    _____
    _____.

44. To be in dynamic balance, the centerline of the weight mass must be_____
    _____
    _____
    _____.

45. A wheel and tire assembly with excessive _____ or _____ runout cannot be balanced.

45. _____
    _____

46. Runout may be checked by using a(n) _____ _____.

46. _____

47. When balancing the rear wheels on the car, remember that when one wheel is on the floor, the other is free to _____.

47. _____

48. When using an on-the-car balancer on cars equipped with the traction-type differential (posi-traction), raise _____ _____ to prevent the car from running off the jack.

48. _____
    _____

49. Identify the tire inflation conditions illustrated below.

(A) _____

(B) _____

(C) _____

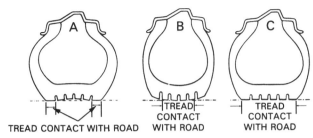

(Rubber Mfg. Association)

50. Draw the lines and arrows showing how the tires below should be rotated.

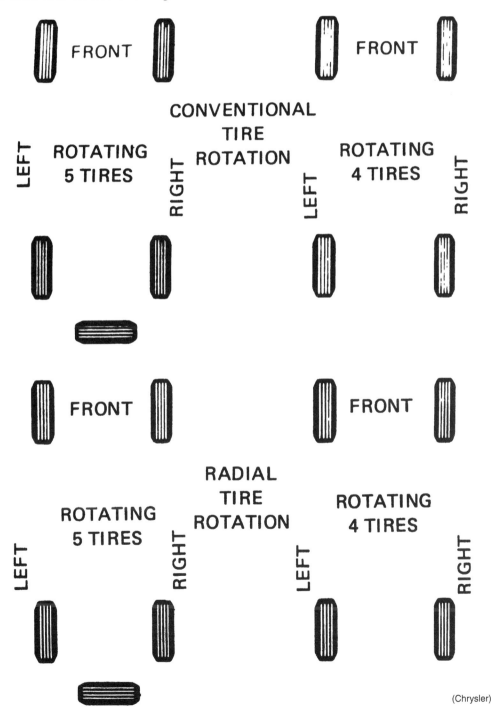

(Chrysler)

Name _____

Date _____ Period _____

Instructor _____

Score_____

Text pages 849-869

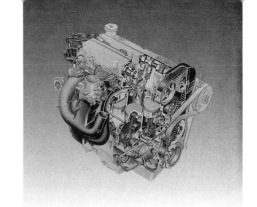

39

Wheel Alignment

Objectives: After studying Chapter 39 in the textbook and completing this section of the workbook, you will be able to:

- Explain the importance of wheel alignment.
- Summarize wheel alignment procedures.
- Explain the difference between two-wheel and four-wheel alignment.
- Diagnose common alignment-related problems.

Tech Talk: Alignment is critical to vehicle handling and tire wear. Modern vehicles use lighter components and are, therefore, easier to knock out of alignment. Many late-model vehicles have front-wheel drive. Rear wheel alignment is also adjustable on these vehicles. These new alignment factors make it imperative that you study this chapter thoroughly.

Instructions: Study Chapter 39 of the text; then answer the following questions in the spaces provided.

Defining Wheel Alignment

1. Wheel alignment refers to the process of _____

   _____

   _____

   _____.

2. Improper alignment can cause _____.   2. _____
   (A) rapid tire wear
   (B) wandering
   (C) hard steering
   (D) All of the above.

3. Technician A says that adjustable alignment angles include   3. _____
   caster, camber, and toe-out on turns. Technician B says that
   nonadjustable alignment angles include steering axis incli-
   nation and toe-in. Who is right?
   (A) A only.
   (B) B only.
   (C) Both A & B.
   (D) Neither A nor B.

4. Define *caster.*_____

_____

_____

5. _____ caster occurs when the tire support centerline inter-
sects the roadway at a point ahead of the tire.

5. _____

6. _____ caster is produced by tilting the spindle so that the
tire support centerline strikes the road behind the tire.

6. _____

7. Positive caster tends to assist the wheels in maintaining
a(n) _____ _____ position.

7. _____

8. Improper caster angle can cause all of the following, EXCEPT:
(A) high-speed instability.
(B) tire wear.
(C) wandering.
(D) hard steering.

8. _____

9. Define *camber.*_____

_____

_____

10. Negative camber occurs when the _____ of the wheel is
tilted inward.

10. _____

11. Camber angles, whether negative or positive, are usually
quite small, averaging from around _____.
(A) 1°
(B) 5°
(C) 10°
(D) 15°

11. _____

12. Makers often recommend setting around _____ more positive camber in the left wheel to compensate for road crown.

12. _____

13. Steering axis inclination is formed by tilting the _____ ball
joint or strut mount inward.

13. _____

14. Technician A says that steering axis inclination (SAI) is
adjustable on most vehicles. Technician B says that com-
mon causes of incorrect SAI include a bent spindle, frame,
or strut. Who is right?
(A) A only.
(B) B only.
(C) Both A & B.
(D) Neither A nor B.

14. _____

15. Toe is the relative position of the _____ and _____ of a tire
in relation to the tire on the other side of the vehicle.

15. _____
_____

16. Rear-wheel drive vehicles are usually toed _____. Many
front-wheel drive vehicles are toed _____.

16. _____
_____

17. When a car rounds a corner, the inner front wheel is forced
to follow a smaller _____ than the outer wheel.

17. _____

18. Although toe on turns specifications vary, they usually call for around a _____°-_____° difference between the inner and outer wheel turning angles.

18. _____

19. Wheel _____ is the ability of the rear wheels to follow directly in the path of the front wheels.

19. _____

20. Why was the two-wheel alignment the only type performed in the past? _____

_____

_____

21. Technician A says that on a four-wheel alignment, the settings that can be adjusted on the front axle are caster, camber, and toe. Technician B says that on a four-wheel alignment, the settings that can be adjusted on the rear are caster and toe. Who is right?
    (A) A only.
    (B) B only.
    (C) Both A & B.
    (D) Neither A nor B.

21. _____

22. What is the purpose of turning plates? _____

_____

_____

23. Label the caster-related items shown in the following illustration.

    (A) _____
    (B) _____
    (C) _____
    (D) _____
    (E) _____

(Perfect Equipment Corp.)

Performing Wheel Alignments

24. Technician A says that before beginning the alignment, the vehicle should be checked for worn parts. Technician B says that a suspected alignment problem can often be traced to tires, brakes, or other unrelated parts. Who is right?
    (A) A only.
    (B) B only.
    (C) Both A & B.
    (D) Neither A nor B.

24. _____

25. During prealignment checks, inspect the tires for _____, _____, and other damage.

25. _____

26. All of the following statements about alignment are true, EXCEPT:
    (A) a four wheel alignment should always begin with the front wheels.
    (B) some imports are aligned with weight in the vehicle.
    (C) wheel rims always have some runout.
    (D) never attempt to align a vehicle with mismatched tires.

26. _____

27. Technician A says that curb weight is obtained with a full tank of gas and the driver in the vehicle. Technician B says that toe should always be set first. Who is right?
    (A) A only.
    (B) B only.
    (C) Both A & B.
    (D) Neither A nor B.

27. _____

28. If the engine has power steering , _____ the _____ before centering the steering wheel.

28. _____
    _____

29. Rear toe and camber are set by _____ _____ or _____ _____.

29. _____
    _____

30. If the vehicle has four-wheel steering, the rear gearbox must be _____ with a special tool before camber and toe are set.

30. _____

31. Some rear ends can be adjusted by the use of _____.

31. _____

32. Never attempt to make non-factory adjustments by _____ or _____ parts.

32. _____
    _____

Wheel Alignment

33. The following illustration shows the alignment tool being attached to the _____ _____. Label the parts indicated.

33. _____

    (A) _____
    (B) _____
    (C) _____
    (D) _____

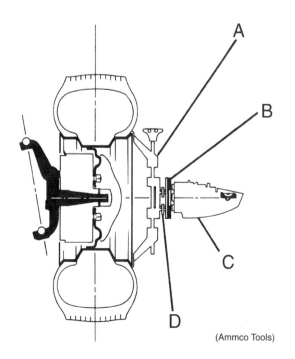

(Ammco Tools)

34. The following illustration shows a method of adjusting _____. Label the indicated parts.

34. _____

(A) _____

(B) _____

(C) _____

(D) _____

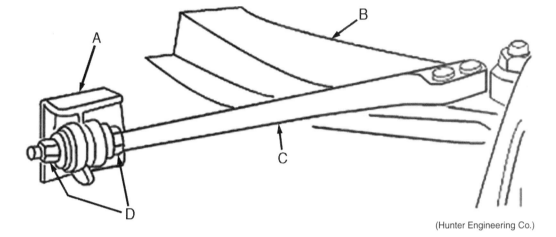

(Hunter Engineering Co.)

35. The following illustration shows a method of adjusting the _____. Label the indicated parts.

35. _____

(A) _____

(B) _____

(C) _____

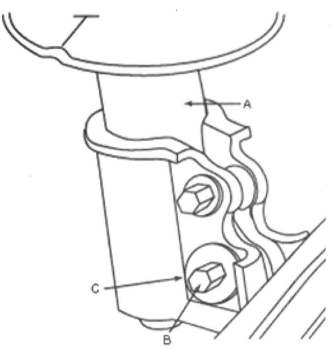

(Hunter Engineering Co.)

Name _____

Date _____ Period _____

Instructor _____

Score_____

Text pages 871-911

40

Air Conditioning and Heater Service

Objectives: After studying Chapter 40 in the textbook and completing this section of the workbook, you will be able to:

- Explain basic refrigeration theory.
- Identify major air conditioning system components.
- List the safety rules for air conditioning service.
- Inspect an air conditioning system for problems.
- Recover, evacuate, and recharge an air conditioning system.
- Service air conditioning and heater parts.
- Install air conditioning system parts.
- Service refrigerant oil.
- Diagnose air conditioning and heating problems.

Tech Talk: Automotive air conditioning is almost universal: it is installed in approximately 90% of new cars and 70% of new light trucks. An automotive technician will often be asked to diagnose and repair an air conditioning system. Understanding the material in this chapter is necessary to service air conditioners and avoid equipment damage, personal injury, and environmental damage.

Instructions: Study Chapter 40 of the text; then answer the following questions in the spaces provided.

Principles of Air Conditioning

1. Basic air conditioning is a process in which air entering the vehicle is _____, _____, and _____.

   1. _____
      _____

2. When a substance changes from a vapor to a liquid or from a liquid to a vapor, it is said to change _____.
   (A) form
   (B) standard
   (C) state
   (D) None of the above.

   2. _____

3. Technician A says that older air conditioning systems use a refrigerant called R-12. Technician B says that newer systems use a refrigerant called R-134a. Who is right?
   (A) A only.
   (B) B only.
   (C) Both A & B.
   (D) Neither A nor B.

3. _____

4. When the pressure of a refrigerant is lowered, its boiling point is _____.

4. _____

5. If the restrictor is not variable, the _____ is turned on and off to control refrigerant flow
   (A) compressor
   (B) blower
   (C) condenser cooling fan
   (D) None of the above.

5. _____

6. Identify the parts in the air conditioning system in the following illustration.
   (A) _____
   (B) _____
   (C) _____
   (D) _____
   (E) _____
   (F) _____
   (G) _____

(Geo)

Major Components of the Air Conditioning System

7. Most automotive compressors are _____ types.

7. _____

8. The condenser is mounted in front of the _____.

8. _____

9. The expansion valve admits refrigerant into the evaporator based on evaporator _____.

9. _____

10. Define *air conditioning muffler.* _____
    _____
    _____

11. The receiver-drier acts as a(n) _____ for liquid refrigerants and removes _____ from the refrigerant system.

11. _____
    _____

12. Technician A says that the sight glass is used to check the refrigerant for bubbles or foam. Technician B says the sight glass is always located on the low side of the system. Who is right?
(A) A only.
(B) B only.
(C) Both A & B.
(D) Neither A nor B.

12. _____

13. One purpose of the accumulator is to prevent _____ damage.

13. _____

14. If evaporator temperature drops below 32°F (0°C), condensation on the evaporator core will _____.

14. _____

15. Technician A says that the suction throttling valve is no longer used. Technician B says that the pilot-operated absolute valve is no longer used. Who is right?
(A) A only.
(B) B only.
(C) Both A & B.
(D) Neither A nor B.

15. _____

16. Define *thermostatic switch.* _____

_____

_____

17. The compressor magnetic clutch can be disengaged at full throttle to eliminate compressor _____ when the vehicle is being accelerated.

17. _____

18. Label the parts of the expansion valve illustrated below.

(A) _____

(B) _____

(C) _____

(D) _____

(E) _____

(F) _____

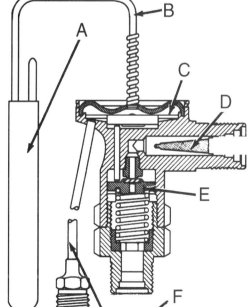

(Chevrolet)

19. Label the parts of the fixed orifice tube illustrated below.

(A) _____

(B) _____

(C) _____

(General Motors)

Air Conditioning System Service

20. Always wear _____ when working on an air conditioner.

20. _____

21. Refrigerant should never be discharged directly into the _____.

21. _____

22. If refrigerant vapor contacts an open flame, it will produce _____ gas.

22. _____

23. All of the following statements about refrigeration system service are true, EXCEPT:
(A) as soon as a line or part is disconnected, it should be capped.
(B) the system should be flushed with refrigerant to remove moisture.
(C) refrigerant lines should be close to room temperature before they are disconnected.
(D) the receiver-drier should be connected into the system last.

23. _____

24. Technician A says that compressor oil containers should be capped. Technician B says that the system should be evacuated before recharging. Who is right?
(A) A only.
(B) B only.
(C) Both A & B.
(D) Neither A nor B.

24. _____

25. A manifold gauge set is needed for _____

_____

_____.

26. Technician A says that the low-pressure gauge is graduated in pounds per square inch. Technician B says that the low-pressure gauge is graduated in inches of vacuum. Who is right?
(A) A only.
(B) B only.
(C) Both A & B.
(D) Neither A nor B.

26. _____

27. The center manifold connection is _____ to both valves.

27. _____

28. Define *Schrader valve.*_____

_____

_____

29. Technician A says that on late-model air conditioners, the Schrader valve may have different threads on the high side than on the low side. Technician B says that R-12 and R-134a service fittings are the same and caution is necessary when attaching them. Who is right?
    (A) A only.
    (B) B only.
    (C) Both A & B.
    (D) Neither A nor B.

29. _____

30. Label the parts of the manifold gauge set illustrated below.

    (A) _____

    (B) _____

    (C) _____

    (D) _____

    (E) _____

    (F) _____

    (G) _____

    (H) _____

    (I) _____

(Ford)

Leak Detectors

31. A liquid leak detector is used to detect _____ leaks.

31. _____

32. The flame of a halide torch produces _____ gas when it contacts refrigerant.

32. _____

33. The air conditioning system must be at least partially _____ before leak testing can be done.

33. _____

34. If the flame of a halide torch becomes yellow green, the leak is _____.
    (A) small
    (B) medium
    (C) large
    (D) None of the above. The detector is out of adjustment.

34. _____

35. Some _____ leak detectors can only detect one type of refrigerant.

35. _____

Discharging the System

36. When can air conditioning refrigerant be legally discharged into the atmosphere?
    (A) When recovery equipment is not available.
    (B) When recovering the refrigerant would contaminate the recovery equipment.
    (C) When the refrigerant is contaminated with moisture or dirt.
    (D) None of the above.

36. _____

37. Why is it important not to mix different types of air conditioning refrigerant in a recovery unit? ____

_____

_____

Evacuating the System

38. Technician A says that system evacuation is done to remove air and moisture. Technician B says that the evacuation process requires a compressor. Who is right?
    (A) A only.
    (B) B only.
    (C) Both A & B.
    (D) Neither A nor B.

38. _____

39. What are some reasons that an air conditioning system cannot be drawn down to 29″ (711mm) at sea level? _____

_____

Refrigerant Charging

40. What are the three possible sources of refrigerant for system charging?

    (A) _____

    (B) _____

    (C) _____

41. Unless specifically recommended, never allow liquid refrigerant to enter the _____ side of the system.

41. _____

42. List the steps that must be taken when the refrigeration system must be opened for part removal and replacement.

    (A) _____

    (B) _____

    (C) _____

    (D) _____

    (E) _____

    (F) _____

43. Always use two wrenches when loosening a(n) _____.

43. _____

Component Replacement

44. The compressor clutch can be removed without removing the _____ _____.

44. _____

45. Technician A says that R-12 and R-134a refrigerant oils are the same. Technician B says that all parts of a refrigeration system contain some oil. Who is right?
    (A) A only.
    (B) B only.
    (C) Both A & B.
    (D) Neither A nor B.

45. _____

46. Oil can be lost from a refrigeration system by _____.
    (A) a leak in the system
    (B) discharging too fast
    (C) replacing a part
    (D) All of the above.

46. _____

47. Technician A says that the oil level in many compressors can be checked with a dipstick. Technician B says that compressors with a dipstick must be pressurized before checking oil level. Who is right?
    (A) A only.
    (B) B only.
    (C) Both A & B.
    (D) Neither A nor B.

47. _____

48. Many manufacturers recommend flushing the air conditioning system with _____.

48. _____

49. Adapting an R-12 system to operate on R-134a is called _____. This may become necessary as the supply of R-12 _____.

49. _____
    _____

Heater System

50. Technician A says that in most vehicles, the heater system relays on engine coolant to provide heat. Technician B says that the job of the heater shut-off valve is to control the flow of air through the heater core. Who is right?
    (A) A only.
    (B) B only.
    (C) Both A & B.
    (D) Neither A nor B.

50. _____

51. If the heater core is suspected of leaking, conduct a(n) _____ system pressure test.

51. _____

Blower Motor Service

52. If the blower motor is inoperative, check the _____ first.

52. _____

53. A defective _____ or burned _____ are common causes when the blower has some speeds but not others.

53. _____
    _____

Air Distribution and Control System Service

54. The air conditioner control system blend door blends air from the _____ _____ and the _____.

54. _____
    _____

55. The air conditioner and heater are operated by the vehicle occupants through _____.
    (A) vacuum switches
    (B) electrical switches
    (C) cables
    (D) All of the above.

55. _____

Name _____

Date _____ Period _____

Instructor _____

Score_____

Text pages 913-925

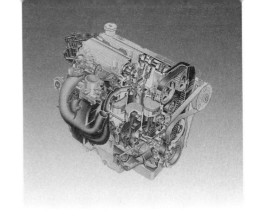

41

Preventive Maintenance

Objectives: After studying Chapter 41 in the textbook and completing this section of the workbook, you will be able to:

- Describe the purpose of preventive maintenance.
- List the basic parts of a lubrication system.
- Explain oil filtration systems and their service.
- Describe oil classifications.
- Explain how to change engine oil and filter.
- Explain how to lubricate front suspension fittings.
- Describe other preventive maintenance procedures.

Tech Talk: As the name implies, preventive maintenance involves preventing problems by properly maintaining a vehicle. Thanks to improved designs and materials, modern automobiles and trucks require fewer preventive maintenance services than vehicles of 20 or 30 years ago. However, the preventive maintenance services that must still be performed are vital. Study this chapter to learn how to perform preventive maintenance on modern vehicles.

Instructions: Study Chapter 41 of the text; then answer the following questions in the spaces provided.

Protecting the Engine Lubrication System

1. In a full flow system, all of the oil must pass through the _____.

   1. _____

2. What is the purpose of the bypass valve? _____

   _____

3. Technician A says that a surface filter consists of treated paper accordion folded to trap particles. Technician B says that a depth filter consists of a number of fibers with different filtering abilities. Particles are trapped at different layers of the material. Who is right?
   (A) A only.
   (B) B only.
   (C) Both A & B.
   (D) Neither A nor B.

   3. _____

4. When a spin-on filter is used, the _____ is discarded when it is time to change the filter.
   (A) element
   (B) housing
   (C) pressure regulator
   (D) Both A & B.

4. _____

5. Techncian A says that if engine oil is too thick, the starter will have a hard time cranking the engine. Technician B says that if the oil is too thin, it will not protect the engine under light loads and low temperatures. Who is right?
   (A) A only.
   (B) B only.
   (C) Both A & B.
   (D) Neither A nor B.

5. _____

6. Motor oil must seal the area between the _____ _____ and _____ _____.

6. _____
   _____

7. Motor oil must carry away _____ and keep impurities in _____.

7. _____
   _____

8. Viscosity is an oil's resistance to _____.
   (A) heat
   (B) dirt
   (C) flow
   (D) sludging

8. _____

9. The W of 10W-30 motor oil stands for _____.

9. _____

10. Light oils should be used in engines that are _____.
    (A) worn
    (B) in good condition
    (C) smoking
    (D) All of the above.

10. _____

11. Technician A says that the S in motor oil service grades indicates that it is designed for use in a diesel engine. Technician B says that the C in motor oil service grades indicates that it is designed to be in an engine with compression ignition. Who is right?
    (A) A only.
    (B) B only.
    (C) Both A & B.
    (D) Neither A nor B.

11. _____

12. When a motor oil is capable of holding impurities in suspension, it is called a(n) _____ oil.

12. _____

13. A reasonable oil change interval would be _____.
    (A) 500 miles (805 km)
    (B) 7500 miles (12,000 km)
    (C) Somewhere between A and B.
    (D) None of the above.

13. _____

14. If the engine operating conditions are not ideal, oil change intervals should be _____.

14. _____

15. A full-flow lubrication system is shown in the following illustration. Identify the parts indicated.

(A) _____

(B) _____

(C) _____

(D) _____

(E) _____

(F) _____

(Wix)

Changing the Oil and Filter

16. All of the following statements are true, EXCEPT:
    (A) some disposable filter elements are located inside the oil pan.
    (B) oil should be changed when the engine is cold.
    (C) before installing a new spin-on filter, a thin film of oil should be rubbed on the sealing ring.
    (D) removing a spin-on oil filter requires a special wrench.

16. _____

17. Technician A says that a new filter requires between one-half and one quart of additional oil. Technician B says that after a spin-on filter engages the base, it should be tightened one full turn. Who is right?
    (A) A only.
    (B) B only.
    (C) Both A & B.
    (D) Neither A nor B.

17. _____

18. After changing the oil and filter, run the engine for a few minutes and check for leaks around the _____ _____ and _____.

18. _____
    _____

Other Services during Oil and Filter Changes

19. Front suspension and steering parts often contain _____ _____, which should be lubricated on a regular basis.

19. _____

20. Some suspension and steering parts have _____, which should be replaced with _____ _____ for lubrication.

20. _____
    _____

21. Modern greases are called _____ _____ greases.

21. _____

22. If a joint has a sealed boot, apply the grease until the boot _____ slightly.

22. _____

23. If grease squirts from around the grease gun and fitting, the fitting is _____.

23. _____

24. Technician A says that a loose suspension part should be overgreased to compensate for wear. Technician B says that a loose suspension part should be replaced. Who is right?
   (A) A only.
   (B) B only.
   (C) Both A & B.
   (D) Neither A nor B.

24. _____

25. While greasing the front suspension, check for grease fittings on the driveshaft _____. If the vehicle is a front wheel drive model, check the _____ _____ boots for damage.

25. _____
   _____

26. The PCV system should be checked at every _____ _____.

26. _____

27. _____ and _____ filters should be changed if they show any sign of restriction.

27. _____
   _____

28. When the oil is changed, check the _____ _____ in the transmission, transfer case, and rear axle.

28. _____

29. Why does the parking brake cable stick? _____
   _____

30. Technician A says that oil should be used to lubricate lock cylinders. Technician B says that graphite can be used to lubricate lock cylinders when oil is not available. Who is right?
   (A) A only.
   (B) B only.
   (C) Both A & B.
   (D) Neither A nor B.

30. _____

Name _____

Date _____ Period _____

Instructor _____

Score_____

Text pages 927-961

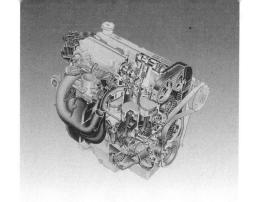

42

Problem Diagnosis Charts

Objectives: After studying Chapter 42 in the textbook and completing this section of the workbook, you will be able to:

- Read a troubleshooting chart.
- Use a troubleshooting chart to compare a problem with its probable cause and correction.

Tech Talk: Competent automotive technicians often know the answer to a problem as soon as they are presented with it. In many cases, however, the problems are not obvious, and the technician must use a problem diagnosis, or "troubleshooting" chart. This is no reflection on the technician, for even the best diagnosticians will encounter problems that they have not seen before. Good technicians are never afraid to admit that they sometimes need to refer to "the book."

Instructions: Study Chapter 42 of the text; then answer the following questions in the spaces provided.

Problem Diagnosis Charts

1. A car is brought into the shop with an overheated engine. After consulting the correct problem diagnosis chart, what would you check *first?*
   (A) Sticking thermostat.
   (B) Low coolant level.
   (C) Head gasket leak.
   (D) Retarded ignition timing.

1. _____

2. If an engine is overcooling or failing to warm up in normal weather, what part is most likely defective or missing?

2. _____

3. If the radiator cap is buzzing, what is wrong?

3. _____

4. If the engine is not getting any fuel, what would you check for *first?*
   (A) Clogged filter.
   (B) Inoperative pump.
   (C) No fuel.
   (D) Clogged tank vent.

4. _____

- Match the problems on the left with the likely causes on the right.

Problem   **Most Likely Cause**

5. Carburetor flooding   (A) Idle speed too low   5. _____
6. Rough idle   (B) Restricted muffler   6. _____
                                     (C) Vapor lock
7. Choke inoperative   (D) Defective needle and   7. _____
8. Poor acceleration   seat   8. _____
                                     (E) Faulty thermostatic
9. Low top speed   spring   9. _____
                                     (F) Defective accelerator
                                         pump

10. In the **Excessive Fuel Consumption** Problem Diagnosis Chart, what is the first *vehicle* defect to be listed as a possible problem? _____

11. If the starter will not crank the engine, what is the *first* thing   11. _____
    to check after consulting the appropriate problem diagnosis
    chart?
    (A) Battery.
    (B) Solenoid.
    (C) Starter.
    (D) Ignition switch.

12. If the charging system is not charging the battery, what is   12. _____
    the *first* thing to check after consulting the appropriate
    problem diagnosis chart?
    (A) Battery.
    (B) Alternator drive belt.
    (C) Regulator.
    (D) Alternator brushes.

13. A combustion knock (pinging) is usually noticed when the   13. _____
    vehicle is being _____.

14. If a vehicle is brought in with a complaint of a slipping clutch, what could be adjusted to correct the problem? _____

15. A truck is brought into the shop with a complaint of hard   15. _____
    shifting in all gears. Technician A says that the problem
    could be in the clutch linkage or disc. Technician B says that
    the driver may not be pushing the clutch pedal all the way to
    the floor. Who is right?
    (A) A only.
    (B) B only.
    (C) Both A & B.
    (D) Neither A nor B.

16. If the vehicle pulls to one side during braking only, what   16. _____
    could the problem be?
    (A) Low tire pressure.
    (B) Worn out brake pads.
    (C) Misaligned front end.
    (D) Defective master cylinder.

17. A vehicle owner says that his vehicle has no power assist in   17. _____
    one direction. The problem is probably a defective _____
    _____.

18. If an air conditioner is overcharged with refrigerant, what should be done? _____

    _____

• Based on the problem diagnosis charts in the text, answer the following questions.

19. List at least three driving habits that cause vehicle problems. _____

    _____

    _____

    _____

20. Name at least two examples of *poor maintenance* that can cause the following problems.

(A) Poor gas mileage. _____

    _____

(B) Overheating. _____

    _____

(C) Automatic transmission slipping. _____

    _____

(D) No brakes. _____

    _____

(E) Uneven tire wear. _____

    _____

(F) Poor power steering operation. _____

    _____

(G) Poor air conditioner cooling. _____

    _____

Name _____

Date _____ Period _____

Instructor _____

Score _____

Text pages 963-968

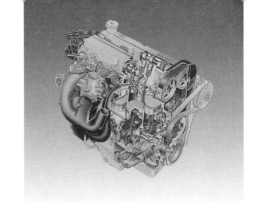

43

Repair Orders and Cost Estimates

Objectives: After studying Chapter 43 in the textbook and completing this section of the workbook, you will be able to:

- Explain the purpose of repair orders.
- Fill out a repair order.
- Explain the purpose of cost estimates.
- Complete a cost estimate.

Tech Talk: You may be able to specialize within the automobile repair business and avoid many repair operations that you are not interested in performing. However, one job you will have to do— no matter how disinterested you are—is the paperwork. Filling out forms is a part of modern life, and you must know how to make out repair orders and cost estimates. This chapter will prepare you for these inevitable paperwork duties.

Instructions: Study Chapter 43 of the text; then answer the following questions in the spaces provided.

Repair Orders

1. Many repair orders are set up to record both _____ and _____ _____ work.

1. _____
   _____

2. Which of the following would *not* be on a repair order?
   (A) Vehicle identification number (VIN).
   (B) Manufacturer of individual vehicle components.
   (C) Vehicle owner and address.
   (D) Vehicle body style.

2. _____

3. When the technician begins the repair, he or she will write or punch in the time _____. When repairs are completed, he or she will write or punch in the time _____.

3. _____
   _____

4. When parts are used, the part _____, _____, and _____ must be listed on the repair order.

4. _____
   _____
   _____

5. The customer will not be billed for parts and labor covered under _____.

5. _____

6. Calculate the labor bill for a 3.5 hour job when the hourly labor rate is:

   (A) $21.00   _____

   (B) $25.00   _____

   (C) $29.50   _____

   (D) $35.00   _____

   (E) $47.50   _____

   (F) $55.00   _____

7. A shop is basing its labor charges on a current flat rate manual. According to the manual, a water pump replacement is supposed to take 2.5 hours. However, one of the pump bolts is rounded off, and removing the bolt increases the total time for the job to 3.0 hours. The labor rate is $30.00 per hour. What will the shop charge the customer for labor?

   (A) $30.00
   (B) $60.00
   (C) $75.00
   (D) $90.00

   7. _____

8. When a shop buys a part for $35.00 and the price to the customer is $42.00, the markup is _____ percent.

   8. _____

9. A deposit on an old part is called the _____ charge.

   9. _____

10. Give some examples of outside service costs. _____

    _____

11. Rags, solvents, and lubricants are examples of _____.

    11. _____

12. A disposal fee may be charged for such things as used _____ or scrap _____.

    12. _____
    _____

13. Sales _____ are levied almost everywhere.

    13. _____

14. Technician A says that if the shop forgets to charge sales tax to the customer, it is not liable for the tax. Technician B says that sales taxes do not apply to some exempt customers. Who is right?

    (A) A only.
    (B) B only.
    (C) Both A & B.
    (D) Neither A nor B.

    14. _____

15. If the local sales tax is 5% on parts and labor, what is the final bill for the following repair jobs?

    (A) $75.00   _____

    (B) $120.00   _____

    (C) $205.00   _____

    (D) $275.50   _____

    (E) $311.00   _____

Cost Estimates

16. Should the technician assume that the customer will want needed repairs done?

16. _____

17. A cost estimate for fuel pump replacement is being made. The power steering pump must be removed to gain access to the pump fasteners. Technician A says that the labor for removing the pump must be included in the cost estimate. Technician B says that the labor for removing the power steering pump is charged at the same rate as the labor for removing the fuel pump. Who is right?
    (A) A only.
    (B) B only.
    (C) Both A & B.
    (D) Neither A nor B.

17. _____

18. If a flat rate manual is not available, the shop can obtain parts prices by calling _____.
    (A) local parts houses
    (B) other repair shops
    (C) vehicle manufacturers
    (D) the information division of the local library

18. _____

19. When listing parts and outside services on an estimate, do not forget to add normal _____.

19. _____

20. What are some things that should be added to the basic parts and labor sections of the cost estimate? _____

_____

_____

Name _____

Date _____ Period _____

Instructor _____

Score_____

Text pages 969-974

44

ASE Certification

Objectives: After studying Chapter 44 in the textbook and completing this section of the workbook, you will be able to:

- Explain why technician certification is necessary.
- Explain the process of registering for ASE tests.
- Explain how to take the ASE tests.
- Identify typical ASE test questions.
- Explain what is done with ASE test results.

Tech Talk: ASE tests are a fact of life for the modern automotive technician. A technician without any ASE certifications will increasingly be looked on as an unskilled laborer. To get the best jobs and stay competitive, you must take and pass the ASE tests. This chapter will help prepare you for ASE certification. Study it carefully.

Instructions: Study Chapter 44 of the text; then answer the following questions in the spaces provided.

Reasons for ASE Tests

1. ASE was established in 1975 to provide a(n) _____ process for automobile technicians.

   1. _____

2. Define *standardized test*. _____

   _____

Applying for the ASE Tests

3. What may be substituted for all or part of the 2 years work experience required to become certified?
   (A) Training courses.
   (B) Apprenticeship courses.
   (C) Time spent on similar work.
   (D) All of the above.

   3. _____

4. ASE tests are given _____ each year.

   4. _____

5. What is the relationship of ACT to ASE? _____

   _____

6. Technician A says that the technician must include payment for the required fees when sending in the application form. Technician B says that the technician should send in the application forms as early as possible to be able to take the test at the test center of choice. Who is right?
(A) A only.
(B) B only.
(C) Both A & B.
(D) Neither A nor B.

6. _____

Taking the ASE Tests

7. All ASE test questions are _____ _____ questions with _____ possible answers.

7. _____
   _____

8. A test question with statements from Technician A and Technician B is a(n) _____ part question.

8. _____

9. In most cases, checking your answers more than _____ is unnecessary.

9. _____

Test Results

10. If you have passed an ASE test, ASE will send you your test report and a(n) _____.
(A) shoulder patch
(B) certificate
(C) pocket card
(D) All of the above.

10. _____

11. All ASE test scores are _____ and are provided to the _____ only.

11. _____
    _____

12. How many times can you take a certification test?

12. _____

Other ASE Tests

13. An alternative fuels test is used to test for proficiency in _____ fuels.
(A) diesel
(B) alcohol
(C) CNG
(D) All of the above.

13. _____

14. Engine machinists can be certified in _____ skill areas.

14. _____

Recertification Tests

15. The certified technician must take a recertification test every _____ years to keep his or her certification.
(A) 2
(B) 5
(C) 10
(D) There is no set limit.

15. _____

Name _____

Date _____ Period _____

Instructor _____

Score_____

Text pages 975-981

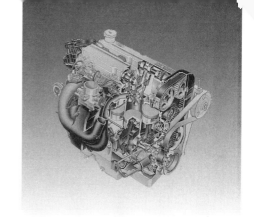

45

Career Opportunities in the Automotive Field

Objectives: After studying Chapter 45 in the textbook and completing this section of the workbook, you will be able to:

* List general classes of jobs in automobile service and repair.
* List areas of specialization in automobile service and repair.
* Explain job working conditions and salaries.
* List addresses of various organizations that offer information on automotive careers.

Tech Talk: Career opportunities in the automotive service industry have been very good in the past. In the future, they look even better. This is obvious when looking in the employment section of almost any newspaper. Openings for qualified automotive service personnel are almost always listed. If you like work that is mentally and physically demanding, diversified, and financially rewarding, auto service and repair may be for you.

Instructions: Study Chapter 45 of the text; then answer the following questions in the spaces provided.

General Classes of Jobs

1. Technician A says that a job in automotive lubrication involves lubricating the working parts of the vehicle. Technician B says that a job in automotive lubrication involves checking the battery, radiator, and brake system. Who is right?
   (A) A only.
   (B) B only.
   (C) Both A & B.
   (D) Neither A nor B.

1. _____

2. A light repair technician's job consists of all of the following, EXCEPT:
   (A) cooling system service.
   (B) muffler installation.
   (C) shock installation.
   (D) differential overhaul.

2. _____

3. Heavy repair technicians are called upon to disassemble, check, repair, and reassemble _____ components.

3. _____

4. When starting as a(n) _____ repair technician, you will probably work under the direction of an experienced technician in this area.

4. _____

Areas of Specialization

5. The specialist will have _____ training in a chosen specialty.

5. _____

6. Driveability technicians must understand _____ systems.
   (A) fuel
   (B) starting and charging
   (C) electronic engine control
   (D) All of the above.

6. _____

7. A transmission/transaxle specialist must be able to work on _____ and _____ units.

7. _____
   _____

8. A front-end technician performs _____ balancing.

8. _____

9. The body and fender technician will repair damage to a vehicle's _____ structure.

9. _____

Supervisory Positions

10. Advancement to a supervisory position is dependent on your _____.
    (A) ability to cope with the problems of the position
    (B) knowledge
    (C) skill
    (D) All of the above.

10. _____

11. Technician A says that the shop supervisor is in charge of all the technicians in the repair department. Technician B says that the shop supervisor does not need to know how to repair vehicles. Who is right?
    (A) A only.
    (B) B only.
    (C) Both A & B.
    (D) Neither A nor B.

11. _____

12. In a small shop, the shop supervisor may divide her time between supervision and _____ work.

12. _____

13. The _____ manager is in charge of the overall service and repair operation.

13. _____

What to Expect from Service Facilities

14. Working conditions for the automotive technician are _____ than they were in the past.

14. _____

15. Technician pay can be based on a(n) _____ wage or on _____.

15. _____
    _____

16. List several examples of job benefits. _____

_____

_____

_____

17. Automotive technicians earn wages that are in line with those earned by other persons employed in _____ jobs.

17. _____

18. Technician A says that it is hard for a good technician to find work. Technician B says that about one third of all technicians work in specialty shops. Who is right?
(A) A only.
(B) B only.
(C) Both A & B.
(D) Neither A nor B.

18. _____

How Does a Person Become an Automotive Technician?

19. A person develops into a good automotive technician by _____

_____

_____

_____.

20. _____ offer opportunities to acquire the training necessary to gain employment as an automotive technician.
(A) Trade schools
(B) Apprentice programs
(C) High schools
(D) All of the above.

20. _____

Job 1

PRECISION MEASURING TOOLS

Name _____

Date _____ Period _____

Instructor _____

TRODUCTION: Precision measuring tools (micrometer, sliding caliper, dial indicator, feeler gauge, etc.) are quently used in auto mechanics. These tools are needed to check various auto parts for wear. If a part is rn beyond manufacturer's specifications, it must be repaired or replaced.
During this job, you will use a micrometer, sliding caliper, and dial indicator to measure several shop units. ce these basic measuring tools have been mastered, you can easily transfer this knowledge and skill to other asuring tasks. Note! Plastigage, feeler gauges, and other more specific measuring devices will be covered other workbook jobs.

JECTIVE: Given the tools and equipment listed below, you will learn to use a micrometer, sliding caliper, d dial indicator.

OLS AND EQUIPMENT: You will need a differential assembly, two large screwdrivers, an instructor prepared of flat feeler gauges (numbered but with sizes removed), six engine valves, six valve spring shims, 0 to 1 h outside micrometer, sliding caliper, and a dial indicator.

STRUCTIONS: Follow the detailed procedures carefully and do NOT hesitate to ask your instructor for help. ke sure that you have completed the textbook and workbook chapters on precision measuring tools BEFORE rking on this Job.

As a quick review, identify the parts of the micrometer in Fig. 1-1. Also, using your own words, describe the four steps for reading a micrometer in the space provided.

1-1   (CENTRAL TOOLS, INC.)

. _____

. _____

. _____

. _____

_____

_____

_____

1. READ: _____

_____

_____

_____

2. COUNT: _____

_____

_____

_____

3. COUNT: _____

_____

_____

_____

4. ADD: _____

_____

_____

_____

2. Inspect your flat feeler gauge set. Ten of the blades should have the factory blade sizes removed (ground off, taped over, etc.). These blades should be renumbered (engraved, labeled using tape, or notched) from one to ten.

3. Before measuring the unsized blades, practice measuring a few of the sized blades. Then, you can get feedback about measuring accuracy by comparing your mike readings to the actual size written on the blades.

4. Now, test your skill. Using the micrometer, measure the thickness of the ten unsized feeler gauge blades and record your measurements in the following chart. If needed, ask your instructor for help getting started.

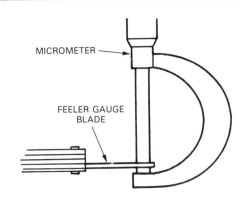

Fig. 1-2. Measure feeler gauge with "mike."

Feeler Gauge Blade Number	1	2	3	4	5	6	7	8	9	10
Your "Mike" Reading										

5. Find the six engine valves. Check that they are numbered from one to six.

6. Measure the valve stems using both the micrometer and sliding caliper, Fig. 1-2 and 1-3. Try to measure the largest (least worn) and the smallest (most worn) part of each valve stem. Only measure on the operational, machined, or shiny portion of the stem. Record your results in the chart.

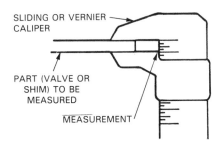

Fig. 1-3. Measure size with caliper.

Valve Number	1	2	3	4	5	6	
Caliper Reading	A.	A.	A.	A.	A.	A.	Largest Reading
	B.	B.	B.	B.	B.	B.	Smallest Reading
"Mike" Reading	C.	C.	C.	C.	C.	C.	Largest Reading
	D.	D.	D.	D.	D.	D.	Smallest Reading

7. Repeat this same measuring and recording procedure on the six valve spring shims.

Shim Number	1	2	3	4	5	6	
Caliper Reading	A.	A.	A.	A.	A.	A.	Largest Reading
	B.	B.	B.	B.	B.	B.	Smallest Reading
"Mike" Reading	C.	C.	C.	C.	C.	C.	Largest Reading
	D.	D.	D.	D.	D.	D.	Smallest Reading

8. Inspect your dial indicator setup. It should have attachments (clamp or magnet) for mounting the indicator on various assemblies.

9. Ask your instructor which differential unit will be used in this section of the Job. Preferably, you will have a bench mounted differential.

10. Mount the dial indicator as shown in the adjacent illustration, Fig. 1-4. The indicator stem should contact the smooth, back side of the ring gear. The base of the indicator should be clamped to or placed on the outer edge of the carrier.

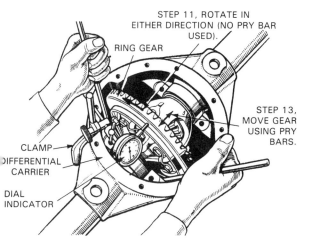

Fig. 1-4. In step 11, rotate or turn ring gear as if it were operating. Amount of runout (wobble) will be measured by indicator. In step 13, you must pry sideways as shown above.

11. Now, adjust the indicator dial to read zero. The face of the indicator should turn and adjust to zero. Slowly rotate the ring gear while watching the movement of the indicator needle. The amount of needle movement indicates the runout (wobble) of the ring gear in thousandths of an inch.

12. How much runout is there on your ring gear?
_____
_____
_____

13. Without changing the indicator mounting, use screwdrivers or small pry bars to move the ring gear sideways. Pry one way and then the other while watching the indicator needle. This will measure gear end play.

14. How much side or end play is there in your case bearings? _____
_____
_____
_____

15. To measure the gear backlash, mount your indicator as shown in Fig. 1-5. The indicator stem should contact one of the ring gear teeth. Hold the pinion gear solid to prevent any movement while moving (wiggling) the ring gear back and forth gently. Do not turn the ring gear, however. The amount of dial indicator needle movement indicates gear backlash.

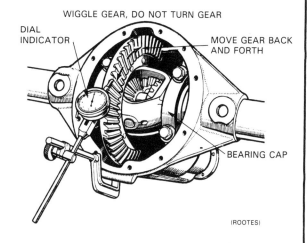

Fig. 1-5. Using dial indicator to measure ring and pinion backlash.

16. What is the amount of backlash between your differential gears? _____
_____
_____
_____

17. Have your instructor initial this Job for credit.

_____
INSTRUCTOR'S SIGNATURE

Job 3

BASIC OHMMETER

Name _____

Date _____ Period _____

Instructor _____

TRODUCTION: Due to the advanced electronic technology used in today's cars, the ohmmeter is becoming increasingly useful tool in auto service and repair. An ohmmeter will measure the electrical resistance (ability stop flow of electricity) in a circuit or component. When tested with an ohmmeter, a good electrical compo-nt should have a resistance value that is within specifications. On the other hand, a defective component ll register either an excessively high or low resistance reading. As you will see in this Job, an ohmmeter can used to test everything from a spark plug wire to an electronic ignition pick-up coil.

BJECTIVE: Employing the listed tools and equipment, you will learn to calibrate and use an ohmmeter.

OOLS AND EQUIPMENT: You will need a box or parts tray containing: short piece of insulated wire, piece rubber vacuum hose, ballast resistor, rheostat (variable resistor), eight resistor spark plug wires, three alter-tor diodes, three makes of distributor pick-up coils from electronic ignition systems, and an ohmmeter.

STRUCTIONS: Ask your instructor for the location of the equipment to be used in this Job and for any lded details: safety precautions, optional steps, etc. Only connect your meter to the components that are men-oned. Remember, NEVER CONNECT AN OHMMETER TO A SOURCE OF VOLTAGE. If an unprotected mmeter is touched to wires or a circuit containing an external supply of electricity, the ohmmeter could be riously damaged.

---

1. Compare your meter face to the one shown in Fig. 3-1.

    Locate the scale for resistance or ohms. It will have a zero on the far right and an in-finity symbol (maximum resistance) on the left. Sometimes, the symbol for infinity (∞) will be placed next to the left side of the ohms scale.

    You may be using a multimeter which in-cludes scales for an ohmmeter, a voltmeter, and an ammeter. If so, make sure that you have found and have STUDIED THE RESIS-TANCE SCALE. It will be used throughout this Job.

2. Describe the resistance scale on the face of your ohmmeter. _____

    _____

    _____

    _____

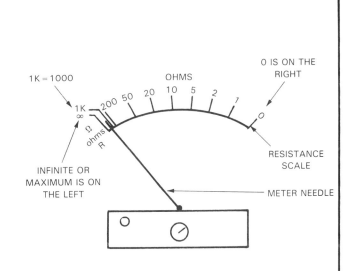

Fig. 3-1. Resistance, ohms, or (Ω) scale will have the zero on the right.

3. Now, set the CONTROL KNOBS on your meter. Use the corresponding illustration, Fig. 3-2, as an example. Turn the range switch to ohms times one (R x 1) and the function switch, if used, to ohms, R, or sometimes + DC. Meter controls and markings will vary with the manufacturer; so alter your control settings accordingly.

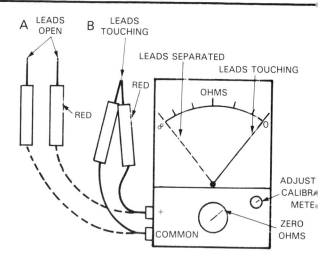

Fig. 3-3. Short ohmmeter leads and adjust zero ohms (≃) knob until until meter needle points at zero. When leads are separated, needle should return to infinite on the left side of the scale.

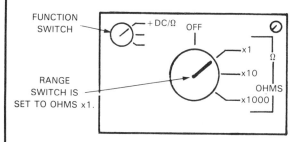

Fig. 3-2. As shown above, set ohmmeter to (R x 1). Some meters use a function switch. It must be set according to particular operator's manual.

4. Next, to compensate for variations in the meter batteries, you may need to CALIBRATE THE OHMMETER.

Touch or short the two test leads of the meter together as in Fig. 3-3. The leads should be plugged into the (+) and (−) jacks on most meters. With the leads shorted together, B in Fig. 3-3, turn the ohms adjust knob (zero ohms knob) until the needle of the ohmmeter is pointing directly at zero.

5. When the leads are separated as in A of Fig. 3-3, the needle should return to infinite on the left side of the scale.

If you have any problems calibrating your meter, ask your instructor for assistance.

6. When you have calibrated your ohmmeter, you have actually measured the resistance of a known conductor (meter test leads = 0 resistance) and a known nonconductor (surrounding air separating untouched test leads = infinite resistance).

Remember! A CONDUCTOR will allow the flow of electricity (current). A resistance unit, or LOAD (lightbulb, electric motor, resistor, etc.), will limit the flow of electricity. An INSULATOR (plastic, rubber, ceramics, etc.) will stop the flow of electricity.

7. When using the ohmmeter, keep in mind that as resistance in a component goes up, current goes down and that as resistance goes down, current increases.

8. Measure the resistance of the following objects with your ohmmeter. Record your results in the provided space. Also explain why the readings varied.

A. Piece of wire _____
_____

B. Piece of rubber vacuum hose_____

C. Explain the difference in your resistance readings._____
_____
_____
_____

9. A BALLAST RESISTOR can be used to control the amount of current flowing into the ignition system. During engine operation, it maintains a constant voltage of around 10 volts at the ignition coil primary (low voltage connection).

A defective ballast resistor can cause a wide range of problems. For example, if the resistance value of the ballast resistor were to drop, excessive current could flow through the ignition coil and distributor contact points. The points could overheat and burn. If a bad ballast resistor developed extremely high resistance, the ignition coil would not receive enough current and the engine might not run.

10. Measure and record the resistance of your ballast resistor as in Fig. 3-4.

Ballast resistor ohms = _____

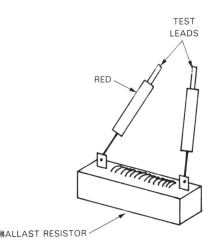

TEST LEADS

RED

BALLAST RESISTOR

Fig. 3-4. Touch your ohmmeter leads on each terminal of resistor. If you were to heat resistor, its ohm value would increase.

11. A RHEOSTAT is a variable resistor (internal resistance of resistor may be changed). It is commonly used as a volume-controlling device in car radios, for example. By turning the control knob on the rheostat, you actually change the internal resistance of the device. As a result, the amount of current that can flow through the rheostat is also changed.

The action of a rheostat can be used to control the volume, treble, light intensity, and current flow in various electrical circuits.

12. Using Fig. 3-5 and the four illustrations in Fig. 3-6, measure and record the resistance values of your rheostat in the given positions.

13. On the remaining ohmmeter measurements, you may need to change or even determine the appropriate range setting on your ohmmeter (R x 1, R x 100, R x 1000, etc.). When you have a general idea of the resistance to be measured, you should adjust the resistance range knob as follows:

OHMS RANGE SETTING	AMOUNT OF RESISTANCE TO BE TESTED
R x 1	1 to 200 ohms
R x 100	200 to 20,000 ohms
R x 1000	anything above 20,000 ohms

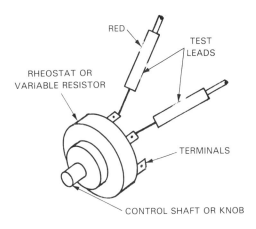

RED

TEST LEADS

RHEOSTAT OR VARIABLE RESISTOR

TERMINALS

CONTROL SHAFT OR KNOB

Fig. 3-5. Touch your ohmmeter leads to rheostat terminals while turning control shaft as described in Fig. 3-6.

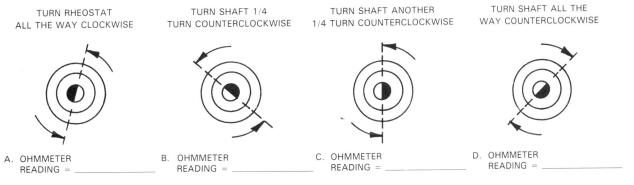

TURN RHEOSTAT ALL THE WAY CLOCKWISE

TURN SHAFT 1/4 TURN COUNTERCLOCKWISE

TURN SHAFT ANOTHER 1/4 TURN COUNTERCLOCKWISE

TURN SHAFT ALL THE WAY COUNTERCLOCKWISE

A. OHMMETER READING = _____

B. OHMMETER READING = _____

C. OHMMETER READING = _____

D. OHMMETER READING = _____

Fig. 3-6. Record ohmmeter readings for these rheostat positions.

14. When you do not have an idea of the resistance value in the component to be measured, turn the resistance range control to various settings. Use trial and error settings until the meter NEEDLE READS NEAR THE MIDDLE of the scale.

    For example, if you measured a resistor spark plug wire (10,000 ohms) with your meter range on R x 1 you would get a false ohmmeter reading. The meter would indicate infinite resistance since the plug wire has over 200 ohms. You would need to change the range setting until the needle read near the middle.

15. Set the range switch on your ohmmeter to R x 100 and recalibrate the meter. Anytime the range setting is changed, you may need to recalibrate the meter.

16. With the range switch set on R x 100, you will need to multiply the meter readings by 100. For example, if the ohmmeter needle points at 70 and the range switch is set on R x 100, the ohmmeter reading would be 70 x 100 or 7000 ohms, NOT 70 ohms.

17. Locate the eight numbered SPARK PLUG WIRES to be tested. Resistance spark plug wires are used to prevent intereference or static in a car's radio or tape player. They keep the high voltage pulses from transmitting into the radio.

18. In general, a GOOD SPARK PLUG WIRE should not have excessive resistance (generally not over 25,000-50,000 ohms depending on manufacturer). When the carbon filled center of a plug wire fails (burns, is pulled apart and separated, etc.), the resistance of the spark plug wire will increase tremendously.

    Quite often, a DEFECTIVE PLUG WIRE will have an infinite amount of resistance and current will not flow through the wire. The engine cylinder with the bad spark plug wire would develop a "dead miss," the engine would idle roughly.

19. Now, measure the resistance of your eight spark plug wires to determine if they are bad or good. See Fig. 3-7. Record your results in the following chart.

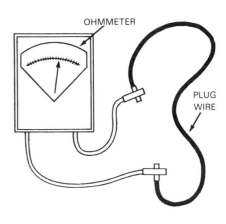

Fig. 3-7. To check plug wire resistance with an ohmmeter, connect meter as shown. Make sure that you have good connections and have your meter on R × 100.

20. How many of the spark plug wires checked OK? _____ Explain. _____
_____

21. How many of the plug wires were defective? _____ Explain. _____
_____

22. A DIODE is an "electrical check valve." It will allow current to flow in one direction but not the other.

    The condition of a diode can be tested with an ohmmeter. A GOOD DIODE will show high resistance with the meter leads connected in one direction and low resistance with the meter leads reversed.

    A BAD DIODE may be either open or shorted. An open diode will exhibit an extremely HIGH RESISTANCE when tested in both directions. A shorted diode will have a LOW RESISTANCE reading in both directions.

23. Now, using Fig. 3-8 as an example, measure the resistance of the three diodes in your equipment box. Connect the ohmmeter leads in both directions and record your readings for both. Unless instructed otherwise, set your ohmmeter range switch to R x 100.

SPARK PLUG WIRE	1	2	3	4	5	6	7	8
OHMMETER READING								

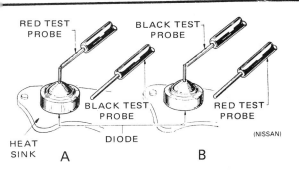

RED TEST PROBE   BLACK TEST PROBE

BLACK TEST PROBE   RED TEST PROBE

HEAT SINK   A   DIODE   B   (NISSAN)

Fig. 3-8. Connect your ohmmeter as shown. Record your readings in the chart. Diodes are used in an alternator to change AC (alternating current) into DC (direct current).

DIODE	1	2	3
FORWARD READING	A.	A.	A.
REVERSE READING	B.	B.	B.

24. Explain the condition of the diodes. _____

_____

_____

25. A distributor PICKUP COIL is one of the more problem prone components in an electronic ignition system. A pickup coil, as the name implies, is nothing more than a long piece of wire wrapped around a permanent magnet. Due to heat, cold, vibration, and movement caused by the distributor vacuum advance, coil windings and output wires can break. When this happens, the ignition system can be rendered inoperable.

An ohmmeter can be used to test the condition of a distributor pickup coil. Depending upon the manufacturer, the resistance specification for your pickup coils may vary from 150 to 1500 ohms.

26. Measure and record the resistance of the three pickup coils. You may need to change the ohmmeter range setting and recalibrate the ohmmeter.

Also, it is a good idea to WIGGLE the output wires of the pickup coil while testing. An internal wire break may only show up when the wires are moved. The reading may fluctuate and show a defect.

PICKUP COIL	1	2	3
OHMMETER READING	A.	B.	C.

27. Explain the condition of the pickup coils.

_____

_____

28. Have your instructor sign this sheet for credit.

_____
INSTRUCTOR'S SIGNATURE

Job 4

VOLTMETER AND AMMETER

Name _____

Date _____ Period _____

Instructor _____

INTRODUCTION: A voltmeter and ammeter are commonly used by the auto technician as testing and diagnostic tools. Hundreds of electronic devices are used in almost every system of today's vehicles, including the ignition system, fuel system, emission control system, starting system, and cooling system. As you will see in this Job, a voltmeter measures "electrical pressure" and an ammeter measures "electrical flow." By measuring actual voltage and current levels in a circuit and comparing them to specs, a technician can quickly determine the source of electrical problems.

OBJECTIVE: Using the materials listed below, you will learn to correctly operate a voltmeter and ammeter.

TOOLS AND EQUIPMENT: You will need a 12-volt car battery, possibly a trickle type battery charger, jumper wires, a light socket with a bulb and a pigtail (taillight type), a remote starter or on/off switch, and a multimeter.

INSTRUCTIONS: Ask your instructor for the location of the equipment to be used and for any additional information (safety precautions, job changes, etc.). Only hook up the circuits that are described in the Job. Always double-check your connections before turning on the power. Also, perform this exercise on an insulated work surface (wooden table, fender cover, etc.).

1. Study the controls, face and scales on your particular meter. They should include settings for those shown in Fig. 4-1. Some meters have one knob control while others use two or three knobs to select measurement type (volts, amps, or ohms) and quantity (100, 50, down to a fraction of a volt or amp).

2. List the following values for the controls or settings on your meter.

3. Set your meter to measure either 15 DC volts or more. A voltmeter, as with any meter, must always be set to measure SLIGHTLY ABOVE the expected maximum value. This will prevent the meter needle from "pegging" or slamming all the way to the right, possibly damaging the meter.

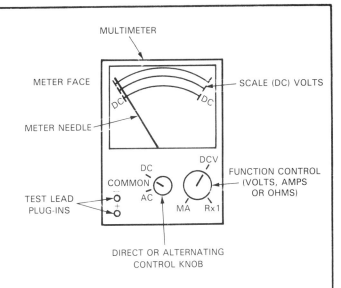

Fig. 4-1. Compare your meter to one shown.

Meter Controls	DC Volts	DC Amps	AC Volts	AC Amps	Ohms(R)
Highest Given Value					
Lowest Given Value					

As an example, if you set your meter to 12 volts and connected it across the output of an alternator, commonly designed to produce over 13-15 volts, your meter needle would strike the stop on the right side of the scale. This could harm the accuracy of the instrument. The same is true for reversing leads.

4. Now that you have your meter set to measure 15 or more volts, connect your test leads across the battery posts, as shown in Fig. 4-2.

Caution! DO NOT reverse your leads or meter damage could occur. The red meter lead should go to positive, and the black lead should go to negative. Remember, a 12-volt battery should have slightly over 12 volts.

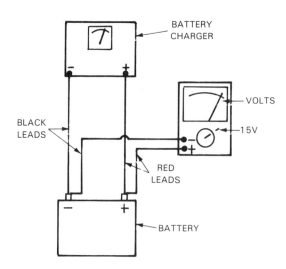

Fig. 4-3. Measure charging voltage as shown.

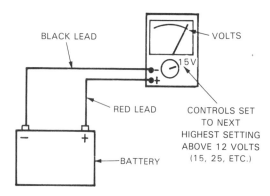

Fig. 4-2. Measure battery voltage as shown.

5. What is the voltage of your battery?

_____

6. Even though your battery is not "dead" or discharged, connect a **BATTERY CHARGER** (trickle charger) to the battery, Fig. 4-3. Then, measure the amount of voltage across the battery posts.

For a battery to be charged, it must have an input voltage higher than its standing potential of 12.6 volts. By forcing voltage into the battery, the battery can normally be returned to a full state of charge.

7. What was your charging voltage reading?

_____

8. How much higher was it than the standing battery voltage (reading you obtained in step 5)? _____

9. Whenever you think of VOLTAGE, try to relate it to water pressure. Voltage is the force that pushes electrons (electricity) through a circuit. It is much like the pressure that pushes water through a garden hose. As water pressure is increased, the amount of flow (current) and the distance that the water will squirt is increased. In an ignition system, this same principle is why 20,000 volts (high electrical pressure) is needed to force the electricity to "squirt" or jump all the way across the gap of a spark plug.

10. Now, connect the light circuit shown in Fig. 4-4. Take your time and try to keep everything organized. Avoid winding all the wires into a bundle of "spaghetti." Also, make sure that none of your "hot wires" are touching ground and shorting out.

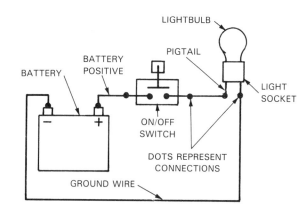

Fig. 4-4. Make sure that none of your connections (dots) are shorting out.

11. Before trying out your circuit or hooking up your meter, ask your instructor to check your work. Also, inquire as to whether the remainder of the Job is to be performed with or without the battery charger in operation.

12. After obtaining INSTRUCTOR APPROVAL, turn on the switch. The lightbulb should light every time the circuit path is connected with the switch. If not, recheck your connections and the bulb.

13. Without changing your meter controls (15 volts or higher), connect your voltmeter as shown in V-1 of Fig. 4-5. Leave the switch open.

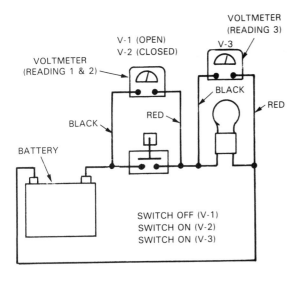

Fig. 4-5. Study required voltage measurements.

14. Record your meter readings in the chart. Then with the switch closed (on), repeat this process on the other two voltage drop measurements (V-2 and V-3).

Voltmeter Connection	V-1 Switch Off	V-2 Switch On	V-3 Switch On
Reading			

15. In the preceding task, you measured three voltage drops in order to grasp a very important point. A VOLTAGE DROP is an indicator of circuit resistance. For example, the voltage drop across the open switch was full battery voltage. The voltage drop across the closed switch was zero. A voltage drop is proportional to the internal resistance of the

tested circuit or component (open switch = infinite resistance = maximum voltage drop and a closed switch = zero resistance = zero voltage drop). In many instances, a voltmeter (voltage drop) is much easier, faster, and more desirable than an ohmmeter. You do not need to disconnect the circuit and voltage source.

16. A high voltage drop indicates _____ component resistance. A low voltage drop indicates a _____ resistance.

17. Next, change your meter controls (range and function) to measure MAXIMUM DC CURRENT (amps, A, or ∓). On some meters, you may need to change the location of the meter test leads in their jacks (plug-in sockets).
    Caution! If your meter DOES NOT MEASURE 10A or more, check with your instructor to prevent meter damage.

18. Unlike the voltmeter which must be connected in parallel, an ammeter must be CONNECTED IN SERIES with the circuit.
    Connect your ammeter in series with the circuit, shown in Fig. 4-6. You must break (disconnect) the circuit at the positive of the battery and insert your meter between the two connections.

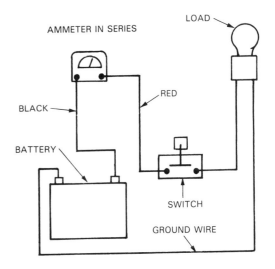

Fig. 4-6. Check that your ammeter is in series and that negative and positive connections are not reversed.

19. Caution! NEVER connect an ammeter in parallel with a circuit. A short circuit may be produced, causing an "electrical fire."

20. Before turning on the power, double-check your meter connections and settings. If they check out OK, turn on the switch and measure the current in your circuit.

21. Record the meter readings for the open and closed switch positions.

Switch Setting	Switch Open	Switch Closed
Meter Reading		

22. From these extremes (infinite resistance with switch open and normal resistance with only resistance of light bulb in circuit), you can easily see the relationship between current and resistance.

A high resistance will lower current. A lowered resistance will increase current.

An auto technician will utilize this principle when using an ammeter. The technician will measure the actual current flowing in a circuit and compare it to specifications. If the tested circuit current is high, then the circuit resistance is low (short, faulty resistor, electric motor, etc.) and vice versa. The technician can then diagnose which component or connection is defective.

23. Have your instructor sign this Job for credit.

_____

INSTRUCTOR'S SIGNATURE

Job 5

WIRE AND TERMINALS

Name _____

Date _____ Period _____

Instructor _____

INTRODUCTION: It is extremely important for an auto technician to be able to properly attach electrical components (one wire to another, wire to terminals, terminals to electrical devices, etc.). Some of the fundamental operations included in this skill are stripping wire insulation, cutting wire, crimping wire terminals, attaching wire connectors, and soldering. During this Job, you will perform all of these basic tasks.

OBJECTIVE: Using the listed tools and equipment, you will develop the skills needed to properly repair automotive wiring.

TOOLS AND EQUIPMENT: You will need safety glasses, a six inch piece of primary wire, old spark plug wire, male slide connector (preferably without insulation), spade connector with insulation, some rosin core solder, soldering "gun", wire strippers, needle nose pliers, small screwdriver, and burn-resistant work surface.

INSTRUCTIONS: You should have covered textbook Chapter 9. It discusses the terminology, operations, terminals, etc. that will be used in this Job. Ask your instructor for any changes or safety precautions. Take your time and do NOT hesitate to ask for help.

---

1. Locate your piece of primary wire. It should be about six in. (152 mm) long. Using your wire strippers, as in Fig. 5-1, cut and pull off about 1/4 in. (6.35 mm) of insulation from each end of the primary wire. Select the correct size stripping jaws.

   If wire strippers are not available, use diagonal cutting pliers. Diagonals may be used to strip insulation by cutting part way through the insulation all the way around the wire. Then, push on the side of the pliers with your thumb. The pressure will force the insulation free of the wire.

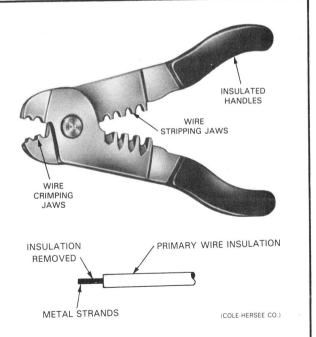

Fig. 5-1. Primary insulation is removed by clamping wire in appropriate size stripping jaw and pulling.

2. Shown in Fig. 5-2, fasten your terminal to the piece of wire. Slide the stripped end of the wire into the connector. Then, using the crimping tool, smash the middle of the terminal tang. This will lock the terminal on the wire. Check your connection by pulling on the wire and terminal lightly.

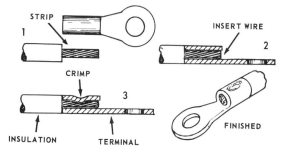

Fig. 5-2. Note, in step three, make sure you crimp middle of terminal tang or connection may not hold.

3. Next, crimp and attach your slide type connector to the other end of the primary wire. If your slide connector has insulation on it, peel off the plastic insulation. You will be soldering the terminal shortly.

4. Inspect the tip of your soldering gun or iron. The tip should be clean and tinned (coated with melted solder). Also, make sure you are using a work surface that will not burn easily.

5. Touch your soldering gun tip on the connection, Figs. 5-3 and 5-4. Pre-heat the wire and terminal. Then, touch the solder on the connection while still applying heat. Heat the connection until the solder melts and flows down into the terminal and wire.

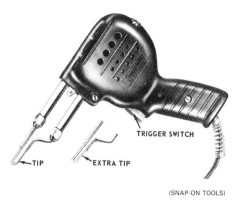

Fig. 5-3. This type soldering gun heats up in a matter of seconds; so be careful. Is your tip clean and tinned?

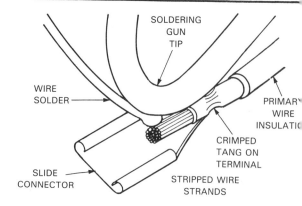

Fig. 5-4. Heat both wire and connector until solder flow into joint.

Note! Avoid moving the wire for a moment after soldering. Movement will weaken the solder joint.

6. The jumper wire that you have just made should be extremely useful. It can be used during a wide range of electrical tests.

7. Locate your piece of secondary wire (spark plug wire), Fig. 5-5. It should be an old discarded wire. In the following directions, you will be required to remove and install the terminals on the ends of the spark plug wire.

8. First, cut the metal terminals off of the plug wire as close to the terminals as possible. Then, strip off about 3/8 in. (9.53 mm) of insulation from each end of the wire, Fig. 5-6. Be careful when stripping a carbon filled spark plug wire as pulling too hard can break and ruin the carbon filled string in the wire.

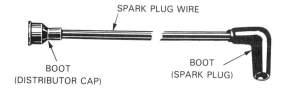

Fig. 5-5. Use an old discarded piece of secondary or spark plug wire.

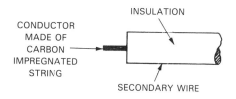

Fig. 5-6. You must use a fairly small size jaw on your strippers since diameter of conductor is small.

9. What does your wire conductor look like?

_____

_____

_____

_____

10. Using needle nose pliers and a small standard tip screwdriver, open and remove the old terminal ends from the spark plug wire. After removal, try to reshape the terminals into their original precrimped shape, Fig. 5-7.

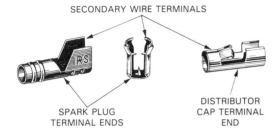

SECONDARY WIRE TERMINALS

R-S

SPARK PLUG TERMINAL ENDS

DISTRIBUTOR CAP TERMINAL END

Fig. 5-7. Try to return used terminals to their original shape for this exercise.

11. Next, slide your rubber boots back on the spark plug wire.

12. Fold the strands of the plug wire over the outside of the insulation and slip the terminal end into position. See Fig. 5-8. The carbon strand should touch the metal portion of the terminal. If a staple is used, it should have been inserted into the center of the carbon impregnated strands before the terminal end.

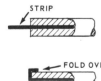
STRIP

STRIP OFF THICK INSULATION WITHOUT DAMAGING CONDUCTOR.

FOLD OVER

FOLD OVER STRAND OF CARBON TREATED STRING.

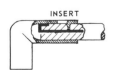
INSERT

INSERT YOUR TERMINAL OVER WIRE WITH CONDUCTOR AND TERMINAL. THEN, CRIMP TERMINAL ON WIRE.

Fig. 5-8. Installing terminal end.

13. Finally, crimp the terminal to the spark plug wire. Be careful not to crush and distort the outer end of the terminal. If distorted, the terminal will not fit into the distributor cap or over the spark plug properly. Quite often the wire stripper jaws will be marked as to which type of opening should be used to crimp spark plug or secondary wiring.

14. As a quick review of this Job, answer the following questions in your own words.

15. What is the difference between primary and secondary type wire? _____

_____

_____

16. What type of solder should be used with electrical wiring? _____

_____

17. Explain how a terminal is fastened to a wire without soldering. _____

_____

_____

18. How can diagonals be used to strip wire?

_____

_____

_____

_____

19. What should be done to the strands of a secondary wire before installing the terminal end? _____

_____

_____

_____

20. Pulling too hard on a secondary wire will cause: _____

_____

21. Show your primary and secondary wire to your instructor and have this Job signed for credit.

_____

INSTRUCTOR'S SIGNATURE

Job 6

SERVICE MANUALS

Name _____
Date _____ Period _____
Instructor _____

RODUCTION: The service manual, also called shop manual or repair manual, is a book containing detailed ctions on how to work on a car. It is an essential reference tool of the auto technician. When a technician t perform an unfamiliar or difficult repair, the service manual can be used to outline what must be done. lso provides specifications, capacities, and other useful information. In a sense, a service manual is like ing an experienced technician standing ready to answer almost any of your questions.

ECTIVE: Supplied with service manuals and vehicle information, you will learn to use the index, contents, ifications, troubleshooting, and repair sections of a service manual.

LS AND EQUIPMENT: You will need a service manual that covers your car or one covering all makes and els of cars.

TRUCTIONS: Use the service manual to look up and list the information requested in the job. Take your . You may need more than one class period to fully grasp the use of a service manual.

INDEX AND CONTENTS SECTIONS

. Ask your instructor for the following vehicle information. You may be able to look up data on a car of your choice, or your instructor may assign a particular make and model car. Record this information in the following space. It will be used for the remainder of the job.

. Car make_____ Car model_____
Year car _____ Engine size _____
Transmission type _____

. Check out a service manual. Then, read the front section explaining how to use the manual. This information is normally inside the front cover or on first few pages of the book.

. What is the title of the service manual you are using? _____
_____

5. What model years does it cover? _____

6. Does your manual contain a table of contents? _____

7. Does your manual contain an index? _____ Where is it located? _____

8. Are there small contents or index pages at the beginning of each repair section?_____

FINDING PAGE NUMBERS

9. On what page is the section covering the repair of your engine? The page number should be given in either the contents or the index. _____

10. List the service manual page numbers that explain the service and repair of the following engine parts. Also, read the instructions covering each area of repair.

AREA OF REPAIR   **PAGE NUMBER**

A. Engine assembly   _____

B. Valve lifters   _____

C. Connecting rods   _____

D. Main bearings   _____

E. Valve guides   _____

F. Timing chain, gears,
   or belt   _____

G. Pistons   _____

H. Camshaft   _____

BOLT TORQUE SPECIFICATIONS

11. Normally given under specifications, list the torque specs for the following engine components.

COMPONENT   **TORQUE SPECS**

A. Cylinder heads   _____

B. Main bearings   _____

C. Intake manifold   _____

D. Connecting rod bolts   _____

E. Flywheel bolts   _____

F. Exhaust manifold   _____

ENGINE TUNE-UP INFORMATION

12. Look up and list the following tune-up information for your engine.

TUNE-UP DATA   **SPECIFICATION**

A. Spark plug type   _____

B. Compression pressure   _____

C. Ignition timing   _____

D. Spark plug gap   _____

E. Fuel pump pressure   _____

F. Idle speed   _____

13. Most service manuals will have a simplified top view illustration of the engine. It gives information on engine firing order. The service manual illustration will usually show cylinder numbers, distributor cap numbers, direction of distributor rotation, timing marks, and spark plug firing order. It should be similar to Fig. 6-1. This type il-

lustration may be needed when installing a distributor, spark plug wires, when adjusting ignition timing (finding number one cylinder), and other related type jobs.

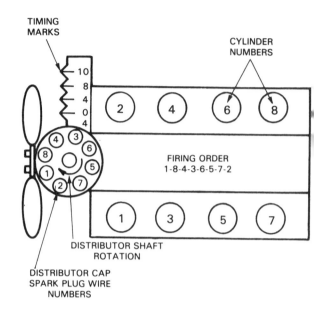

Fig. 6-1. This is an example of how a firing order-timing mark illustration in a service manual might look.

14. Locate the drawing in the service manual for your particular engine. Note how the manual illustration shows cylinder number and firing order information.

15. Draw your engine illustration in Fig. 6-2. Use a ruler to add the shape of the engine to the fan. Then, label the cylinder numbers, distributor cap, and any other data. Finally, draw lines (spark plug wires) from the distributor cap terminals to the correct cylinders.

Fig. 6-2. Draw shape of your engine. Then, add firing order, cylinder numbers, distributor shaft rotation, timing marks, and spark plug wires.

FOOTNOTES

6. When using a service manual, it is very important to pay close attention to footnotes. Footnotes are commonly used with specifications, for example. The footnote will give extra data or special procedures for complying with the specification.

   When a footnote is used, a symbol (@, 1, 2, 0, Δ, □) will be placed next to the specification. You must find another identical symbol elsewhere on the page. It will give the added details for the specification.

7. Find an example of a footnote in your service manual. What page is it on? _____ In your own words, explain the purpose of this footnote. _____
   _____
   _____
   _____
   _____

TROUBLESHOOTING CHARTS

8. Most service manuals have troubleshooting or diagnosis charts. They are helpful when a problem is difficult to locate or pinpoint. The troubleshooting chart will list common causes for particular problems, with needed corrections.

19. Can you find a troubleshooting chart or diagnosis information in your service manual? _____ On what page is it located? _____ In your own words, explain one problem and possible correction.
    _____
    _____
    _____
    _____
    _____
    _____

REVIEW OTHER SERVICE MANUALS

20. When you have spare time, thumb through different service manuals. Inspect the illustrations and repair procedures for various components. Also, compare the organization of one service manual to another.

21. Have your instructor sign this job for credit.

_____
INSTRUCTOR'S SIGNATURE

Job 7

BASIC CYLINDER HEAD

Name _____

Date _____ Period _____

Instructor _____

INTRODUCTION: During a valve job (reconditioning of cylinder head), it is very important to closely inspect
of the components for wear or damage. If a cylinder head is cracked, warped, or burned between the combustion chambers, it must be repaired or replaced. Also, other parts (valves, valve springs, guides, seats, etc.)
should be checked and compared to specifications. A good technician knows that overlooking any problem
can cause engine failure. A poorly completed valve job may have to be done over at the shop's expense.

OBJECTIVE: Using the tools and equipment listed below, you will learn to complete the procedures (inspec-
tions, tests and measurements) essential to cylinder head service.

TOOLS AND EQUIPMENT: You will need a valve spring compressor, brass hammer, safety glasses, straightedge,
flat feeler gauge, ruler, sliding caliper, a ruler and caliper, or micrometer, and cylinder head assembly.

INSTRUCTIONS: During this exercise, you will actually disassemble, inspect, and reassemble an automotive
cylinder head. Ask your instructor for any added details for the Job (head location, make engine, etc.). Remember
to keep all of your parts in a container. If you drop any of the small keepers, make sure that you find them.
Inform your instructor if you lose anything or run into problems.

CHECK FOR HEAD WARPAGE

1. Identify the cylinder head used in the Job by
   listing the following information.

   Engine make_____
   Engine model _____

2. Before disassembling the cylinder head, check
   it for warpage. Lay a straightedge across the
   surface of the head at various angles. Try to
   slide different size feeler gauge blades between
   the straightedge and the head. See Fig. 7-1.

   The LARGEST BLADE that will fit between the straightedge and head indicates the
   amount of cylinder head warpage.

3. When a head is warped more than specifications, it must be milled or machined to
   straighten its deck surface. A warped cylinder
   head often results after an engine has been
   overheating. Cylinder head warpage may

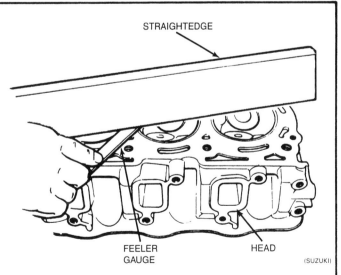

Fig. 7-1. Check your cylinder head surface for warpage.

cause the head gasket to blow, which may
then lead to water and pressure leakage and
more overheating.

4. A small amount of head distortion is acceptable, around .003 in. (0.076 mm) on any 6 in. (152 mm) surface. When machining, always check with specs for maximum amount of milling permissible.

5. When an engine is driven with a "blown" head gasket, serious head and block damage can occur. The surfaces directly opposite the leak can actually be burned away by the hot, high pressure combustion leak. If the burn depth is not too deep, it can be machined away by milling.

6. What was the largest size of feeler gauge that would fit between the straightedge and the head? _____

   _____

7. Explain the condition (straightness) and resulting action that should be taken with your cylinder head. _____

   _____

   _____

   _____

HEAD DISASSEMBLY

8. Now, disassemble the cylinder head.
   Using a brass hammer, so not to damage the valve stems, strike the retainers to free them from their keepers.

9. Using your spring compressor, as shown in Fig. 7-2, squeeze the valve springs and remove the keepers. One end of the compressor fits on the head of the valve and the other over

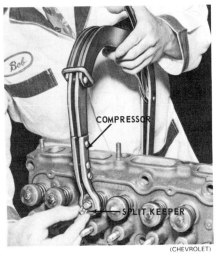

Fig. 7-2. Compress valve spring and remove split keepers.

the spring retainer. Hold on to the compressor firmly and keep it square. If it starts to slip, open and reposition the compressor.

10. After removing the keepers, open the compressor and remove the retainer, spring and the seal. Place all of the organized parts in a container. Note, do not remove the valves from the head at this time.

11. Repeat steps 8 through 10 on the rest of the valves. Don't lose any of the parts!

12. What damage can a blown head gasket cause?

    _____

    _____

    _____

CHECK VALVE GUIDES

13. With the springs removed, you should now check the condition of all of the valve guides. Look at Fig. 7-3. Pull each valve open about 1/4 in. (6.35 mm) and wiggle it sideways and up and down. The valves should NOT be excessively loose in their guides. If a valve wiggles excessively, wear is present in the guide or on the valve stem.

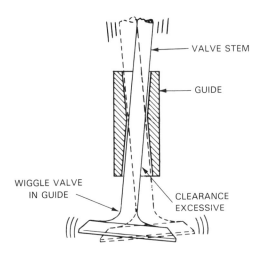

Fig. 7-3. Stem to guide clearance near end of guide must be within limits. Wiggle valve to check for stem on guide wear.

14. When a valve guide is worn beyond specifications, it must be repaired or replaced. When a valve stem is worn, it must be replaced. If this were an actual repair or valve job, you would have to mark any of the worn guides so that they could be serviced. Valves with worn stems would require replacement.

15. List the condition of each of the valve guides. Fill in the following chart. Label the chart and guides as being in GOOD (no wiggle), FAIR (slight wiggle under 1/32 of an inch) or BAD (over 1/32 of an inch wiggle) condition. Start at the punch marked end of the cylinder head and work across. The instructor's punch marks will be on the end of the head, not on the machined face of the head.

GRINDING VALVES

19. If this were an actual reconditioning of a cylinder head (valve job), you would grind the valves and seats at this time. If you are using a shop owned cylinder head, go on to the next step of the Job. If this is a real repair, check with your instructor for additional information. You may be required to complete Job 9, Valve Service, which is in this workbook.

Guide Number	1	2	3	4	5	6	7	8 4 or 8 cyl.	9	10	11	12 6-cyl.
Guide Condition												

INSPECT VALVES

16. Remove one valve at a time, keeping them in order!

    Inspect each valve for wear or damage by comparing them to Fig. 7-4. The surfaces of the stems should not be worn or rough. The faces of the valves should not be excessively burned. The heads of the valves should have a margin.

17. A margin is a flat lip between the face and head of the valve. See Fig. 7-4. If the margin is gone and the valve is relatively sharp, the valve must be replaced. Also, look on the end of the valve stem and check for wear.

18. In the chart, list the condition of each of your valves. Check the condition of the stems, stem tips, margins, and faces. Categorize them as being in GOOD (no detectable wear), FAIR (normal amount of correctable wear) or BAD (unrepairable wear or damage) condition.

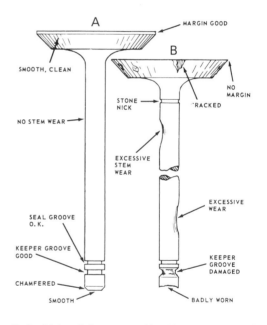

Fig. 7-4. Valve A is acceptable. Valve B is not. Study the problems.

Valve Number	1	2	3	4	5	6	7	8 4 cyl	9	10	11	12 6 cyl
Stem Condition												
Margin Condition												
Face Condition												

Note! DO NOT attempt to use valve grinding equipment without your instructor's permission.

20. To assure that you can identify the parts of a cylinder head correctly, use a ruler, sliding caliper, or micrometer to measure the following dimensions.

A. Intake Valve Head Diameter ＿＿＿＿＿＿

B. Exhaust Valve Head Diameter ＿＿＿＿＿

C. Valve Length ＿＿＿＿＿＿＿＿＿＿

D. Valve Stem Diameter ＿＿＿＿＿＿＿

E. Valve Margin Width (Maximum) ＿＿＿＿

F. Valve Margin Width (Minimum) ＿＿＿＿

G. Intake Port Height ＿＿＿＿＿＿＿＿

H. Valve Spring Free Height ＿＿＿＿＿＿

REASSEMBLE HEAD

21. Now, you can begin reassembly of the cylinder head. Oil the valve stems and install the valves into their original guides.

22. Basically, there are two types of valve seals in present use: umbrella and O-ring types. Look at Fig. 7-5. Naturally, the umbrella type is installed before the valve spring. However, the O-ring type seal must be installed after the spring and retainer.

    If you install an O-ring type seal before compressing the spring over the valve, the seal may be cut and damaged. The engine may smoke and consume an excessive amount of oil.

23. Explain how you installed your oil seals.

＿＿＿＿＿＿＿＿＿＿＿＿＿＿＿＿＿＿

＿＿＿＿＿＿＿＿＿＿＿＿＿＿＿＿＿＿

＿＿＿＿＿＿＿＿＿＿＿＿＿＿＿＿＿＿

＿＿＿＿＿＿＿＿＿＿＿＿＿＿＿＿＿＿

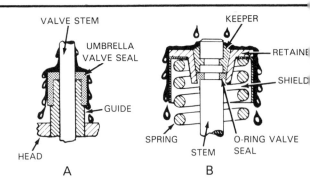

Fig. 7-5. A — This type valve seal is placed on stem before other components. B — This type seal can be easily installed incorrectly. It must be installed after compressing spring and retainer over stem.

24. Reassemble the rest of the parts of your cylinder head. To seat the keepers in their retainers, tap the ends of the valve stems with a brass hammer. A steel hammer can damage the stems.

CHECK FOR VALVE LEAKAGE

25. OPTIONAL: The heads can be tested for compression leaks by pouring water or parts solvent into each of the ports in the head. Place the head with the ports facing up and pour the water or parts cleaner into the ports. If fluid leaks out around the head of any of the valves, the valve or seat must be reground or lapped. This operation can save you the unpleasant task of having to repeat the valve job.

26. Have your instructor sign this sheet for credit.

＿＿＿＿＿＿＿＿＿＿＿＿＿＿＿＿＿＿

INSTRUCTOR'S SIGNATURE

Job 8

ENGINE TOP END

Name _____

Date _____ Period _____

Instructor _____

RODUCTION: The top end of an engine typically includes the cylinder head(s), intake manifold, exhaust ifold, valve train, and other upper parts of the engine. Proper assembly methods must be used to ensure cient, dependable engine operation. For example, the cylinder head, intake manifold, rocker assembly, and aust manifold bolts must be torqued to exact specifications and in the correct sequence. If not done proper-water leaks, oil leaks, vacuum leaks, combustion leaks, part warpage or even breakage can result.

JECTIVE: Given the listed tools and equipment, you will be able to install the cylinder heads and intake ifold on a V-type engine.

TRUCTIONS: This Job will outline the most important steps for assembly of an engine top end. Take your and follow each step carefully. Refer to a shop manual for added instructions if needed. Also, feel free sk your instructor for help if you have difficulty.

SERVICE MANUAL INFORMATION

1. Ask your instructor for the location of the engine to be used during the job and for its year, make, and displacement (size). Record the engine information in the space below.

A. Engine Make_____

B. Engine Year _____

C. Engine Size _____

TORQUE SPECIFICATIONS

2. Look up the following torque specifications in your shop manual. Record the data in the following chart.

A. Cylinder Head Torque_____

B. Intake Manifold Torque _____

C. Rocker Arm Torque_____
(if applicable)

3. Locate the picture in your shop manual that illustrates the head bolt tightening sequence (order) for your engine. Also, find a similar top view illustrating the torque sequence for

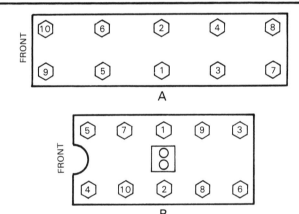

Fig. 8-1. A — Numbers indicate tightening order of head bolts. B — Numbers show torquing sequence for intake manifold bolts.

the intake manifold. They will look somewhat like those in Fig. 8-1. Notice the basic crisscross pattern.

4. Using your shop manual illustrations, complete the drawings in Fig. 8-2. Place CIRCL-ED NUMBERS on the illustrations to represent the bolt tightening order for your particular engine.

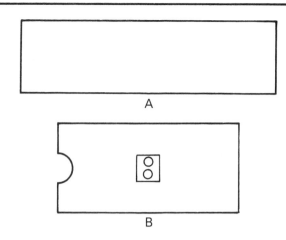

Fig. 8-2. A—Shop manual torquing order for your cylinder head. B—Shop manual tightening sequence for your intake manifold.

5. You are now ready to begin the hands-on section of the job. Check out and take the listed tools to the shop engine to be worked on.

TOP END DISASSEMBLY

6. If the engine is mounted in a car rather than on an engine stand, remove any hoses, lines, linkages, pipes, brackets, or wires that would prevent the removal of the cylinder heads and intake manifold. Note, if you are working on a V-8 or V-6 engine, you only need to remove the parts and cylinder head on one side.

7. Remove the valve covers. Loosen the rocker arms and remove the push rods. Lay them on your bench IN ORDER or use organizing racks. They should be reinstalled in the same location during assembly.

8. Break the intake bolts loose with a flex handle. Spin them the rest of way out with a speed handle. Preferably, use a six-point socket to prevent damage to the bolt heads.

9. What is the size of the intake bolts?

_____

10. What size socket did they take? _____

_____

11. Remove the intake manifold. If it is stuck and you must pry, be careful not to damage the gasket sealing surfaces.

12. Using a six point socket and breaker bar, break loose the head bolts by following the reverse sequence used in tightening. Use your flex handle first. Then spin the head bolts out with a speed handle. Note, your instructor may only want you to remove one head on a V-8 or V-6 engine.

13. Without bumping the head on the block, lift it from the engine. If both heads are to be removed, keep them in order so that they can be replaced in the same position on the block. Numbering the heads with punch marks on an unmachined surface can avoid later confusion.

PART MEASUREMENT

14. Use a ruler and caliper, or a sliding caliper to measure the basic dimensions of the following engine components. If you have been trained, you could also use micrometers to measure some of these parts. Ask your instructor for help, if needed.

A. Intake Valve Head Diameter _____
B. Exhaust Valve Head Diameter _____
C. Push Rod Length _____
D. Cylinder Bore _____
E. Engine Stroke (Piston BDC) _____
F. Valve Lifter Length _____
G. Valve Spring Height (Compressed) _____
H. Valve Spring Diameter _____
I. Valve Stem Diameter _____
J. Intake Port Height _____
K. Intake Port Width _____
L. Exhaust Port Height _____

15. If this is an EXERCISE instead of an actual repair, you will NOT have to scrape the mating surfaces clean or install new gaskets.

16. Place the head gasket on the block. There will usually be writing on the gasket to let you know how it should face (word top, front, etc.). Carefully position the cylinder head on the block. Squirt a small amount of oil on the head bolt threads and spin them in with your speed handle. NOTE! Use gasket sealer only if recommended by manufacturer.

TORQUING CYLINDER HEADS

17. Using the torque wrench, tighten the head bolts to one-half of their torque specification. Follow the order or sequence that you listed in step four of this job.

18. What is one-half of the head bolt torque specification? _____

19. Where is the location of the first bolt to be tightened? _____

20. Next, torque the head bolts to three-fourths of the torque specification. Follow the correct sequence.

21. Tighten the head bolts to their full torque value. Then, go over each bolt a second time to complete the head installation. Some manufacturers recommend that the head bolts are re-torqued after the engine has been started and has reached full operating temperature. The instructions with the new head gaskets will normally give this information.

22. What is the full tightening specification of the head bolts? _____

23. Did any of the bolts turn when torquing the second time? _____

INSTALLING INTAKE MANIFOLD

24. Install the intake gaskets and manifold. Refer to your shop manual for exact details (sealer use, etc). Start all of the bolts with your fingers before tightening any of the bolts.

25. Refer back to step four of the job to obtain the tightening sequence for the intake manifold bolts.

26. First, torque the intake bolts to one-half of their full torque specification in the prescribed order.

27. What is one-half of the full intake manifold torque? _____

28. Where is the first intake bolt that should be tightened? _____
_____
_____
_____

29. Tighten the intake bolts to about three-fourths of the full torque specification.

30. Torque the intake bolts to their full specification following the correct sequence. Go over all of the bolts one or two times to finish the installation. As with the cylinder head, some manufacturers recommend bolt re-tightening after engine operation.

31. What is the full torque specification for the intake bolts? _____

32. Did any of the bolts turn during the second or third full torque sequence? _____
_____
_____
_____

ASSEMBLE VALVE TRAIN

33. Install the push rods and rocker arms in their original locations. If a rocker shaft is used, start the rocker bolts with your fingers. Then sequence tighten them a little at a time. Start in the middle and tighten each bolt in ten pound steps. This will prevent a strain on any one bolt. Remember, the pressure of the compressed valve springs will be pushing against the rocker shaft assembly.

34. How many ten pound steps did it take to reach the full torque spec? _____
_____

35. If this were an actual repair you would have to adjust the valves on some engine makes. In your shop manual, look up the valve clearance adjusting procedure for your engine.

36. In your own words, how do you adjust the valves? _____

_____

_____

_____

_____

37. Install any remaining engine parts. Clean and return all of the tools before having your instructor sign the job sheet for credit.

_____

INSTRUCTOR'S SIGNATURE

Job 9

VALVE SERVICE

Name _____

Date _____ Period _____

Instructor _____

INTRODUCTION: This exercise, along with the Cylinder Head and Engine Top End Jobs, should give you enough experience and knowledge to perform an actual engine valve job. Remember though, the fit between a valve face and its seat is critical. The slightest mistake can cause a compression leak, rough idle, poor gas mileage, and increased emissions.

OBJECTIVE: Employing a shop cylinder head and the listed tools, you will learn to recondition a cylinder head assembly.

TOOLS AND EQUIPMENT: Check out safety glasses, valve spring compressor, brass hammer, steel rule, valve grinding machine, valve seat grinder, air or electric drill, rotary carbon brush, and old, shop owned cylinder head assembly.

INSTRUCTIONS: Ask your instructor for the location of the cylinder head to be utilized in this Job. Note! You should have completed the Jobs on Cylinder Head Service and Engine Top End before doing this Job. You should have also seen demonstrations on the use of valve and seat grinding equipment.

CYLINDER HEAD DISASSEMBLY

1. Clean the carbon from the combustion chamber, using your drill and wire brush, Fig. 9-1. Wear eye protection as carbon and wire bristles can fly. Even if the head is already clean, practice using a wire brush.

2. Using a valve spring compressor, remove TWO valve springs from your cylinder head. Remove them from one intake and one exhaust valve in a common combustion chamber. If the retainers are stuck to the keepers, tap the retainers with a brass hammer.

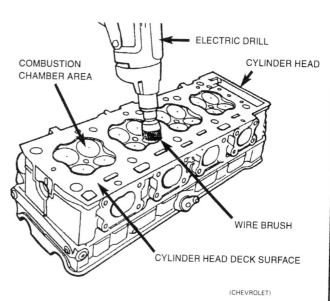

(CHEVROLET)

Fig. 9-1. Using an electric drill and a wire brush to remove carbon from a cylinder head combustion chamber.

CHECK GUIDE WEAR

3. Pull each valve open about one-quarter of an inch and check for valve guide and stem wear. See Fig. 9-2.

   There should not be detectable movement when the valve is wiggled sideways and up and down. A loose valve can result in valve breakage, excessive oil consumption, lifter-like clattering noise, and compression loss.

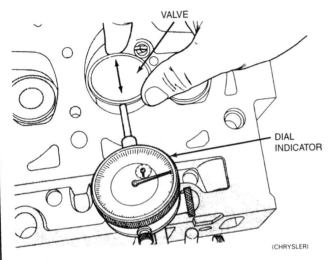

(CHRYSLER)

Fig. 9-2. A dial indicator can be used to measure actual guide wear. If available, you may use this method during your job.

4. What is the condition of your valve guides?

   _____

   _____

   _____

CHECK VALVE CONDITION

5. Inspect valve condition. Slide the valves out of the cylinder head and inspect them for rough and worn stems, burned faces, worn stem tips, etc., as in Fig. 9-3.

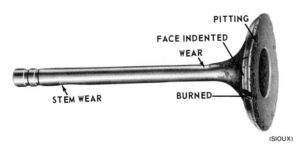

(SIOUX)

Fig. 9-3. Always check for all above mentioned valve conditions.

6. Note! If the valve will not pull out of the head freely, check to see if the stem is "mushroomed." If so, you will need to file off and chamfer the end of the valve stem with a hand file. Never hammer a valve out of a head or the guide can be broken.

7. Now, clean any carbon from the valve heads. Use an electric wire wheel, Fig. 9-4. Wear leather welding gloves and eye protection. Also, check that the tool rest on the wire wheel is close to the wire wheel.

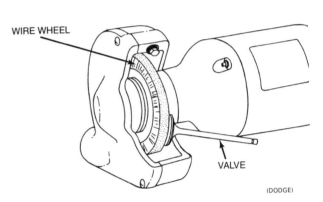

(DODGE)

Fig. 9-4. A pedestal wire wheel will quickly remove carbon from a valve, be careful!

GRINDING VALVES

8. Go to your valve grinding machine and prepare it for operation by checking the fluid levels and plugging it in. Also, familiarize yourself with its controls (chuck lever, grinding wheel, depth wheel, on/off switch, etc.). Move the lever and turn the control wheel while watching the resulting movement of the machine.

9. Unless instructed otherwise, skip the stone dressing operation. Stone dressing is normally done during a real valve job.

10. Insert the valve into the valve grinder. Check that the chuck jaws grasp the valve stem on the shiny, machined portion of the stem nearest the valve head. This operation is illustrated in Fig. 9-5.

    Do not let the valve protrude out or slide in too far.

11. Turn the grinder on and see if the valve is wobbling in the chuck. If it is, check for dirt on the stem or chuck. Remount the valve and try again. When wobble cannot be corrected, the valve is bent and must be replaced.

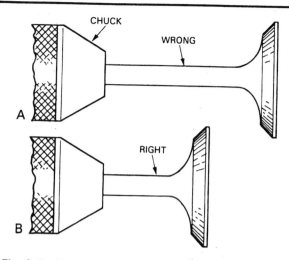

Fig. 9-5. Mount clean valve to proper depth or valve wobble can result. A — Valve protruding too far out of the chuck. B — Valve depth is correct.

12. Now, determine your valve face angle. Look it up in a service manual. Compare the valve face angle to the angle on the grinding stone. The two should be perfectly parallel, as in Fig. 9-6.

Most valves, except some high performance ones, use a 45° angle.

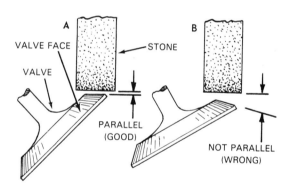

Fig. 9-6. To adjust chuck angle, loosen hold-down nut and swivel chuck until proper degree marks are lined up. Stone should line up with valve face.

13. Adjust your grinder to the appropriate angle by loosening the chuck hold-down nut and swiveling the chuck mechanism until its degree marks line up accordingly.

If the valve seat is to be cut at 45°, you should set the chuck on the valve grinder at 44°. This will provide an interference angle. If in doubt, refer to service manual.

14. What can cause a valve to wobble in a grinding machine? _____
_____

15. When beginning to grind the valve, feed the valve into the stone VERY SLOWLY. Make sure cooling fluid is flowing over the valve head. The valve should be positioned in front of the stone, while turning the depth wheel a little at a time.

As soon as the stone touches the valve, start moving the valve back and forth, Fig. 9-7. Valves and stones can be easily ruined on this step of the repair, so TAKE YOUR TIME.

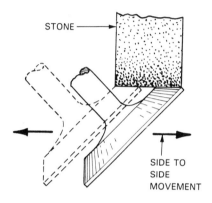

Fig. 9-7. Keep valve directly in front of grinding wheel and feed in slowly.

16. What is your valve face angle?
_____
_____

17. While continuing to move the valve back and forth, slowly feed the valve into the spining stone, Fig. 9-8. Go VERY SLOWLY while noting the depth of cut (markings on feed wheel).

Watch the face of the valve carefully. As soon as the face is "cleaned up" (black pits and marks removed), stop! Back out the depth wheel. You only want to grind off enough metal to true the face of the valve — the LESS material ground off, the BETTER.

18. How much material did you have to grind off your valve face? _____
_____
_____

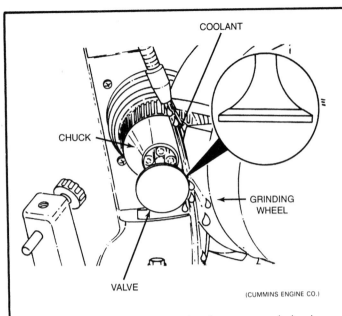

Fig. 9-8. When grinding a valve face, proceed slowly and grind a little at a time.

(CUMMINS ENGINE CO.)

19. Stop the machine and inspect the VALVE MARGIN, as in Fig. 9-9. Measure it with your steel rule. In general, if the margin is less than 1/32 in. (0.79 mm), the valve should be replaced. A thin valve margin will quickly overheat and burn when operating in an engine. There is not enough metal left to dissipate combustion heat, especially on the exhaust valves.

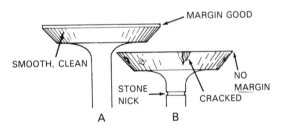

Fig. 9-9. Your valve should look like A not B. Notice that valve B is sharp and could NOT be used.

20. How wide is your valve margin? _____
    Is this satisfactory? _____
    _____
    _____

21. Next, dress or true up the end of your valve stem. Mount the valve in the V-block on the opposite end of the grinder chuck, Fig. 9-10.

Again, grind off as little metal as possible (generally less than .010 in. or 0.25 mm). Excessive grinding will remove the thin, hardened outer surface of the stem, causing rapid stem wear.

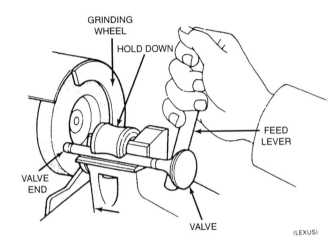

Fig. 9-10. Keep count of how many "thousandths" is removed from stem.

(LEXUS)

22. How much material did you grind off the stem? _____
    _____
    _____

GRINDING SEATS

23. To begin the grinding operation of the valve seat, find the correct size stone or cutter. The cutter should be SLIGHTLY LARGER than the valve seat and head of the valve.

    Never use a stone that is too small or it will rapidly cut into the port area of the head. Refer to Fig. 9-11.

24. After cleaning the guide, install your pilot, stone, and sleeve, Fig. 9-11. Then, inspect the fit of the stone closely, Fig. 9-12. Turn the stone with your hand to check its operation. Also, check that it has the correct angle.

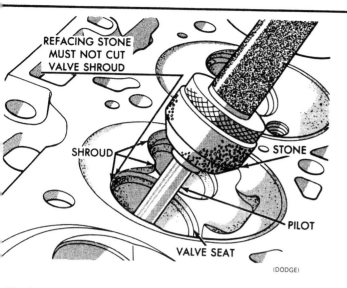

Fig. 9-11. Refacing (grinding) a valve seat. Wear safety glasses.

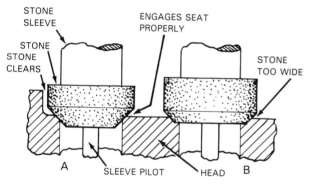

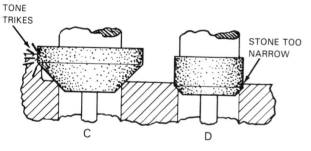

ig. 9-12. Stone must be of correct width. A — Stone .K. B — Too wide. C — Too wide. Will produce a orizontal step at bottom of seat. D — Too narrow. Makes a vertical step at the top of the seat.

5. What diameter and angle stone did you select?

_____

_____

_____

_____

26. If this were an actual repair and not an exercise, you would dress your seating stone at this time. However, to avoid the waste of stones and cutting diamonds, DO NOT DRESS YOUR STONE. Ask your instructor for help.

Usually, the stone dressing tool is adjusted to the valve face angle (30° or 45°). However, a 1° interference angle is sometimes used on the stone when not ground on the valve face.

27. What angle should be ground on the stone?

_____

_____

_____

28. Place a drop of oil on the pilot shaft. Insert your stone assembly over the pilot. Then, using your drive motor, spin the stone in the seat for a second OR LESS. Do NOT push down on the drive motor, let the weight of the motor do the cutting.

Again, grind off as little metal as needed to clean up the seat. The finished seat should be free of pits (black spots). Remember, grinding the seats sinks the valve down into the head. This will change engine compression ratio, fuel mixture, flow characteristics, etc.

CHECKING VALVE CONTACT

29. To check your work (face-to-seat contact), place pencil marks on the valve face, as shown in Fig. 9-13. With the valve in place in the cylinder head, give the valve about one-fourth of a turn while holding down on the valve.

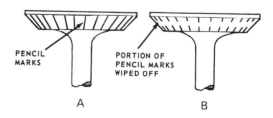

Fig. 9-13. Pencil marks on valve face will determine valve face to seat accuracy. A — Marks applied. B — Portion of marks wiped off by placing valve in seat and giving it one-quarter turn.

30. Remove the valve and inspect the pencil marks on the face of the valve. The portion of the pencil marks rubbed off indicates the contact point between the valve face and the seat. The contact point should be in the middle of the valve face. It should be about 1/16 in. (1.59 mm) wide and should extend all the way around the face, Fig. 9-14.

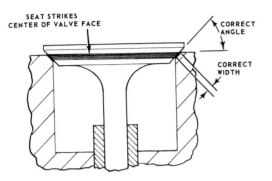

Fig. 9-14. Correct contact width should be about 1/16 in. (1.59 mm). Top and bottom portions of seat can be removed to change seat width and location.

31. Was the pencil mark wiped off all the way around the valve? _____

32. Explain your valve face-to-seat contact point.

_____
_____

33. Repeat operations eight through 18 on the other valve.

34. As a quick review, answer the following questions on valve service.

35. What is the function of a valve margin?

_____
_____
_____
_____

36. What is an interference fit between a valve and seat? _____

_____
_____
_____

37. Explain a good contact surface between a valve and seat. _____

_____
_____
_____

38. Before reassembling your head, ask your instructor to initial this Job and check your work.

_____
INSTRUCTOR'S SIGNATURE

Job 10

PISTON AND CYLINDER SERVICE

Name _____

Date _____ Period _____

Instructor _____

INTRODUCTION: Have you ever seen blue-grey smoke blowing out a car's tail pipe? Blue smoke implies that excess oil is entering and being burned in the engine combustion chambers. Possibly, the piston rings and cylinders are worn and need service. However, other problems (leaking valve stem seals, leaking intake manifold gasket on V-type engine, etc.) can also cause blue smoke. You would need to complete diagnostic tests to pinpoint the problem. Your tests will let you find out if the engine needs a "ring job" (piston and cylinder service).

OBJECTIVE: Given an engine short block and set of tools, you will learn to recondition a piston assembly and cylinder.

TOOLS AND EQUIPMENT: Check out a ridge reamer, hammer, safety glasses, ring expander, inside micrometer, outside micrometer, set of flat feeler gauges, ring compressor, some engine oil, cylinder hone, low speed electric drill, ratchet and socket set, two short pieces of fuel line hose, torque wrench and shop owned engine assembly.

INSTRUCTIONS: Before beginning this Job, identify the parts in Fig. 10-1. If not already briefed, ask your instructor for any added directions and for the location of the special equipment and engine to be used. This is a rather long and time consuming exercise. If you see that time is running out, inform your instructor so that the engine parts may be stored.

PART DISASSEMBLY

1. Since you are going to service only one piston and cylinder, position that piston at BDC (bottom dead center).

    The crankshaft may be turned with a breaker bar and socket which fits the large bolt on the front of the crankshaft snout. If needed, a large pry bar can be wedged between the flywheel bolts to turn the crank. A special flywheel tool may also be used to grasp the teeth of the flywheel for turning.

2. How did you position your piston at BDC?

    _____
    _____
    _____
    _____

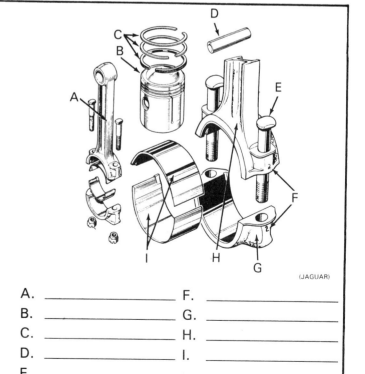

(JAGUAR)

A. _____ F. _____
B. _____ G. _____
C. _____ H. _____
D. _____ I. _____
E. _____

Fig. 10-1. Identify these parts as a review.

INSPECT CYLINDERS

3. Inspect the engine cylinder for wear or damage (scratches, grooves, etc.). To check for excessive cylinder wear, rub your fingernail across the top of the cylinder. This will show any ridge formed in the top of the cylinder. See Fig. 10-2.

A RING RIDGE is formed by the wearing action of the piston rings. If a ring ridge is present, it must be removed before piston removal. Forcing the piston out of the cylinder and over a ring ridge can break the rings and damage the piston grooves and lands.

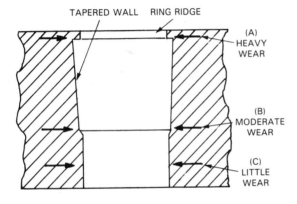

Fig. 10-2. Typical cylinder wear pattern. Diameter through A (top of ring travel), minus B (bottom of ring travel), indicates amount of taper. Note sharp edge formed by upper ring ridge. Ridge at bottom of ring travel is less pronounced.

4. Does your cylinder have a ring ridge?

_____

_____

_____

_____

REMOVE RING RIDGE

5. To remove the ring ridge, stuff rags into the bottom of the cylinder bore. Insert your ridge reaming tool into the cylinder, Fig. 10-3.

Adjust the cutters out against the ridge. Then, turn the reamer with your ratchet and socket until the ridge is cut flush with the worn part of the cylinder wall.

Important: the new reamed surface must blend smoothly with the existing cylinder.

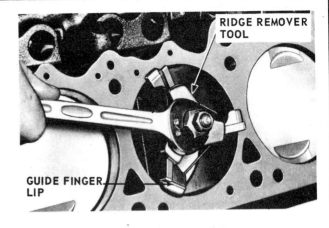

Fig. 10-3. Removing a ring ridge. This reamer is supported by lips on top of guide fingers. (Chrysler)

6. Remove your rags and blow out the cylinder to remove metal shavings that might scratch the cylinder during piston removal.

REMOVE CONNECTING RODS

7. Now, unscrew the nuts holding the rod cap on the connecting rod. Keep them in order and right side up. It is desirable to replace the connecting rod nuts exactly as removed.

8. Also, check that the rod cap and rod are numbered, Fig. 10-4. During a complete service of all of the pistons and cylinder, it is essential that all of the caps, connecting rods, pistons, and related fasteners are installed as removed.

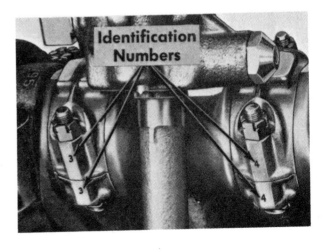

Fig. 10-4. Check connecting rods for correct identification numbering. (G.M.C.)

9. What is the number of the rod you are removing? _____

MEASURE CYLINDER WEAR

10. Measure the diameter of your cylinder with an inside micrometer or telescoping gauge and outside mike, Fig. 10-5. You must take measurements in the cylinder locations described in Fig. 10-6.

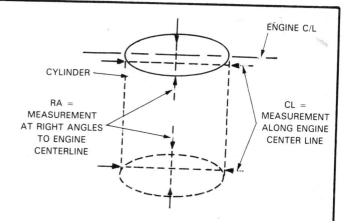

Fig. 10-6. Measure diameter as indicated by the four dotted lines and arrows.

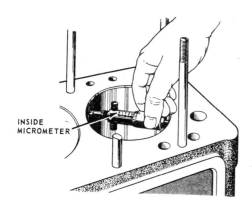

Fig. 10-5. Use your inside micrometer or outside mike and telescoping gauge to measure bore diameter.

11. Make measurements at right angles to and along the engine centerline, near the top of ring travel. This will let you calculate how much the cylinder is OUT-OF-ROUND.

12. When checking CYLINDER TAPER, "mike" at the top and bottom of ring travel at right angles to the engine centerline.

13. CYLINDER OVERSIZE is determined by measuring the diameter of the cylinder bore at right angles to the engine centerline near the bottom of ring travel. Subtract this measurement from standard bore size.

14. Record your measurements in the appropriate space in the following chart.

15. Now, calculate the out-of-round, taper and oversize of your cylinder. Subtract the chart values. The difference will indicate these three conditions in your cylinder. Your standard cylinder diameter will have to be obtained from your service manual or instructor.

HONE CYLINDER

16. To hone or deglaze your cylinder, clamp the hone into a low speed electric drill. Install the hone, Fig. 10-7, in the cylinder bore. Squirt a moderate amount of hone oil in the cylinder. Turn ON the drill. At the same time, move the drill up and down the full length of the cylinder. However, be careful not to pull the hone too far out of the bore or hone damage may result.

    Move the hone up and down at a rate that will produce a 50 degree crosshatch pattern as shown in Fig. 10-8. This will help the rings seat and seal during engine start up.

17. Before withdrawing the hone, hand squeeze or adjust the stones together to prevent vertical scratches.

MEASUREMENT	RESULT	MEASUREMENT	RESULT	MEASUREMENT	RESULT
Top of cylinder R/A	A. ____	Top of cylinder R/A	D. ____	Bottom of cylinder R/A	G. ____
Top of cylinder C/L	B. ____	Bottom of cylinder R/A	E. ____	Standard bore specs	H. ____
Out-of-round	C. ____	Taper in cylinder	F. ____	Cylinder oversize	I. ____

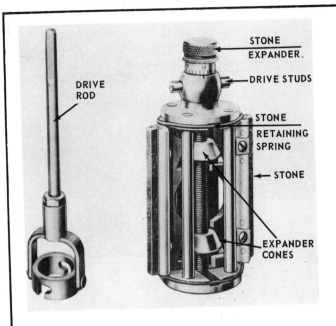

Fig. 10-7. Note parts of hone.

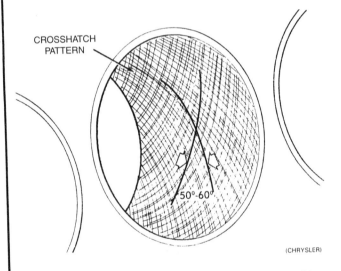

Fig. 10-8. A spring-loaded hone was used to create this desirable crosshatch pattern.

18. At about what angle are the hone marks in your cylinder? _____

_____

_____

CLEAN CYLINDER

19. After honing, always CLEAN the cylinder thoroughly. Any grit left in the engine will act as grinding compound that can wear moving parts of the engine. Scrub the cylinder with soap and hot water and then rinse with clean hot water. Wipe the cylinder dry with a clean rag.

20. Finally, wipe the cylinder with a clean OIL-SOAKED RAG. Wipe until all of the grit is removed. The oil will help pick up heavy particles from inside the hone scratches.

FIND PISTON CLEARANCE

21. Next, determine the PISTON CLEARANCE. Measure the diameter of your piston across the skirts, even with the piston pin. Use a large outside micrometer. Then, record this measurement in the following chart. Go back to Step 8 through 12 of the Job and look up your cylinder diameter (bottom of cylinder R/A). Record it in the chart.

22. Finally, subtract cylinder bore diameter by piston diameter to determine piston clearance.

	CYLINDER DIAMETER A.	_____
minus	PISTON DIAMETER B.	_____
equals	PISTON CLEARANCE C.	_____

CHECK PISTON PINS

23. To check the general WRIST PIN FIT in the piston, clamp the rod I-beam lightly in a vise, as in Fig. 10-9. Try to rock the piston sideways (opposite normal swivel). Any detectable movement would indicate piston pin looseness. During an actual repair this would require service (pin or bushing replacement).

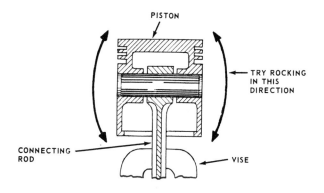

Fig. 10-9. Rock piston as shown to check for pin looseness.

24. Explain the condition of your piston pin.

_____

_____

_____

_____

25. Position the piston and rod assembly in the vise so that the piston skirt is resting on top of the vise jaws and cannot swivel. Clamp the jaw around the connecting rod. Using your ring expander, Fig. 10-10, remove the piston rings from the piston. To prevent ring breakage, open the rings only enough to clear the piston lands. Keep them in order and right side up.

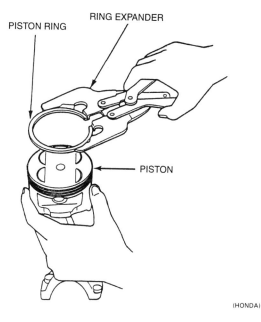

(HONDA)

Fig. 10-10. Avoid over expansion of rings.

CLEAN RING GROOVES

26. Clean the carbon from the inside of your ring grooves with a ring groove cleaner, Fig. 10-11. Select the correct width scraper for each groove and be careful not to cut too much. Ideally, you do not want to cut any of the metal in the groove, just the carbon.

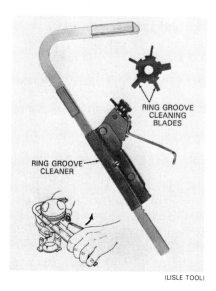

(LISLE TOOL)

Fig. 10-11. Try to remove all of the carbon but none of the metal from grooves.

27. If a groove cleaner is not available, an old broken ring can be used to scrape carbon from inside the grooves.

CHECK RING GROOVE WEAR

28. Measure your RING SIDE CLEARANCE as demonstrated in Fig. 10-12. Fit a ring into the top and middle ring grooves. Determine the largest size feeler gauge that will fit between the side of the groove and ring. The largest size feeler gauge blade that fits will determine your ring side clearance. Your top piston groove will usually be the most worn.

29. What is your top ring side clearance? ___

_____

30. What is your second ring side clearance?

_____

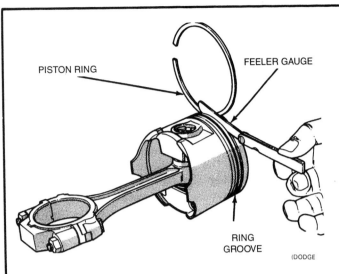

Fig. 10-12. Ring side clearance is checked as shown.

CHECK RING GAP

31. Next, determine your PISTON RING GAP. Install the compression ring into the cylinder squarely. Push it to the bottom of ring travel with the head of your piston.

   Determine the largest size feeler gauge that will fit between the gap in the ends of the ring, Fig. 10-13. When a ring gap is too small, the heat of operation will cause expansion. This expansion could crush the ring outward against the cylinder wall with tremendous force, damaging or scoring the ring and cylinder.

32. What is your upper compression ring gap?

_____

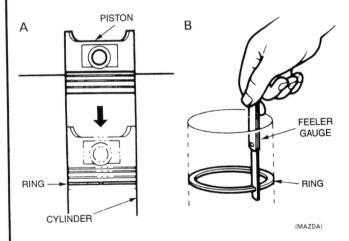

Fig. 10-13. Measuring ring gap. A — Using a piston to push the ring to the bottom of ring travel in the cylinder.
B — Measuring the ring gap with a feeler gauge.

33. What is your lower compression ring gap?

_____

34. What can happen when a ring gap is too small? _____

_____

_____

_____

INSTALL PISTON RINGS

35. Now that you have cleaned the piston grooves and fit the rings, you can INSTALL THE RINGS on the piston. Take your time and follow the directions given in the Fig. 10-14. Start with your oil rings, making sure that you butt the ends of the expander.

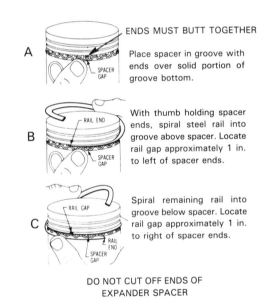

Fig. 10-14. Note basic steps for installing oil ring.

36. With the oil ring in place, you may either install your compression rings by hand or with your ring expander. The ring expander is faster and reduces the chance of ring breakage.

37. If you must spiral the rings on by hand, be careful not to extend the rings too much.

Double-check that you have the rings right-side up. They are sometimes marked with a dot or small circle on the top. Space the ring gaps away from each other as described in Fig. 10-14. Ask your teacher for help if in doubt about any task.

INSTALL PISTONS

38. Oil the piston, pin, and rings generously, Fig. 10-15. Then, tighten your ring compressor around the piston rings as shown in Fig. 10-16. Check that the small identations on

(FEDERAL MOGUL)

Fig. 10-15. Cylinder, piston, rings, pin, and rod bearings must be heavily oiled.

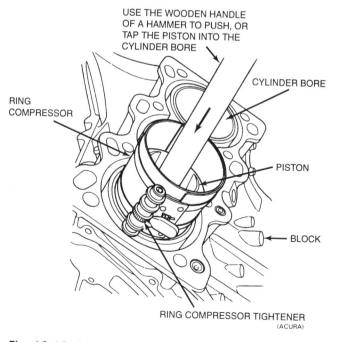

USE THE WOODEN HANDLE OF A HAMMER TO PUSH, OR TAP THE PISTON INTO THE CYLINDER BORE

CYLINDER BORE

RING COMPRESSOR

PISTON

BLOCK

RING COMPRESSOR TIGHTENER
(ACURA)

Fig. 10-16. Properly adjusted ring compressor makes piston installation easy. Hold compressor tightly against block surface.

your ring compressor are DOWN near the bottom of the piston. These small lips prevent the compressor from sliding into the cylinder with the piston.

39. Remove your rod cap. Install the bearing. Then, oil the outside surface of the bearing. Slide two pieces of rubber gas line hose (or other suitable protector) over the rod bolts to protect the crank, Fig. 10-17.

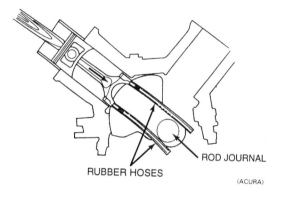

ROD JOURNAL

RUBBER HOSES

(ACURA)

Fig. 10-17. Pulling or pushing rod into contact with crankshaft journal.

40. With the piston marking to the front of the engine, INSTALL YOUR PISTON in the cylinder. Tap lightly on the piston head with a hammer handle, Fig. 10-16. Keep the compressor flat on the block. If the oil ring pops out between the compressor and cylinder, reinstall the compressor and try again.

41. Important! DO NOT hammer the piston to the bottom of the bore until you can reach under the engine to guide the rod over the crank. If a rod bolt is hammered into the crank, the crank can be damaged.

42. While carefully guiding the connecting rod over the crank journal with the bearing insert in place, tap the piston fully down into the cylinder, Fig. 10-16. Double-check that the piston and rod assembly is facing in the proper direction. Reversing the rod can cause bearing and crankshaft damage.

43. How do you know that the piston and rod assembly is facing in the right direction?

_____

_____

_____

CHECK BEARING CLEARANCE

44. Now, determine your ROD BEARING CLEARANCE, using Plastigage. With the rod cap bearing insert clean and dry, lay a strip of Plastigage across the bearing. Then install and torque the rod cap to specifications. Remove the cap and compare the flattened Plastigage to the paper scale provided with the Plastigage, Fig. 10-18.

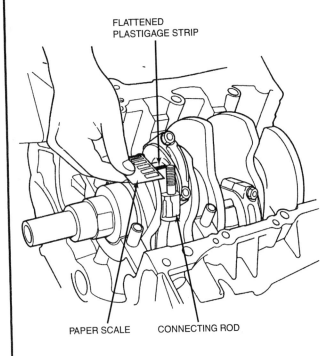

FLATTENED
PLASTIGAGE STRIP

PAPER SCALE   CONNECTING ROD

Fig. 10-18. Check the width of flattened Plastigage with paper scale.

45. As you can see, when the bearing clearance gets smaller, the width of the crushed Plastigage gets wider and vice versa. Also note, a two on the Plastigage scale would equal a bearing clearance of .002 of an inch (1 = .001, 1.5 = .0015, etc.).

46. What is your rod bearing clearance?

_____

TORQUE CONNECTING RODS

47. Remove the flattened Plastigage from the rod insert carefully. Oil the bearing and crank journal and install the rod cap. The rod identification numbers should be lined up. Torque the rod cap nuts to service manual specifications. Then, make sure the crank will still rotate.

48. What is your rod bolt torque specification?

_____

49. Clean your work area and tools, and have your instructor sign this Job.

_____

INSTRUCTOR'S SIGNATURE

Job 11

TIRE CHANGE AND REPAIR

Name _____

Date _____ Period _____

Instructor _____

INTRODUCTION: Changing, repairing, and balancing a tire are fundamental automotive service and repair operations. Damaged or improperly maintained tires frequently cause numerous drivability problems, such as wheel tramp, shimmy, vibration, hard steering, poor steering recovery, steering pull, steering wander, tire squeal, hard ride, tire wear, lowered gas mileage, and on-the-road breakdowns in the form of flats or blowouts. As you can see, anyone who plans on becoming a well qualified auto technician and problem troubleshooter should learn as much as possible about basic tire service.

OBJECTIVE: Given an old tire, a wheel, and the listed tools, you will learn to properly service and repair a wheel and tire assembly.

TOOLS AND EQUIPMENT: You will need a wheel and tubeless tire, tire changer, valve core tool, tire plugging tool kit, wheel weight pliers, small steel ruler, tread depth gauge or a Lincoln-head penny, soapy water, safety glasses, tire pressure gauge, diagonal cutting pliers, and shop rags or paper towels.

INSTRUCTIONS: Ask your instructor for the location of the particular tire and wheel to be used in the Job and for any other details. You should have seen a demonstration on the safe and proper use of your tire changer. Be sure to wear safety glasses, especially while inflating the tire.

REVIEW OF TIRE AND WHEEL

1. As a review and to help you better understand the procedures given in the Job, identify the parts of the cutaway tire, wheel, and valve stem assembly in Fig. 11-1. The parts that you cannot label from memory should be studied.

A. _____
B. _____
C. _____
D. _____
E. _____
F. _____
G. _____
H. _____
I. _____

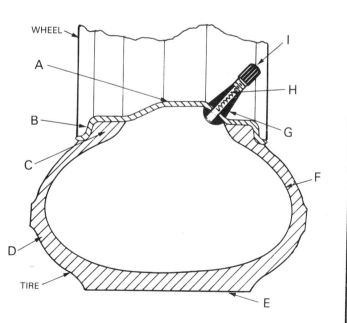

Fig. 11-1. Identify the parts of the wheel and tire assembly.

2. Check out the tools, equipment, tire, and wheel to be used for the Job.

3. From the information printed on the sidewall of the tire, fill in the following data on your tire.
   A. Brand name _____
   B. Wheel diameter _____
   C. Ply information _____
   D. Construction type _____
   E. Load range _____
   F. Maximum air pressure _____
   G. Maximum load _____
   H. DOT number _____

CHECK TIRE WEAR

4. As previously mentioned in your textbook, tire wear patterns are indicators of suspension, inflation, alignment, and driving problems. Compare your tire wear pattern to the ones given in Fig. 11-2. Diagnose the cause of any irregular tire wear.

5. What type of wear pattern does your tire have? _____
   _____
   _____
   _____

6. What was the most likely cause for the wear pattern? _____
   _____
   _____

7. Can you find any tire damage (cuts, cracks, etc.) other than wear? _____
   _____
   _____

8. As a rule of thumb, if the tread on a tire, at any point, is less than 1/16 in. (1.59 mm) deep, the tire is unsafe. It should be replaced.

9. A "trick of the trade" is to insert a Lincoln-head penny into the tire tread at various locations. If the top of Mr. Lincoln's head shows, then the tread is less than 1/16 in. (1.59 mm) deep and tire is unsafe for use. If the tread covers part of Lincoln's head, the tire is usually considered safe.

10. Use your depth gauge, steel rule, or Lincoln penny to measure the tread depth at its deepest and shallowest points.

11. What is the measured tread depth at its shallowest point? _____
    _____

12. What is the measured tread depth at its deepest point? _____

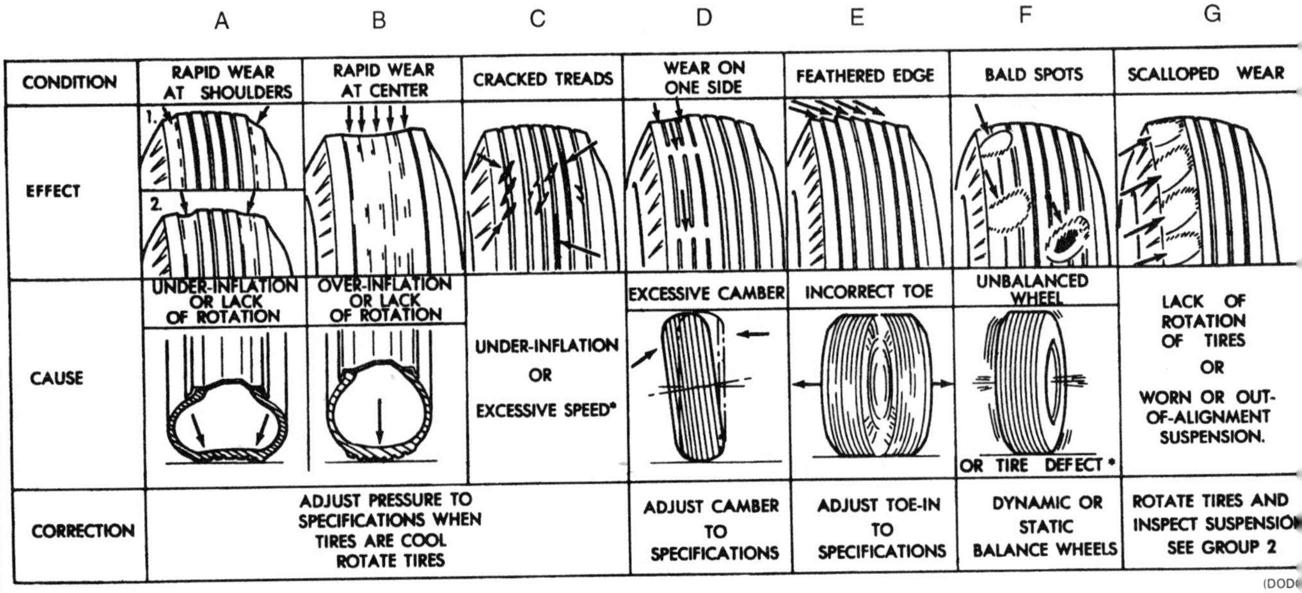

	A	B	C	D	E	F	G
CONDITION	RAPID WEAR AT SHOULDERS	RAPID WEAR AT CENTER	CRACKED TREADS	WEAR ON ONE SIDE	FEATHERED EDGE	BALD SPOTS	SCALLOPED WEAR
EFFECT							
CAUSE	UNDER-INFLATION OR LACK OF ROTATION	OVER-INFLATION OR LACK OF ROTATION	UNDER-INFLATION OR EXCESSIVE SPEED*	EXCESSIVE CAMBER	INCORRECT TOE	UNBALANCED WHEEL OR TIRE DEFECT*	LACK OF ROTATION OF TIRES OR WORN OR OUT-OF-ALIGNMENT SUSPENSION.
CORRECTION		ADJUST PRESSURE TO SPECIFICATIONS WHEN TIRES ARE COOL ROTATE TIRES		ADJUST CAMBER TO SPECIFICATIONS	ADJUST TOE-IN TO SPECIFICATIONS	DYNAMIC OR STATIC BALANCE WHEELS	ROTATE TIRES AND INSPECT SUSPENSION SEE GROUP 2

(DOD

Fig. 11-2. Tread wear patterns indicative of pressure, alignment, or driving problems.

13. Explain the tread condition of the tire. __

_____

_____

REMOVE TIRE

14. While wearing safety glasses, remove the valve stem core with your core tool. This will let the air out of the tire. Also, remove any wheel weights with your wheel weight pliers.

15. Use your tire changer to break or push the tire bead away from the lip or flange of the wheel. Follow the specific instructions provided with the tire changer.
    Keep your fingers out of the way and follow all safety rules.
       If you are using a power tire changer, do not catch the bead breaker on the edge of the wheel. It can bend a steel wheel or break an alloy wheel.

16. Rub some special lubricant or soapy water on the tire bead and the wheel flange. This will ease tire removal. Then, use the proper end of the large steel bar of your tire changer to remove the tire from the wheel, Fig. 11-3.

(HUNTER ENGINEERING CO.)

Fig. 11-3. When demounting a tire, work carefully and wear safety goggles.

   Note, you must use one hand to HOLD THE TIRE DOWN into the drop center of the wheel while prying off the opposite side of the tire.
       Be careful not to cut or split the tire bead. If you run into difficulty, ask your instructor for help.

17. After the tire is off of the wheel, inspect the inside of the tire for splits, cracks, punctures, patches, or repairs.

REPAIRING A PUNCTURED TIRE

Note: In the past, tires were repaired by inserting a rubber plug in the puncture without demounting the tire. This practice is no longer acceptable. Tires must be repaired from the *inside* only. The following procedure is for repairing a puncture with a plug and a patch. If available, a one-piece head-type plug can be used. This type of plug eliminates the need for a separate patch. Follow the manufacturer's directions.

18. After removing the tire from the rim, remove the puncturing object and note the angle of penetration. Clean the area to be repaired.

19. From the inside of the tire, fill the puncture with a plug or a liquid sealer. After filling the hole, cut off the plug (if used) slightly above the tire's inside surface.

20. Scuff the inside surface of the tire well beyond the repair area. Clean the scuffed area thoroughly.

21. Apply cement to the scuffed area and place a patch over the damaged area. Use a stitcher to help bond the patch to the inner surface of the tire. See Fig. 11-4.

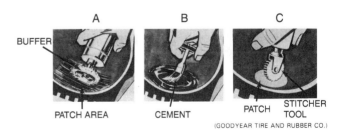

(GOODYEAR TIRE AND RUBBER CO.)

Fig. 11-4. Installing a tire patch. A — Buff an area slightly larger than the patch and clean the buffed area thoroughly. B — Apply the cement with a brush (allow for recommended drying time.) C — Install the patch. Use the stitcher tool to firmly roll the patch into contact with the cement. Roll over the entire surface of the patch.

22. Clean the outer pressure sealing edge of the wheel as needed. See Fig. 11-5. Wipe it off with your rags or towels or if rusted or dirty, clean it with steel wool.

STEEL WOOL

Fig. **11-5**. Clean and check rim before mounting tire. Remember rim is part of air chamber.

23. Check the condition of the valve stem. Bend it sideways and look for weather cracks or splits.

    If this were an actual repair, you would remove and replace a cracked or weathered valve stem. Unless instructed to do so, DO NOT remove the valve stem.

24. What is the condition of your valve stem?

    _____

    _____

    _____

MOUNTING TIRE

25. To remount the tire, wipe soapy water on the tire bead and the flange of the wheel. Use the particular procedures for your tire changer to pry the tire back on the wheel.

    Remember! Push the tire bead (bead opposite the pry bar) down in the drop center of the wheel or the tire will NOT go on the rim.

26. With the tire on the rim, pull up on the tire while twisting it. Try to get the tire to catch on the upper safety ridge. You want the upper tire bead to catch and hold on the upper flange of the rim. Then, the tire can be filled with air.

27. Inject air into the tire. If you can hear air rushing out of the tire, push IN lightly on the leaking part of the tire. When the tire begins to take air, do not over inflate it and loosen the wheel holddown cone. Be careful not to get your fingers caught between the tire and the wheel. Go to step 28 if your tire will not take air and expand.

28. If your tire will NOT hold enough air to expand and seal on the wheel, you may need to use a bead expander.

    Clamp the expander around the outside of the tire. This will push the tire bead against the wheel flange. Again inject air into the tire.

    DANGER! As soon as the tire begins to expand, RELEASE the bead expander. If not released immediately, the expander can break and fly off of the tire with unbelievable force.

29. While inflating the tire, lean away from the tire to prevent possible injury. The tire could blow out. DO NOT INFLATE THE TIRE OVER 40 TO 50 PSI! Check that the bead ridge on the sidewall of the tire is even or true with the wheel. If not, remount the tire on the wheel.

30. After the bead has popped over the safety ridges, screw in the valve core and snug it up.

CHECKING TIRE PRESSURE

31. Use your pressure gauge to check tire pressure. The tire pressure should be a few pounds under the maximum pressure rating labeled on the sidewall of the tire. As a tire is operated, it can heat up. This may cause the pressure in the tire to go up.

32. What is the inflation pressure for your tire?

_____

33. To check for leaks, pour water over the tire beads, puncture repair, and valve stem. Watch for bubbles. Air bubbles indicate a leak.

34. Is your tire holding air? Why or why not?

_____

_____

35. Have your instructor sign this sheet for credit before leaving class.

_____
INSTRUCTOR'S SIGNATURE

Job 12

AIR CONDITIONING SYSTEM SERVICE

Name _____

Date _____ Period _____

Instructor _____

INTRODUCTION: We have seen recent changes in automotive air conditioning systems in an effort to reduce air pollution. R-134a has been assigned as a replacement for R-12. This is because R-12 has been blamed for contributing to the depletion of the earth's ozone layer. As a result, you must be aware that two different refrigerants are now in use and that these refrigerants cannot be interchanged. You must also know how to recover old refrigerant to keep it from entering the atmosphere.

OBJECTIVE: Given the needed tools and equipment, you will be able to recover, evacuate, and recharge an automobile's air conditioning system.

TOOLS AND EQUIPMENT: You will need a basic set of hand tools, a gauge mainifold, a recovery/recycling unit, a vacuum pump, a charging station, a thermometer, a leak detector, safety glasses, and gloves.

INSTRUCTIONS: After getting your instructor approval, obtain the needed tools and equipment. Find out which shop-owned or customer car you will use and proceed carefully.

SERVICE MANUAL INFORMATION

1. In a service manual, look up the information on servicing your vehicle's air conditioning system. What type refrigerant does your vehicle use? _____

A/C SYSTEM INSPECTION

2. Start the engine. Turn the air conditioning system to high cool. Allow the system to run for about 10 minutes with the windows up.

3. Using a thermometer, measure the air temperature leaving the center vent. What was the vent temperature reading? _____

4. Is the temperature measured in the previous step within specifications? _____

5. Inspect the air conditioning system for signs of obvious troubles. Summarize the condition of the following:

Compressor drive belt

_____

_____

Compressor and clutch

_____

_____

Wiring and vacuum hoses

_____

_____

Condenser

_____

_____

Dash controls

_____

_____

6. Which parts do you think might be in need of service or replacement?

_____

_____

DISCHARGING AN AIR CONDITIONING SYSTEM

Note: When discharging an air conditioning system, a refrigerant recovery unit must be used. See Fig. 12-1. Always follow the manufacturer's instructions when using a recovery unit.

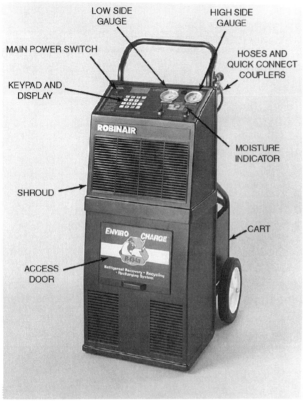

(ROBINAIR DIV., SPX CORP.)

Fig. 12-1. One type of refrigerant recovery unit. Always follow the manufacturer's operating procedures.

7. Attach a manifold gauge set, Fig. 12-2, to the appropriate service fittings.

8. Connect the center hose of the manifold gauge to the recovery unit as outlined in the manufacturer's instructions.

9. Turn on the recovery unit.

10. Open both manifold gauge valves slightly to allow refrigerant to slowly escape from the system.

11. After all refrigerant has been recovered, the air conditioning system will go into a slight vacuum. This can be verified by the readings on the manifold gauges. At this point, shut off the recovery unit.

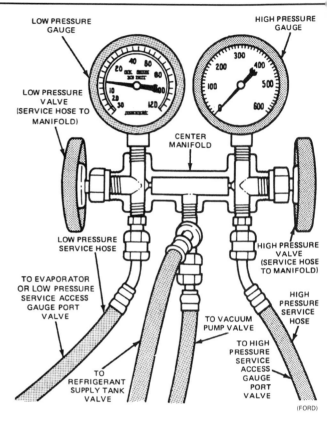

(FORD)

Fig. 12-2. Typical manifold gauge set.

12. Close the manifold gauge valves and allow the system to remain closed for approximately two minutes.

13. If vacuum remains constant, disconnect the manifold gauge from the recycling unit. If vacuum drops, repeat steps 12-15 until vacuum remains constant.

14. Was there any refrigerant in the car's system?

_____

15. Using the information in your textbook, explain what could happen if refrigerant squirted into your face and eyes. _____

_____

_____

EVACUATING THE SYSTEM

Note: This section covers evacuation of an air conditioning system using a vacuum pump. However, most refrigerant recovery/recycling units have the capability to evacuate the system, making a eparate vacuum pump unnecessary. When using a recovery/recycling unit to evacuate an air conditioning system, follow the manufacturer's instructions.

16. Before evacuating the air conditioning system, make sure that both gauge valves are off. Attach the manifold gauge set to the system service fittings.

17. Attach a vacuum pump to the center connection of the manifold gauge set. See Fig. 12-3.

18. Open the high-side manifold gauge valve slowly to remove pressure.

19. Close the high-side valve and start the pump.

20. Slowly open both manifold gauge valves. While the pump is running, slowly open the pump shutoff valve to prevent oil from being drawn from the pump.

21. Watch the vacuum reading on the low-side gauge. When the gauge reads 29 in. Hg., allow the pump to run for an additional 15 minutes.

22. Close the gauge set shut-off valves; then shut off the vacuum pump.

23. After shutting off the vacuum pump, the system vacuum should not drop more than 2 in. Hg. in 5 minutes. If it does, there is a leak in the system.

CHARGING THE SYSTEM

Note: This section covers charging systems with a refrigerant cylinder. If using a pound can or a

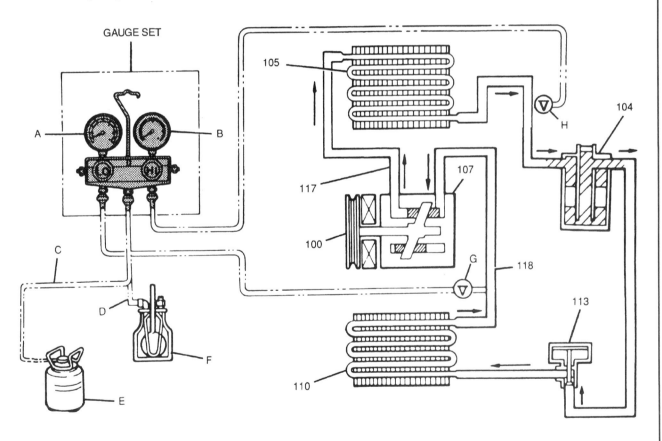

A	LOW-SIDE GAUGE	G	LOW-SIDE SERVICE VALVE	110	EVAPORATOR
B	HIGH-SIDE GAUGE	H	HIGH-SIDE SERVICE VALVE	113	EXPANSION VALVE
C	USED WHEN CHARGING	100	A/C COMPRESSOR CLUTCH	117	COMPRESSOR DISCHARGE PIPE
D	USED WHEN EVACUATING	104	RECEIVER/DRYER	118	COMPRESSOR SUCTION PIPE
E	REFRIGERANT DRUM	105	CONDENSER		
F	VACUUM PUMP	107	COMPRESSOR		

(GEO)

Fig. 12-3. Typical setup for system evacuating. Always follow the procedure recommended by the manufacturer.

recycling unit, discuss the charging procedure with your instructor.

24. Install a safety valve on the refrigerant cylinder, if necessary.

25. Disconnect the center hose from the manifold gauge set to the vacuum pump and attach it to the refrigerant cylinder.

26. Open the high-side manifold gauge valve. This will allow the refrigerant vapor to enter the high side of the system.

27. When refrigerant stops flowing into the system, shut off the high pressure gauge valve.

28. Start the engine and run it at 1500 rpm. Set the air conditioner for maximum cooling with the blower at high speed.

29. Open the tank valve and the low-side manifold gauge valve to draw additional refrigerant into the suction side of the system.

30. While charging the system, watch the gauge to determine when the system is properly charged. What should the gauges read with a properly charged and functioning system

_____

_____

31. When the system is properly charged, shut off the engine and disconnect the manifold gauge set.

32. Turn on the air conditioning system to maximum cooling and check the thermometer reading at the center air duct. Normal reading should be between 35° and 45°F with the blower at low speed. What does your thermometer read after charging? _____

33. Return all tools and equipment to their storage areas.

_____
INSTRUCTORS SIGNATURE

Job 13

OIL AND FILTER CHANGE, GREASE JOB

Name _____

Date _____ Period _____

Instructor _____

'RODUCTION: Lubrication service is one of the most important and common maintenance operations per-
med on a car. Changing the engine oil, filter, and lubricating the various high friction points at prescribed
ervals will prolong the useful life of an automobile. "You can pay now or you can pay later" is an automotive
ing that relates to lubrication service. Anyone that fails to spend a few dollars to change their oil and have
ir car "lubed" will end up paying several hundred dollars for mechanical repairs.

JECTIVE: Given an automobile and the listed tools, you will learn to change the engine oil and filter and
form a grease job.

OLS AND EQUIPMENT: You will be needing an oil filter wrench, box end wrench, oil can spout, grease
1, oil squirt can, oil drain pan, some door latch lubricant, a few shop rags, and eye protection. If you are
forming a live service, you should obtain the manufacturer designated type and amount of oil and an oil filter.

STRUCTIONS: Ask your instructor for details of the Job. Your instructor may want you to perform the
on a customer car or just go through the motions on a shop owned auto or stand mounted engine.

DRAINING OIL

1. During an actual oil change, the engine should
   be warmed to operating temperature. Then,
   any dirt or contaminants will be picked up,
   suspended, and drained out of the engine with
   the oil.

2. Normally, you will have to raise the car on
   a lift or with a jack and then secure it on jack
   stands. In either case, the car should be level
   when raised to allow all of the oil to drain
   from the pan.

   To prevent accidental starting without oil
   in the pan, remove the key from the ignition
   switch.

3. Place your oil drain pan under the engine oil
   pan. Check that you are not looking at the
   transmission pan. Put the drain pan slightly
   to one side of the engine pan, as in Fig. 13-1.

4. With a box end wrench of the correct size,
   turn the oil drain plug counterclockwise and
   remove it, Fig. 13-2.

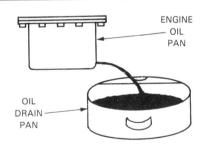

Fig. 13-1. Be careful, at first hot oil will pour out to one
side of oil pan.

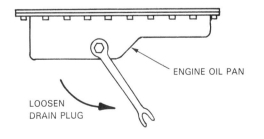

Fig. 13-2. An oil pan drain plug will strip easily. Looking
at it from the front, turn plug counterclockwise for
removal.

CAUTION! Keep your arm out of the way of the HOT OIL as is flows from the engine oil pan.

5. While the oil is draining for three or four minutes, inspect the drain plug. The plastic washer or seal should be uncracked and unsplit or it will leak. Check the threads for damage and wear.

During an actual oil change, you would have to replace a damaged washer seal or drain plug.

6. What is the condition of your drain plug and seal? _____

_____

7. Being extremely careful not to cross thread, overtighten, and strip its threads, install and snug the oil drain plug. Note! The drain plug only needs to be tight enough to slightly compress the plug seal. Overtightening will cause part damage and leakage.

8. Move the oil drain pan under the engine oil filter. Loosen the oil filter using your filter wrench, Fig. 13-3. Being careful not to let HOT OIL run down your arm, spin the filter the rest of the way off.

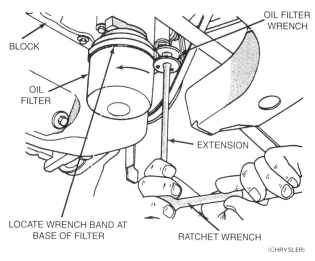

Fig. 13-3. Use oil filter wrench to unscrew old filter. Turn counterclockwise.

REPLACING OIL FILTER

9. Wipe off the mounting base for the oil filter to remove any dirt and contaminated oil, Fig. 13-4. Also, check that the old filter seal is NOT stuck on the engine.

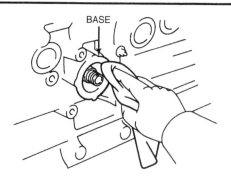

Fig. 13-4. After removing oil filter, clean off filter mounting base to help prevent leakage.

10. Make certain that your new filter is a proper replacement. Always check that the rubber O-ring seals are identical. The diameters of each should measure the same.

11. What is the measured diameter of your filter seal? _____

_____

12. What is the measured diameter of the threaded hole in the filter? _____

_____

13. If the filter fits on the engine upright, fill the new filter with oil. This prevents a temporary lack of oil pressure while the empty filter is filling.

14. How or at what angle is your oil filter mounted on the engine? _____

_____

_____

_____

15. Wipe some clean engine oil on to the new oil filter rubber seal. This will assure proper tightening of the filter and help prevent leaks. See Fig. 12-5.

16. Without cross threading it, screw on and hand tighten the new oil filter (reuse old filter if just an exercise). Your hands and the filter should be clean and dry. Look at Fig. 12-6.

After the seal makes contact with the engine base, use a rag or towel to help turn the filter an additional 1/2 to 3/4 turn.

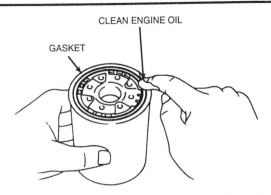

Fig. 13-5. Place some clean oil on seal of new filter. This will assure proper tightening.

Fig. 13-6. With your hands and filter free of oil, tighten filter by hand. Turn 1/2 to 3/4 turn after seal touches base.

17. Avoid tightening the filter with an oil filter wrench or the rubber seal can be smashed, causing a serious oil leak.

GREASE JOB

18. If you have your instructor's OK and a front end teaching unit or automobile, you can perform a grease job. Locate and lubricate the grease fittings on the upper and lower ball joints.

Caution! Do not overfill the rubber boots or they can rupture. As soon as you see them swell a little — stop!

19. Look for other components needing lubrication. Sometimes tie rods ends, idler arm, or universal joints can be lubricated.

20. If the car has never been lubed, the small hex head screws will have to be removed so that fittings can be installed. Fig. 13-7 shows the most common location of grease fittings.

21. How many grease fittings did you find?

_____

22. Where were they located? _____

_____

_____

_____

23. Wipe up any spilled oil or grease and empty your oil drain pan.

If this is a learning exercise on a shop owned engine, your instructor may want you to reinstall the same oil in the engine.

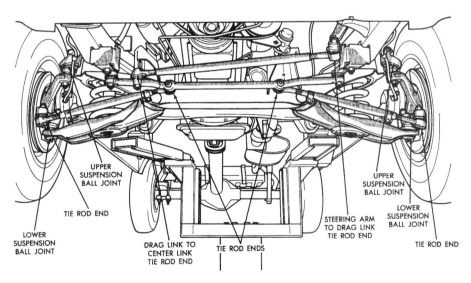

Fig. 13-7. Dots indicate possible grease fitting locations.

24. Lower the car to the ground and remove the filler cap. It is usually on valve cover.

INSTALLING OIL

25. Make sure that you have the right type, weight, and quantity of engine oil. Use the type oil recommended by the auto manufacturer or customer. Engine oil capacity (amount of oil sump will hold) can vary from only 4 quarts in small, gasoline engines to 7 quarts in larger automotive diesel engines. If in doubt, refer to the specifications given in an owner's manual or service manual.

26. What type, weight, and brand of oil should be installed in this engine? _____
_____
_____
_____

27. Push your oil fill spout into a can of oil. Wrap a rag or paper towel around the two to prevent drippage. Pour the oil into the filler opening in the engine. Repeat this operation until the engine is filled to the proper level.

28. How much oil does your engine require?
_____

29. Replace the filler cap and wipe off any oil that you might have dripped on the engine, workbench, or floor.

30. Start the engine and watch the oil pressure indicator light or gauge. The oil warning light should go out within 15 or 20 seconds. A gauge should begin to register almost immediately. If not, SHUT OFF THE ENGINE and find the problem.

31. How long did it take for the engine to develop oil pressure? _____
_____

LUBRICATE OTHER UNITS

32. Let the engine run for about 5 minutes while you CHECK FOR LEAKS under the engine. Also, lubricate other high friction and wear points (hinges, latches, etc.) on the car.

33. Did you find any leaks? _____
_____
_____
_____

34. If this is actual service of a customer car, place a small amount of grease between the parts that rub on the hood hinges and hood latch. Squirt a small amount of oil on the door hinges and rub a little nonstain lubricant on the door latches and posts.

35. If this is an actual oil change, fill out a service sticker including the date, mileage, type, weight, and brand of oil. Stick it on the edge of the driver's door above the latch.

36. Shut off the engine. Wipe off the hood and fenders and have your instructor sign your job sheet for credit before leaving class.

_____
INSTRUCTOR'S SIGNATURE

Job 14

COOLING SYSTEM SERVICE

Name _____

Date _____ Period _____

Instructor _____

INTRODUCTION: An automotive cooling system must be serviced periodically. The cooling system has the awesome task of removing around 30 percent of all of the heat energy produced by combustion. If unserviced, the cooling system can cause serious mechanical breakdowns in a short period of time. Deteriorated hoses and belts, system leaks, bad water pump, faulty radiator cap, and a stuck thermostat can all cause sudden and complete failure of the system. After extended service, antifreeze can break down, forming an acid that attacks and rusts the system. It is important that you know how to service a cooling system.

OBJECTIVE: Given the proper tools and equipment, you will learn to service an automotive cooling system.

TOOLS AND EQUIPMENT: Obtain a cooling system pressure tester, safety glasses, cooling system hydrometer or antifreeze tester, basic set of hand tools, and shop owned cooling system. For the out-of-car thermostat test, you will need a thermostat, a heat resistant container (beaker, pan, can), piece of mechanic's wire, and source of heat (oven or hot plate).

INSTRUCTIONS: Since this Job contains two sections, your instructor may want you to perform the thermostat test at home on a stove as a homework assignment. Ask about these details. The other, cooling system testing and inspecting portion of the Job will be performed in the shop on a school owned assembly.

REVIEW OF PARTS

1. As a quick review of cooling system parts, identify the parts in Fig. 14-1.

A. _____

B. _____

C. _____

D. _____

E. _____

F. _____

G. _____

H. _____

I. _____

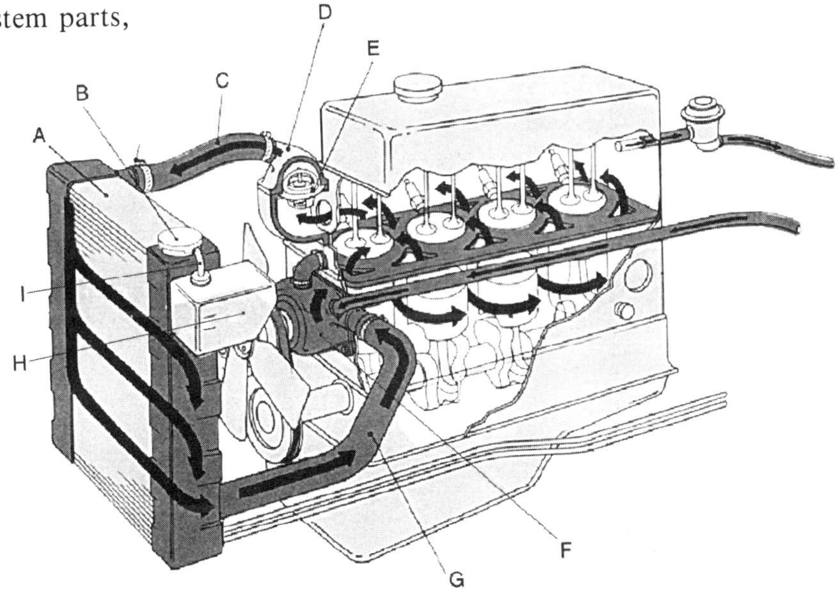

Fig. 14-1. Can you name the components?

INSPECT COOLING SYSTEM

2. Visually inspect your cooling system. Squeeze the hoses to check for hardness, cracks, or softness. Look at Figs. 14-2 and 14-3.

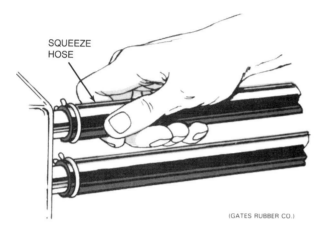

SQUEEZE HOSE

(GATES RUBBER CO.)

Fig. 14-2. Check hardness and condition of all hoses.

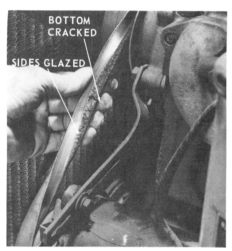

BOTTOM CRACKED

SIDES GLAZED

(GATES RUBBER CO.)

Fig. 14-3. Check belts for cracks, splits, glazing, low tension, and other problems.

3. If the system is cool, check the condition of the coolant. There should be no signs of rust and the system should be filled properly.

4. The percent of antifreeze should be appropriate. Measure the mixture or percentage of antifreeze with an antifreeze tester. Since testers vary, follow manufacturer's operating instructions.

5. Check that the radiator fins are free of leaves and bugs. The rubber seal on the radiator cap should be soft and unbroken.

6. Explain the condition (good, fair, replace) of each of the system check points in the spaces provided in the following chart.

CHECK POINT	CONDITION	
Radiator Hoses	A.	
Heater Hoses	B.	
Water Pump Bearings	C.	
Coolant Level	D.	
Coolant Condition	E.	
Antifreeze Protection	F.	
Radiator Cap	G.	
Radiator Fins	H.	
Belt Condition	I.	
Belt Tension	J.	

REMOVE BELTS

7. Remove the belts from the engine by loosening the bracket bolts on the alternator, air conditioning compressor, power steering pump, or other unit. You may need a droplight so that you can find all of the bolts.

8. With your belts removed, measure and determine the length of each of the belts. If a tape measure or special belt scale is not available, use a ruler to get an estimate. Walk the ruler around the belt carefully keeping track of the total measurement.

9. What are the lengths of each of your belts?

_____

_____

_____

_____

10. Why did any of the cooling system check points fail in Step 6? _____

_____

_____

_____

_____

11. Reinstall your belts and adjust their tension. Special belt tension gauges are available that will measure exact tension. To adjust belts by hand, refer to Fig. 14-4. In general, a belt,

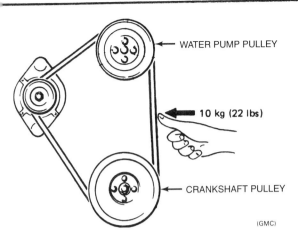

WATER PUMP PULLEY

10 kg (22 lbs)

CRANKSHAFT PULLEY

(GMC)

Fig. 14-4. Checking belt tension. A loose belt can cause slippage and overheating. An overtightened belt can cause premature bearing wear in water pump and alternator.

depending on length, should deflect about 1/2 to 5/8 in. (13 to 9.5 mm) with 25 pounds (11 Kg) of push applied.

12. Ideally, strive to adjust the belts as loose as possible without allowing them to slip, squeal, or flop in operation. This will lengthen the life of the alternator, A/C compressor, water pump, and power steering pump bearings.

Note! The alternator bearings are NOT submerged in lubricant, as with the A/C compressor, water pump, and power steering pump. Thus, the alternator belt should NOT be tightened as much as the other belts.

13. List the types of belts (alternator, power steering) used on your engine. _____

_____

_____

_____

_____

THERMOSTAT SERVICE

14. Now, remove your thermostat from under the top radiator hose fitting. This fitting is also called a thermostat housing. Scrape off all of the old gasket material from both the engine and the thermostat housing.

15. To make a new gasket, obtain a piece of gasket material, a pair of scissors, and a small ball peen hammer. Lay your thermostat housing over the gasket material and trace the outside shape of the housing with a pencil or pen. Cut out this shape with scissors.

Hold this pattern over the thermostat opening in the engine, Fig. 14-5. Then, to cut out the inside holes for the thermostat and bolts, tap lightly around the edge of the openings with the peen end of your hammer. Make sure that you do not shift the gasket while tapping or the holes will be misaligned.

After tapping and perforation, the inside of the gasket holes will easily tear out, Fig. 14-6.

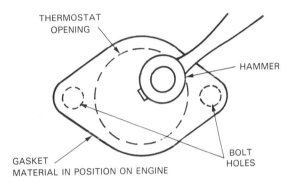

THERMOSTAT OPENING

HAMMER

GASKET MATERIAL IN POSITION ON ENGINE

BOLT HOLES

Fig. 14-5. Lay piece of gasket material over thermostat opening on engine and tap along hole edges (dotted lines) to cut out gasket.

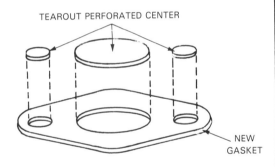

TEAROUT PERFORATED CENTER

NEW GASKET

Fig. 14-6. After tapping with your hammer, tear out center of your holes.

16. Reinstall your thermostat, making sure that it is right-side up (pellet toward engine or pin pointing toward radiator) as shown in Fig. 14-7. Coat your sealing surfaces with non-hardening sealer and fit the gasket and housing into place.

When tightening the thermostat housing bolts, be extremely careful not to overtighten the bolts. Snug them a little at a time to pull the housing down straight and prevent distortion. Overtightening the housing can cause breakage.

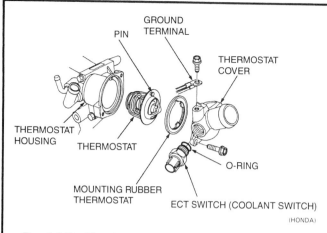

Fig. 14-7. Check that you are fitting thermostat into engine right-side up.

17. How do you know the thermostat is NOT installed backwards? _____

_____

_____

PRESSURE TEST SYSTEM

18. Using a system pressure tester, check the condition of your radiator cap. Mount it on the tester as in Fig. 14-8. Pump up pressure until the pressure needle levels off at a specific pressure.

A good radiator cap will hold the pressure listed on top of the cap and will not leak. A bad cap, besides leaking, may not hold pressure within specified limits (pressure high or low).

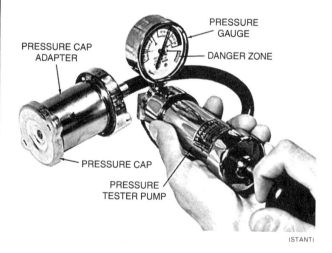

Fig. 14-8. A good radiator cap will hold specified pressure labeled on cap lid.

19. Explain the results of your pressure cap test.

_____

_____

_____

20. Again using your pressure tester, test for cooling system leaks by mounting the tester on the radiator. See Fig. 14-9. Pressurize the system to the pressure rating given on the top of the radiator cap (around 8 to 15 psi). If the pressure holds for two minutes without bleeding off, the system is not leaking. While waiting, always visually watch for leaks.

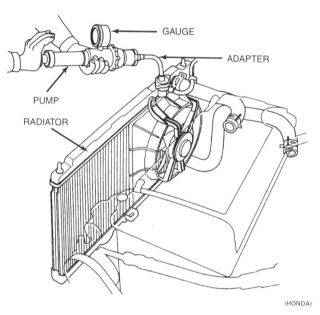

Fig. 14-9. Pump same amount of pressure as is listed on radiator cap and no more.

21. Explain the holding pressure and condition of your cooling system. _____

_____

_____

22. Turn in all of your tools and equipment and have your teacher sign this job for credit. You may also need to ask about the details of the second portion of the Job on thermostat testing.

THERMOSTAT TESTING

3. First, visually inspect your thermostat. Hold it up to the light and check to see if there is a gap or opening around the edge of the sealing valve. If there is, then the thermostat may be defective and may require replacement. No matter what the condition, it will be tested.

4. What is the visual condition of your thermostat? _____
_____
_____

5. Mount your water or coolant filled container, thermostat, and thermometer as shown in Fig. 14-10. Stir the water gently while heating and watching the thermostat.

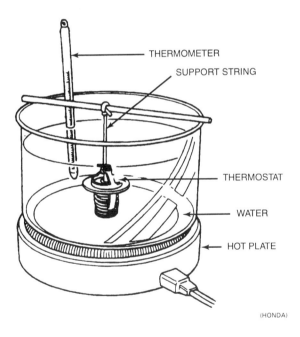
(HONDA)

Fig. 14-10. Checking thermostat opening temperature. Note that both thermometer and thermostat are kept free of container sides and bottom.

26. Record whether the valve is closed, starting to open, or fully opened in the following chart. Write your answer next to the appropriate temperature.

   For example, the valve may be closed at 100°F (37.3°C) and open at 200°F (93.3°C). Watch very closely for the opening temperature when the valve first starts to open. It is important.

WATER TEMPERATURE	VALVE POSITION
100 °F.	A. _____
150 °F.	B. _____
170 °F.	C. _____
175 °F.	D. _____
180 °F.	E. _____
185 °F.	F. _____
190 °F.	G. _____
195 °F.	H. _____
200 °F.	I. _____
205 °F.	J. _____
210 °F.	K. _____
212 °F.	L. _____

27. At what temperature did your thermostat start to open? _____
_____

28. At what temperature did it fully open?
_____
_____

29. A good thermostat should start to open around 5 to 10° above or below the operating temperature stamped on the thermostat. It should be fully open at a temperature 20 to 25° above the opening temperature.

30. Explain the condition of your thermostat.
_____
_____
_____
_____

31. Ask your instructor to sign this portion of the job for credit.

_____
INSTRUCTOR'S SIGNATURE

Job 15

CARBURETOR REBUILDING

Name _____

Date _____ Period _____

Instructor _____

'RODUCTION: Millions of older cars and trucks are still equipped with carburetors. Because most of these buretors are several years old, they require frequent repairs. To be able to service carburetors, you must lerstand basic rebuilding and adjustment methods. This job will help you learn to follow basic instructions ile servicing a carburetor. The ability to follow written instructions will help you when servicing many other dern automotive assemblies.

JECTIVE: Furnished with a shop owned carburetor and the following tools, you will learn to disassemble, ntify, and reassemble the components of an automotive carburetor.

'OLS AND EQUIPMENT: You will need a carburetor, service manual, set of screwdrivers, combination enches, safety glasses, needle nose pliers, ruler, and a parts tray.

STRUCTIONS: Ask your instructor for the location and type carburetor that will be used during the job. If u run out of class time, before finishing, place all of the parts in a tray and store them in a safe place.

CARBURETOR LINKAGE

1. What type carburetor will you be using for this job? _____

   _____

2. Before removing anything, study the carburetor linkage mechanism. Make a mental note or sketch how the rods fit together.

   Linkage rods are commonly used to operate the choke, fast idle cam, and accelerator pump.

3. On your carburetor, which components are operated by linkage rods?_____

   _____

   _____

CARBURETOR CHOKE

4. Observe the operation of the choke. Many carburetors use a thermostatic coil spring to control choke closing and opening. The temperature sensitive spring may be located on the carburetor or in the intake manifold.

5. When the spring is cold, it holds the choke closed to prime the engine with extra fuel. This aids engine starting. Then, when the engine and spring warm up, the spring tension changes to push the choke open.

6. If used on your carburetor, note the position (index marks) on the plastic choke spring housing, Fig. 15-1. Loosen the housing screws and rotate the housing one way and then the other. This should move the choke plate opened and closed.

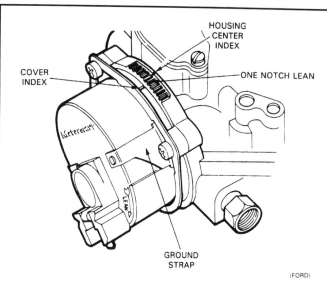

Fig. 15-1. Index marks help during choke adjustment. Turning choke spring cover one direction leans fuel mixture. Turning it the other way richens mixture.

7. When the choke setting is too lean (choke too far open when cold), the engine can stall or die during cold weather starting.

   If the choke setting is too rich (choke closes too much), the engine can flood, miss, stall, and emit black smoke when warm. An excessive amount of fuel will pour into the engine.

8. What does your choke plate do when the thermostatic spring housing is turned clockwise? _____

   _____

   _____

9. Does the choke open or close when the thermostatic spring housing is turned counterclockwise? _____

   _____

   _____

CHOKE VACUUM BREAK

10. Sometimes, a choke vacuum break (diaphragm) is used to partially open the choke upon engine starting. One type is shown in Fig. 15-2.

    As soon as the engine begins to run, engine vacuum acts on the choke diaphragm. The diaphragm pulls on and cracks

open the choke. This prevents engine flooding which could occur if the choke remained fully closed.

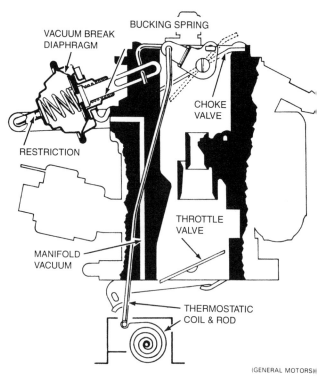

Fig. 15-2. Choke vacuum break diaphragm operates off of engine vacuum. It opens choke as soon as engine starts.

11. If your carburetor has a vacuum break, apply vacuum to the diaphragm chamber. Use either your mouth or a hand vacuum pump. Suction should make the choke swing partially open.

12. What happened when vacuum was applied to your choke break? _____

    _____

    _____

    _____

CHOKE UNLOADER

13. A mechanical choke unloader may also be used to crack open the choke at wide open throttle. When the car's gas pedal is pushed to the floor for maximum power, the carburetor throttle lever pushes on the choke linkage. This cracks the choke and avoids an overrich mixture. Refer to Fig. 15-3.

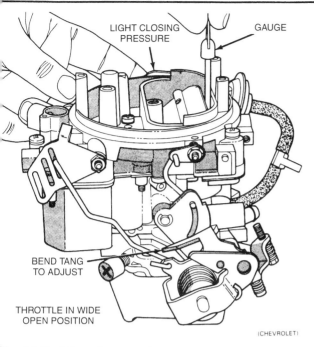

LIGHT CLOSING PRESSURE

GAUGE

BEND TANG TO ADJUST

THROTTLE IN WIDE OPEN POSITION

(CHEVROLET)

Fig. 15-3. When throttle is fully open, choke should be cracked open by unloader. Technician is measuring choke unloader adjustment.

4. Check the action of your choke unloader, if used. Hold the choke closed with one hand and swing the throttle plates wide open with the other hand. This should make the choke open a fraction of an inch.

5. If use, how far does the unloader open your choke? _____
_____
_____

FAST IDLE CAM

. Locate and inspect the operation of the fast idle cam. It is a mechanism that increases idle speed when the engine is cold and the choke is closed. The fast idle cam smooths cold engine operation and speeds warm-up.

. A misadjusted fast idle cam setting can cause the engine to stall upon initial cold starting. If set too high, the engine would "race" (run at high speed) when first started.

18. Does your carburetor have a fast idle cam? _____ If so, does it work? Explain.
_____
_____
_____

THROTTLE PLATES

19. Check the condition of your throttle plates and throttle shafts. The plates must not be bent or nicked. The shafts should be unworn and tight in the carburetor body. Problems with the throttle plates or shafts will usually upset carburetor operation at idle. The engine may idle roughly or at a high rpm.

20. When working on a carburetor, be careful not to bump the throttle plates on the workbench. They can be damaged easily.

21. Can you detect any throttle shaft wear or plate damage? _____
_____
_____

IDLE SPEED SCREW

22. Locate your idle speed screw, Fig. 15-4. It is normally mounted on or against the throttle plate lever. The idle speed screw can be turned to open the throttle plates (increase idle speed) or close the throttle plates (decrease idle speed).

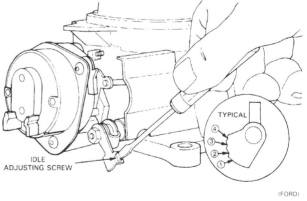

TYPICAL

IDLE ADJUSTING SCREW

(FORD)

Fig. 15-4. Idle RPM adjustment. Note the four different cam steps. Each step will change the speed setting.

23. Turn your idle speed screw while watching the throttle plates.

24. What do the throttle plates do when the idle speed screw is turned clockwise? _____

_____

_____

25. Suppose your carburetor was on a running engine. What would happen to engine speed if the idle speed screw was turned in a counterclockwise direction? _____

_____

_____

IDLE MIXTURE SCREWS

26. Now, remove and inspect one of the idle mixture screws, Fig. 15-4. They usually screw into the carburetor body.

27. The idle mixture screws are used to set the air-fuel mixture at idle. The pointed screw fits into and partially blocks the idle passage in the carburetor.

    Normally, when the screw is turned in, it cuts off more fuel and leans out the idle mixture. Turning it out would allow more fuel flow and would richen the idle mixture.

28. To install the mixture screw, turn the mixture screw in until it bottoms lightly. Then, back the screw out about 1 1/2 to 2 1/2 revolutions. This should rough adjust the idle mixture enough for engine starting.

29. NOTE! Most new carburetors have sealed mixture screws. A metal plug is press fit over the screws to prevent idle mixture adjustment. This prevents tampering with the fuel-air setting which could increase exhaust emissions.

30. Look inside the air horn of your carburetor. Find the small holes or slots for the idle circuit. They will be next to the throttle plates. These small holes feed fuel when the engine is running slowly.

31. Does your carburetor use idle mixture screws? _____ Where are they located on the carburetor? _____

_____

_____

FUEL FILTER

32. Many carburetors have a fuel filter at the inlet to the fuel bowl. The filter may screw onto the outside of the carburetor or may fit under the large fuel line fitting,

33. Does your carburetor have an integral (built-in) fuel filter? _____ Where is it located?

_____

_____

CARBURETOR DISASSEMBLY

34. Now, unscrew and remove the air horn or body cover from the carburetor. See Fig. 14-10. As you lift it off, watch under the cover. Study how the internal parts of the carburetor fit together. You may need to swing the cover into various positions to free the linkage rods.

FLOAT MECHANISM

35. Remove the float mechanism, Fig. 15-5 Unscrew the float needle seat with the proper size screwdriver. Check that the float is not damaged. Hold the float (hollow type only) next to your ear and shake it. If the float is leaking, you will be able to hear fuel splashing around inside the float.

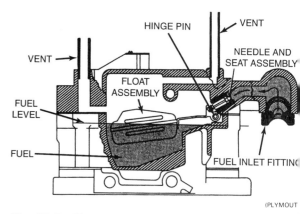

Fig. 15-5. Float may be mounted on body cover or i top of fuel bowl. Removal of hinge pin will normally allo removal of float, needle, and seat.

36. An improperly adjusted float can cause a wide range of performance problems. If set too high, the fuel mixture could be too rich or the engine may even flood with raw fuel. If the float is set too low, the engine coul

starve for gasoline at high speeds or may stall when rounding a sharp curve. The fuel could splash to one side of the bowl, uncovering the main jets.

MAIN JETS

. Using a large screwdriver or jet tool, unscrew the carburetor main jets. They are usually located in the bottom of the fuel bowl.

Notice whether your jets are numbered. The number on the jet indicates the size hole in the jet. A larger number and hole would produce a richer high speed fuel mixture.

8. Main jet size is seldom changed. Only when attempting to improve race car performance or an unusual drivability problem would jets sizes be altered.

9. What size main jets are in your carburetor?

_____

ACCELERATOR PUMP

0. Locate the accelerator pump. It may be one of two common types — piston or diaphragm.

The accelerator pump is simply a squirt gun like device. It squirts a stream of gasoline into the air horn whenever the throttle plates swing open. This primes the engine with fuel and gives the high speed circuit time to start working.

1. If an accelerator pump is not functioning properly, the engine may stumble or hesitate upon initial acceleration. The car may loose power momentarily, before accelerating normally.

42. What type accelerator pump is in your carburetor? _____

CARBURETOR ASSEMBLY

43. Now, find a service manual that details the service of your carburetor. Use the specific directions in the manual to reassemble and adjust the carburetor. You will need to set the float level, float drop, choke, and any other major adjustments.

44. Look up and list the following carburetor specifications.
    A. Float level setting _____
    B. Accelerator pump setting _____
    C. Choke vacuum break adjustment _____

    _____

45. What other carburetor adjustments are described in the service manual? _____

    _____

    _____

    _____

46. Show the assembled carburetor to your instructor and get this job signed for credit.

_____
INSTRUCTOR'S SIGNATURE

Job 16

FUEL INJECTION SERVICE

Name _____

Date _____ Period _____

Instructor _____

INTRODUCTION: Fuel injection systems have replaced carburetors on modern cars. This makes it critical that you know how to troubleshoot and repair these systems. Keep in mind that many carburetor systems can be compared to the parts and operating modes of a fuel injection system. Knowledge about one can be transferred to the other when troubleshooting and servicing.

OBJECTIVE: Given the needed tools and equipment, you will be able to troubleshoot and repair typical fuel injection system problems.

TOOLS AND EQUIPMENT: You will need a basic set of hand tools, a fuel pressure gauge, a hand vacuum pump, a fuel injection system tester, and test vehicle—preferably a shop-owned vehicle.

INSTRUCTIONS: After getting your instructor's approval, use the following instructions and a service manual to analyze the operation of the vehicle's fuel injection system.

FUEL SYSTEM INSPECTION

1. In the appropriate service manual, read the service information on the fuel injection system for your test vehicle.

   Vehicle Make: _____

   Vehicle Model: _____

   Vehicle Year: _____

   Engine Size: _____

   Transmission Type: _____

2. Begin fuel injection service by inspecting the system for obvious problems. If possible, start the engine. Look for fuel leaks, disconnected wires, leaking vacuum hoses, and similar troubles.

3. Could you find any visible problems with the fuel injection system? If so, explain what was found. _____
   _____
   _____
   _____
   _____

4. Have someone turn the key to the run position while you listen for the electric fuel pump. Can you hear the fuel pump running?
   _____

5. Start the engine and use a stethoscope to listen to each one of the injectors. Each injector should make a clicking sound, which indicates that it is open and closing. The noise from each injector should also be similar.

6. Did all the injectors make the appropriate sound? _____ If not, which injectors are defective? _____

_____

CHECKING FUEL PRESSURE

7. Locate the fuel service port on the engine. It is usually on the fuel rail.

   Note: Some vehicles do not have a service port. When servicing a system without a service port, follow the manufacturer's instructions carefully.

8. Using service manual instructions, relieve fuel pressure from the fuel system. See Fig. 16-1.

   Warning: Extreme care must be taken when relieving fuel system pressure. Always wear eye protection and keep an appropriate fire extinguisher handy. When loosening a fuel fitting or service port, cover the area with a shop cloth to contain any fuel that may spray out. Dispose of fuel-soaked cloths properly.

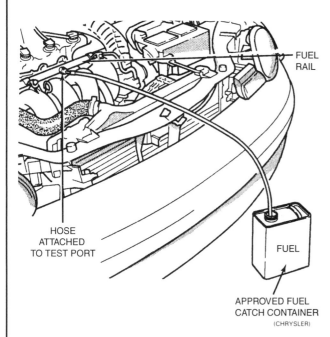

Fig. 16-1. Using an approved fuel container to catch fuel during the pressure release procedure. Always relieve fuel pressure before working on the system.

9. Explain how you relieved fuel pressure? ___

   _____

   _____

   _____

10. Connect your fuel pressure gauge to the service port.

11. Start the engine and read fuel pressure at idle. Write down fuel system pressure. _____

   _____

12. How does your fuel pressure reading compare to specifications? _____

   _____

13. Install a hand vacuum pump on the vacuum fitting to the fuel pressure regulator, which is usually on the fuel rail. See Fig. 16-2. Measure fuel pressure as you apply vacuum to the regulator. Explain what happens as you apply vacuum. _____

   _____

   _____

   _____

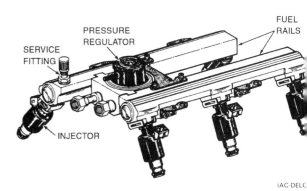

Fig. 16-2. A multiport fuel injector pressure regulator as mounted by one manufacturer.

14. Find and remove the main fuel filter, not the in-tank filter. If clogged, it can reduce fuel pressure. Where was the main fuel filter located? _____

   _____

15. Reinstall the fuel filter, Fig. 16-3, and check for fuel leaks.

TESTING FUEL INJECTORS

16. What type of fuel injector tester are you going to use? _____

   _____

17. Read the owner's manual for the injector tester.

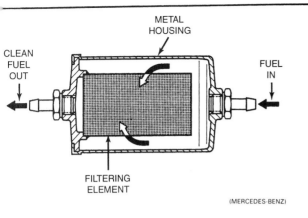

CLEAN
FUEL
OUT

METAL
HOUSING

FUEL
IN

FILTERING
ELEMENT

(MERCEDES-BENZ)

Fig. 16-3. A cross section of a gasoline filter. The entire filter assembly must be discarded when clogged. Be sure to install the new filter with the flow arrows pointing in the right direction.

18. Install the injector tester on the engine according to the manufacturer's instructions.

19. Start the engine and use the injector tester to check each injector. What did the tester tell you about the condition of each injector?

_____

_____

_____

20. Remove the tester from the vehicle. Return all equipment to its proper storage location.

21. Have your instructor check your work.

_____

INSTRUCTOR'S SIGNATURE

Job 17

ELECTRONIC IGNITION SYSTEM SERVICE

Name _____

Date _____ Period _____

Instructor _____

TRODUCTION: Electronic ignition systems have replaced contact point systems. Electronic parts are more pendable and faster than mechanical contact points, which wear and burn.

JECTIVE: Given the needed tools and equipment, you will be able to service an electronic ignition system.

OLS AND EQUIPMENT: You will need a basic set of hand tools, a multimeter, dielectric grease, and an EI distributor.

STRUCTIONS: After getting your instructor approval, obtain the needed tools and equipment. Do not be aid to ask your instructor questions. You will be rebuilding and testing an HEI system in this learning experience.

---

1. Find and read a service manual that covers the service of a General Motor's High Energy Ignition System.

2. Remove the distributor cap from the distributor body. How is this done?
   _____
   _____

3. Inspect the inside of the cap for signs of cracks, carbon traces, and burning. Can you find any signs of failure? _____
   _____
   _____

4. Remove the ignition coil from the distributor cap. How do you remove the coil and the wire leads? _____
   _____
   _____

5. Using an ohmmeter, check the internal resistance of the coil windings. See Fig. 17-1.
   Coil Primary Winding Resistance _____
   Coil Secondary Winding Resistance _____

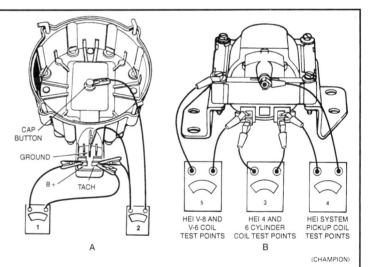

Fig. 17-1. Using an ohmmeter to check for specified resistance values. 1 — Primary resistance. 2 — Secondary resistance. 3 — Primary resistance. 4. — Secondary resistance. 5 — Replace coil if resistance is less than infinite.

6. Is the coil resistance within specs? _____

7. Check the distributor shaft bushings for wear. Try wiggling the top of the shaft sideways

while you watch for movement in the distributor body. If the shaft wiggles sideways, the shaft bushings are worn.

8. Explain the condition of the distributor shaft bushings. _____

_____

_____

_____

9. Remove the distributor shaft.

10. What do you have to do before removing the distributor shaft? Refer to your service manual if needed. _____

_____

_____

11. Inspect the shaft itself for signs of wear at the bushing bearing surfaces. Use a micrometer to measure shaft diameter at its most worn point and on an unworn point.

    Shaft diameter (most worn) _____

    Shaft diameter (unworn)_____

12. Is the distributor shaft worn beyond specifications? Explain. _____

_____

_____

13. Use a telescoping gauge and micrometer to measure distributor bushing inside diameter. Record your measurements below.

    Lower bushing inside diameter _____

    Upper bushing inside diameter _____

14. Use your ohmmeter to check the condition of the pickup coil. See Fig. 17-2.

    Pickup coil resistance _____

15. Wiggle the pickup coil wires while measuring resistance. Sometimes the pickup coil wires can break internally and cause a resistance fluctuation. What did your wiggle test show you? _____

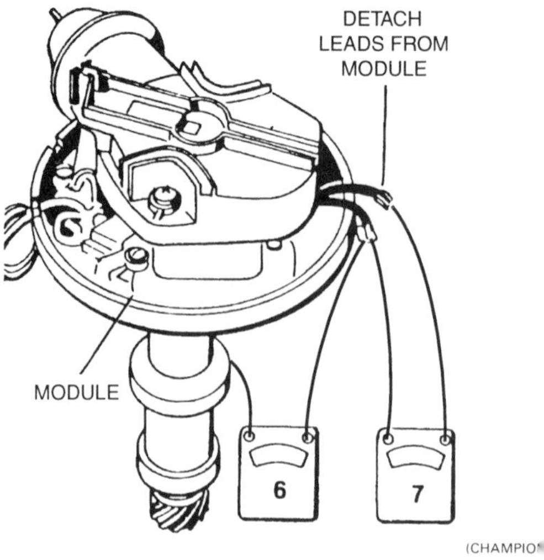

_____

_____

DETACH LEADS FROM MODULE

MODULE

6   7

(CHAMPION)

Fig. 17-2. Using an ohmmeter to check the pickup coil
1 — Replace pickup coil if resistance is less than infinite
2 — Should read between 500 and 1500 ohms for this particular coil.

16. Remove the ignition module. How many wires are connected to the module? _____

_____

_____

17. Using a high impedance ohmmeter, measure the resistances across the terminals of the ignition module. Record your readings.

_____

_____

18. How does the service manual say to test an HEI module? _____

_____

_____

19. To install the module, wipe a thin layer of dielectric grease across the bottom of the unit. This helps keep it from overheating. Install the module and tighten each fastener equally.

20. Reassemble the HEI distributor following service manual instructions.

21. Have your instructor check your work and sign this worksheet.

INSTRUCTOR'S SIGNATURE

Job 18

COMPUTER SYSTEM SERVICE

Name _____

Date _____ Period _____

Instructor _____

RODUCTION: Computers are now used to monitor and control all major systems of a modern car — from engine systems, to the suspension, to anti-lock brakes. This makes it critical for today's technician to be versed in analyzing and repairing computer problems.

JECTIVE: Given the needed tools and equipment, you will be able to retrieve and use trouble codes on a puter controlled vehicle system.

OLS AND EQUIPMENT: You will need a basic set of hand tools, a thermometer, a multimeter, a heat gun, anner, and a shop-owned vehicle.

TRUCTIONS: After getting your instructor's approval, use the shop's scanner to analyze the operation of vehicle's computerized engine control system.

SERVICE MANUAL INFORMATION

. In a service manual, read the service information and look up the computer trouble codes for your test vehicle.

. If you were not going to use a scanner for this job, how would you pull up trouble codes on this vehicle? _____

_____

_____

. On your test vehicle, how would you know when a computer trouble code existed?

_____

_____

. The location of the diagnostic connector on one particular vehicle is shown in Fig. 18-1. Where is the diagnostic connector, or assembly line diagnostic link (ALDL), on your test vehicle? _____

_____

. Obtain and read the owner's manual for the shop's scanner. See Fig. 18-2.

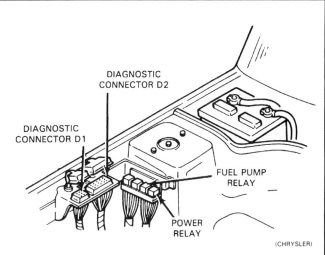

Fig. 18-1. Some diagnostic connectors are located on a wheel well. This vehicle is equipped with two separator diagnostic connectors.

6. Do you need to install a new scanner cartridge for this particular vehicle? If so, explain how this is done. _____

_____

_____

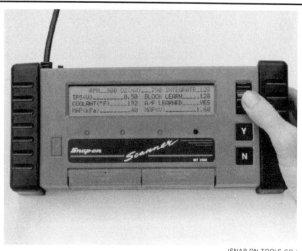

(SNAP-ON TOOLS CO.)

Fig. 18-2. Many manufacturers recommend the use of scan tools to retrieve trouble codes from the computer control system.

ENGINE-OFF SCAN

7. Connect the scanner to the diagnostic connector on the vehicle. The ignition switch should be in the *off* position.

8. To perform an engine-off scan test, turn the ignition to the *on* position and trigger the scanner to retrieve trouble codes.

9. Does the scanner show any trouble codes? If so, what trouble code numbers are given?

_____

_____

10. Using a service manual, explain what each trouble code number indicates. _____

_____

_____

_____

ENGINE-RUNNING SCAN

11. Next, do an engine-running scan. Start and warm the engine to full operating temperature to move the computer system into its normal operating mode.

12. Trigger the scanner to read trouble codes.

13. Does the scanner show trouble codes? If so, explain what each code means. _____

_____

_____

_____

_____

WIGGLE TEST

14. To perform a wiggle test, wiggle the wires the sensors and actuators while scanning f trouble codes. This test might help you u cover an intermittent problem.

15. Did you find any problems during the wi gle test? If so, explain. _____

_____

_____

_____

_____

SWITCH TESTS

16. In some cases, the scanner can be used to per form a switch test. Basically, you must follo scanner instructions to turn each switch o and *off*. The scanner will then tell you if th switches are working properly.

17. Can you perform a switch test on the tes vehicle? If so, explain your results. _____

_____

_____

_____

_____

ACTUATOR TESTS

18. To test the actuators, perform an output cy cling test. During this test, the scanner wi signal the car's computer to fire the injectors idle solenoid, and other actuators. Since mos actuators convert electrical signals int physical movements, they can be seen o heard moving when cycled on and off.

19. If your scanner does not have the capabilit to perform an output cycling test, many ac tuators can be tested by measuring their in ternal resistance or by using jumper wires t apply an external voltage. Follow th manufacturer's instructions.

20. Explain the results of your actuator tests

_____

_____

_____

_____

PINPOINT TESTS

21. After you have retrieved trouble codes, you must do pinpoint tests to find the exact source of the trouble. A trouble code simply indicates which circuit might be at fault. Using the service manual for reference, remove the coolant temperature sensor from the engine. See Fig. 18-3.

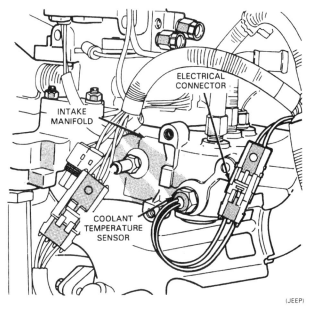

(JEEP)

Fig. 18-3. This coolant temperature sensor is mounted in intake manifold coolant passage area. Disconnect the wires at the electrical connector before removing the sensor.

22. To simulate a test of the sensor, place the tip of the sensor in a beaker of heated water while measuring its internal resistance with your ohmmeter. Take resistance readings at the following temperatures and record them in the chart.

Water Temperature	Sensor Resistance
80°F	_____
100°F	_____
120°F	_____
140°F	_____
160°F	_____

23. Does your service manual give resistance specifications for the sensor? If so, how do your readings compare to specifications?

_____

_____

_____

24. Next, disconnect the wires to a fuel injector. Using your ohmmeter, measure and record the injectors internal resistance. _____

_____

25. Does the injector resistance indicate a good or bad injector? Explain. _____

_____

_____

_____

ERASING COMPUTER TROUBLE CODES

26. Reconnect all wires.

27. Read the service manual instructions for erasing stored trouble codes. How do you erase stored trouble codes on the test vehicles?

_____

_____

_____

_____

28. Erase any codes in your test vehicle following the instructions outlined in question 27.

29. Return all equipment to its proper location.

30. Have your instructor check your work.

INSTRUCTOR'S SIGNATURE

Job 19

UNIVERSAL JOINT, CV JOINT SERVICE

Name _____

Date _____ Period _____

Instructor _____

INTRODUCTION: A faulty propeller shaft universal joint can cause a wide range of problems. It may produce a high pitch chirping sound similar to the sound made by small birds. If highly worn, a bad U-joint can also cause a metallic crunching or grinding sound which resembles the sound of popcorn popping. Upon total failure, a universal joint may break and separate from the remainder of the drive train. The drive shaft could then pound large dents in the floorboard of the car or break the rear housing of the transmission. As you can see, proper diagnosis, inspection, and repair of universal joints is very important.

OBJECTIVE: Using the listed tools and equipment, you will learn to properly disassemble, inspect, and assemble the parts of a propeller shaft universal joint and a ball-type CV joint.

TOOLS AND EQUIPMENT: You will need a basic set of hand wrenches, large brass or ball peen hammer, safety glasses, large screwdriver, pin punch, needle nose pliers or snap ring pliers, one small and one large socket, large driving punch, and a vise.

INSTRUCTIONS: Ask your instructor for the location of the drive shaft and universal joint assembly to be used. It may be located in or out of the automobile.

Caution! If you must clamp the drive shaft in the vise, make sure that you do not dent or bend the drive shaft. Shaft unbalance and vibration may occur when the shaft is returned to service.

REVIEW OF PARTS

1. As a short review of universal joints, identify the parts in Fig. 19-1.

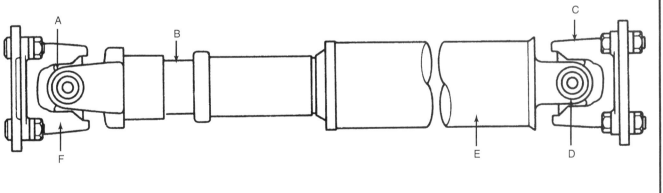

A. _____   D. _____
B. _____   E. _____
C. _____   F. _____

Fig. 19-1. Identify these parts. Restudy them if needed.

REMOVE DRIVE SHAFT

2. If your propeller shaft is installed in a car, it is a very good idea to MARK the mating surfaces of the differential yoke and drive shaft yoke. This will allow reassembly in exact alignment and prevent a possible imbalance and vibration.

3. Remove the two U-bolts holding the rear joint. Pry the drive shaft away from its yoke and slide the drive shaft out of the car. Be careful not to scrape the transmission slip joint on the ground or drop the roller ends.

DISASSEMBLE U-JOINT

4. Lay your propeller shaft assembly on the back of a vise. Using a large punch or shaft and hammer, tap each roller inward to free up the locking rings. They may be located either on the inside or outside of the yoke.

5. Where are your lock rings located? ____

_____

_____

_____

_____

6. Utilizing the appropriate tools (pin punch, needle nose pliers, small screwdrivers, or snap ring pliers), remove your snap rings from the joint.

7. Now, push the rollers and cross out of the yokes. This operation is pictured in Fig. 19-2. Make sure that the small socket is smaller than the roller and that the larger socket is large enough to accept the full roller.
   If stuck, you may need to strike the tightened vise with your brass hammer to free the rollers.

8. Since they will be reused, keep your rollers organized so that they can be replaced in the same location in the yoke. Also, do not drop or lose your needle bearings.

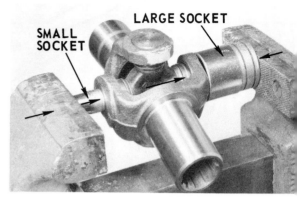

Fig. 19-2. Check that the sockets are correct sizes. Then press out bearings.

9. As an added learning task, remove all of the NEEDLE BEARINGS from one of your rollers. Then, using a very small standard screwdriver and some heavy wheel bearing grease, refit the bearings into place along the inner wall of the roller. The grease will hold the bearings in the joint during assembly.

10. How many needle bearings are there in each roller assembly? _____

_____

_____

_____

11. Explain the condition of your cross journals.

_____

_____

_____

_____

ASSEMBLE U-JOINT

12. Reassemble your universal joint. Being careful not to knock any of the needle bearings loose, force the rollers into the yoke until flush, Fig. 19-3. Then, force the rollers inward just far enough for installation of the snap rings.

Fig. 19-3. Using vise to force rollers inward until flush with yoke lug surface. Do not tighten beyond this point.

13. Important! If you find it difficult to drive the rollers completely into position (clearing snap ring grooves), one of your needle bearings has probably FALLEN SIDEWAYS in the roller. If so, remove the rollers and start over. DO NOT try to force the roller in with excessive force or damage will occur.

14. Refit your snap rings into their grooves. Depending upon the location and type, you may need to alter your procedures from that shown in Fig. 19-4. Needle nose pliers, snap ring pliers, etc. may be required.

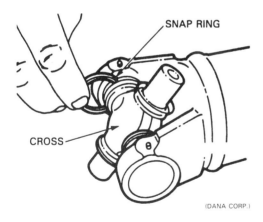

(DANA CORP.)

Fig. 19-4. Reinstall the snap rings.

15. After installing your rollers and snap rings, center your rollers in the yoke by tapping on them until the joint swivels freely.

16. If applicable, reinstall your drive shaft assembly. Check that the slip joint is perfectly clean and coated with a thin layer of grease. Also, check that both rollers are fitted inside their locating tangs.

17. Check out the shop-owned CV axle with a ball-type joint. See Fig. 19-5.

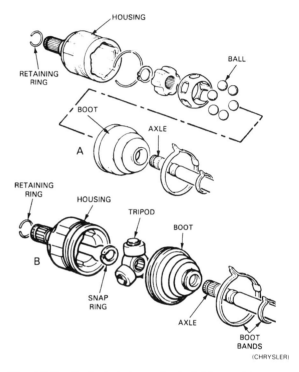

(CHRYSLER)

Fig. 19-5. Exploded view of a ball (Rzeppa) joint.

18. What make and model car is the CV axle from? _____
_____
_____

19. Remove the boot straps from the CV joint.

20. Slide the boot back and remove the C-clips or snap rings that hold the CV joint together, Fig. 19-6.

21. Separate the joint. Refer to the service manual instructions, if needed. Light taps from a brass hammer may be needed.

22. Remove the balls from the cage. This is done by pivoting the joint to free each ball.

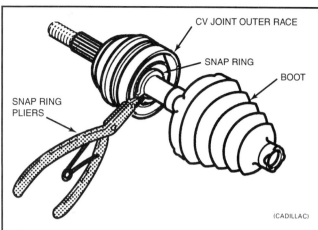

Fig. 19-6. Removing a snap ring so the joint may be disassembled.

23. While wearing rubber gloves and eye protection, clean the CV joint parts in a cold solvent tank or parts washer.

24. Inspect the parts of the joint (bearings, housings, snap rings, ring grooves) for signs of wear. Look for pitting, marring, and other surface imperfections.

25. Describe the condition of the CV joint.

_____

_____

_____

26. If this were an actual CV joint rebuild, you would install a CV joint repair kit containing new parts. Since this is an exercise, simply reinstall the old parts.

27. Grease the bearing race, cage, and bearings. Reinstall the bearings in reverse order of removal.

28. How many ball bearings are used in this joint?

_____

29. Reinstall the snap-rings that secure the joint.

30. Fill the boot with the correct amount and type of grease. Then, reinstall the boot straps, Fig. 19-7.

31. Have your instructor check your work and sign this sheet.

_____

INSTRUCTOR'S SIGNATURE

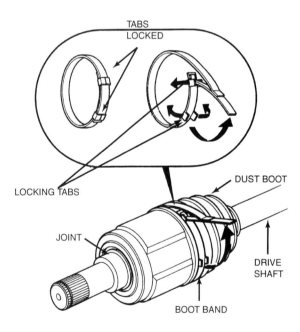

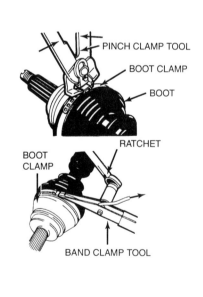

Fig. 19-7. Installing and restraining boot straps with a special strap (band) and pinch tools.

Job 20

DRUM BRAKE SERVICE

Name _____

Date _____ Period _____

Instructor _____

INTRODUCTION: Servicing a drum brake assembly is a fairly simple task, once you have mastered a few basic procedures and tools. Naturally, the first time you try to install brake shoes on a car, it may feel like one of your hands is tied behind your back. However, as with any automotive operation requiring excellent eye-hand coordination, "practice makes perfect." During this Job, you will simulate a brake repair on a shop owned teaching unit.

OBJECTIVE: Given the following list of tools and equipment, you will learn to properly service a drum brake assembly.

TOOLS AND EQUIPMENT: After completing step one, you will need safety glasses, brake retracting spring tool, hold-down spring tool, some heavy wheel bearing grease, brake adjusting spoon, a ruler, small screwdriver, brake adjusting gauge, and possibly a lug wrench, electric drill, brake fluid, and a wheel cylinder hone.

INSTRUCTIONS: Ask your instructor whether or not you will perform the wheel cylinder rebuilding portion of the Job. Also, inquire about the location of the brake assembly to be used. Make sure that you have read the section in the textbook which discusses drum brakes.

Note, if you see that class time is running out, place all of the parts in a can or parts tray so that they will not be lost.

REVIEW OF PARTS

1. As a quick review of the parts to be mentioned in the Job procedures, identify the components in Fig. 20-1.

A. _____

B. _____

C. _____

D. _____

E. _____

F. _____

G. _____

H. _____

I. _____

J. _____

K. _____

L. _____

M. _____

N. _____

O. _____

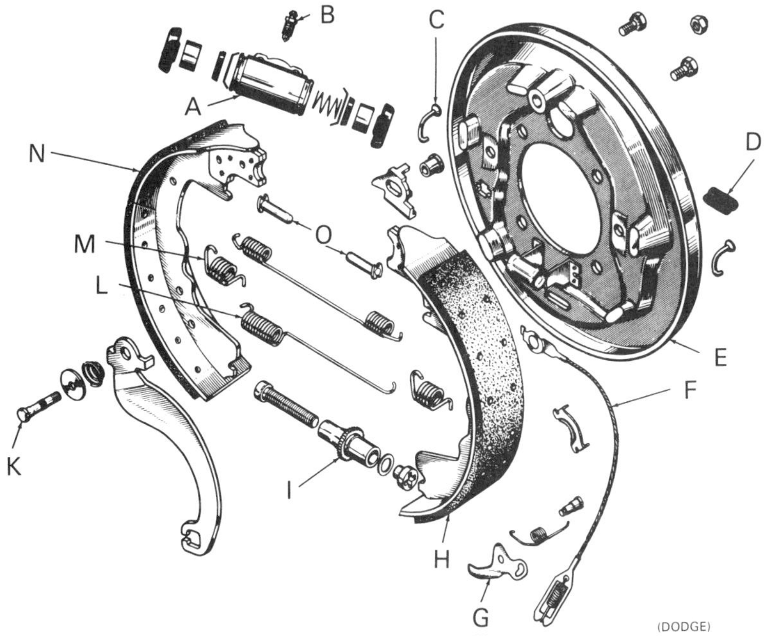

Fig. 20-1. Can you name all of these parts?

(DODGE)

PART DISASSEMBLY

2. Remove the wheel, tire and brake drum. If the drum will not come off, you may need to back up the star wheel, Fig. 20-2. The adjustment may be too tight or the drum may be highly worn and grooved.

   A stuck rear brake drum could also be caused by rust between the axle flange and drum. To free a rusted drum, use light taps with a hammer. Only strike the drum on the edge nearest you or the drum could be broken. The inner edge is not supported and will break off easily.

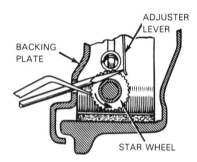

Fig. 20-2. If access hole for brake adjustment is in backing plate, pull up on spoon to loosen brakes. If the access slot is in drum, pry down on brake spoon. Remember to push on adjusting lever with a screwdriver when backing off brakes.

3. Did you have to back off your adjustment to remove the drum? Explain! _____

   _____
   _____
   _____
   _____
   _____

4. Carefully inspect how all of the brake parts fit together, especially the automatic adjuster mechanism and the springs. A few minutes time here can save a lot of time later!

5. If needed (no backing plate stops), install a spring type clamp into the ends of the wheel cylinder, as in Fig. 20-3. This will prevent the pistons and cups from popping out of the cylinder.

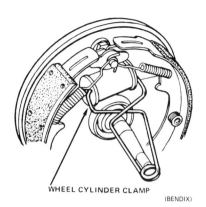

Fig. 20-3. Using a wheel cylinder clamp to hold pistons in cylinder when brake shoes are removed.

6. Measure the dimensions of the following components.
   A. Primary Lining Length _____
   B. Secondary Lining Length _____
   C. Lining Width _____
   D. Lining Thickness _____

7. Using your brake spring tool, Fig. 20-4, remove the upper (primary and secondary) return springs, adjusting cable or lever, etc. It may be a good idea to keep the front and rear springs and other parts separate to simplify reassembly.

   Quite often, the springs may have different tension even though their physical appearance is similar. Always replace brake springs in the exact same location.

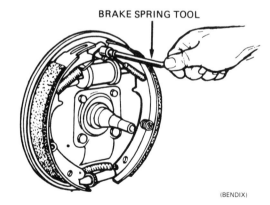

Fig. 20-4. This type of tool is turned or rotated to remove brake springs.

8. Now, remove the hold-down springs with your special hold-down spring tool or with pliers. See Fig. 20-5.

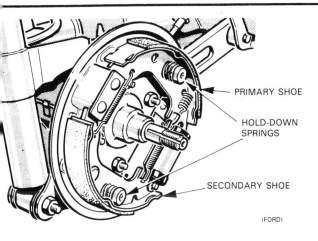

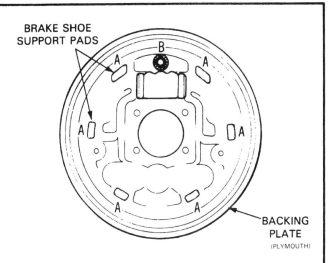

Fig. 20-5. Pliers or a special hold-down spring tool is used to remove the hold-down springs.

Fig. 20-6. Clean and lubricate brake shoe support pads.

Note! To remove the springs, you must use one finger to hold the pin tight against the inside or rear of the backing plate.

9. The brake shoes, star wheel, and lower return spring can now be removed as one unit.

10. Danger! Do not blow off brake parts with compressed air. Brake lining dust normally contains asbestos — a cancer causing agent. Use a special brake vacuum unit to clean the brake assembly.

INSPECT PARTS

11. Check all components for damage (stretched springs, bent parts, frayed cables, etc.).

12. Apply a light coating of high temperature wheel bearing grease on the star wheel threads and raised pads on the backing plate, as in Fig. 20-6. This will help avoid excessive friction, squeaks, and possibly an inoperable automatic brake adjusting mechanism.

13. Are any of your parts damaged? Explain!

_____
_____
_____
_____

REBUILDING WHEEL CYLINDER

14. OPTIONAL! If your instructor has given permission, you may remove and rebuild the wheel cylinder.

After disassembly, check the inside of the cylinder surface for wear, pits, scratches, and scoring. The slightest scratch or score may require cylinder replacement. As in Fig. 20-7, and described in detail in the text, hone the cylinder with your electric drill and a small hone. Be extremely careful not to pull the hone too far out of the cylinder. The hone could break.

When you are done, clean the cylinder with denatured alcohol or brake fluid and wipe dry.

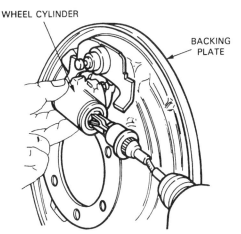

Fig. 20-7. Reconditioning cylinder by light honing. Stones must be fine. Do not pull stones from cylinder while still revolving. Finish with crocus cloth over stones for a smooth finish.

15. What is your wheel cylinder cup size?

_____

16. Reassemble the wheel cylinder. Then, reinstall the cylinder on the backing plate. Naturally, during a real repair, you would always use new wheel cylinder cups and boots.

REASSEMBLE PARTS

17. Place the shoes into position on the backing plate and secure them with their hold-down springs. Check that you have the smaller primary lining towards the FRONT of the car. Also, check that the shoes are completely up into position.

18. Fit the anchor pin plate, adjusting cable or link, and primary and secondary springs into place. See Fig. 20-8. You will need to stretch the springs with a special brake spring tool. With a cable type adjuster, the cable guide must be installed under the rear or secondary return spring.

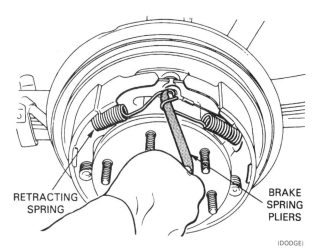

Fig. 20-8. This tool is used to pry and stretch springs over anchor pin.

19. Is your brake mechanism a link or cable type?

_____

_____

_____

_____

20. After screwing it together most of the way, slip the adjusting screw or star wheel between the bottom of the shoes.

21. Fit the short hook end of the lower return spring into its hole in the primary shoe.

Important! The half-hook on the end of the spring must fit (lock) as shown in the lower portion of Fig. 20-9. If the hook is installed WRONG, the spring can easily come off and jam against the rotating brake drum.

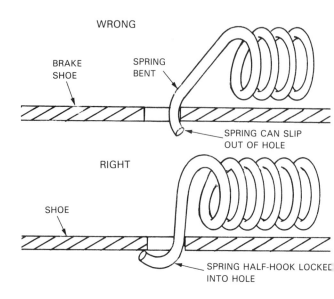

Fig. 20-9. In cutaway views of an installed brake spring, notice how lower spring is installed correctly (locked) into hole in shoe.

22. Attach the other end of the lower spring to the adjusting lever (cable type) or to the other brake shoe (lever type). Complete the assembly of the remaining parts.

23. Do your springs have half-hooks? _____

_____

_____

_____

_____

ADJUSTING BRAKES

24. Now, adjust the brakes by setting the lining-to-drum clearance. Install the special gauge into your brake drum, Fig. 20-10. Then, spread the gauge to the maximum inside diameter of the drum and lock it.

25. Tap the brake shoes from side to side to assure that they are completely seated on the anchor pin and centered on the backing plate.

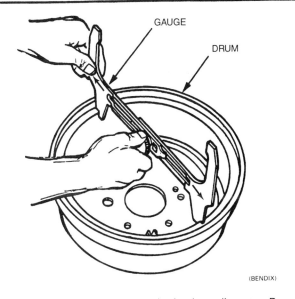

Fig. 20-10. Adjusting gauge-to-brake drum diameter. Be sure to lock securely.

26. Fit the adjusted brake gauge over the brake linings, Fig. 20-11. Then, adjust the star wheel until the linings touch the gauge.

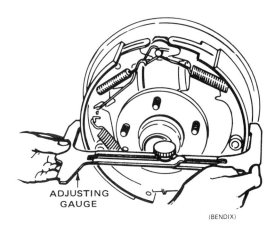

Fig. 20-11. Adjusting shoes to gauge. Check in several directions.

27. Fit the brake drum into place. The linings should almost touch the drum if adjusted properly.

BLEEDING BRAKES

28. If the wheel cylinder or any hydraulic component was removed, you will need to bleed the brakes (remove air from lines). Install the brake drum. Then, as described in the text, have a friend pump the brake pedal as you open and close the bleeding screw, Fig. 20-12. A pressure tank or brake bleeder may also be used.

    After all air bubbles have stopped coming out of the bleeder fitting, snug the fitting and check the feel of the brake pedal. Also, fill the master cylinder with brake fluid.

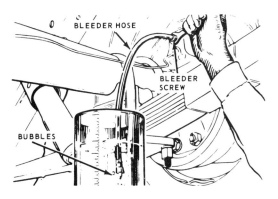

Fig. 20-12. Bleed cylinder until clean fluid, with NO air bubbles, flows from hose. Note bubbles still being forced from this system.

29. How do you bleed brakes? _____
    _____
    _____
    _____
    _____

30. Remove the brake drum and ask your instructor to check your work. Note, do not press the brake pedal with the drum removed or the wheel cylinder will pop apart.

31. Turn in your tools and clean your work area. Ask for your instructor's signature.

INSTRUCTOR'S SIGNATURE

Job 21

DISC BRAKE SERVICE

Name _____

Date _____ Period _____

Instructor _____

INTRODUCTION: Originally, disc type brakes were designed to stop military airplanes during the second world war. As a result, a car equipped with disc brakes will usually have tremendous stopping abilities. Also, disc brakes have a fewer number of parts than drum brakes. This makes them very easy to service.
During this Job, you will actually perform a simulated rebuild on a school owned disc brake unit.

OBJECTIVE: Using the tools and equipment listed for this job, you will learn to service an automotive disc brake assembly.

TOOLS AND EQUIPMENT: After labeling the illustration in step one, check out a basic set of hand wrenches, puller or sliding caliper, large C-clamp, two large screwdrivers, and safety glasses. If your instructor wants you to rebuild the caliper, you will also need an air nozzle, brake fluid, electric drill, cylinder hone and possibly, a special seat-piston installation tool.

INSTRUCTIONS: Ask your teacher whether or not you will rebuild the caliper and for the location of the disc brake unit to be serviced. If you run into any problems, feel free to ask for help.

REVIEW OF PARTS

1. To assure that you know the major components of a disc brake assembly, identify the parts in Fig. 21-1.

   A. _____
   B. _____
   C. _____
   D. _____
   E. _____
   F. _____
   G. _____
   H. _____
   I. _____
   J. _____
   K. _____

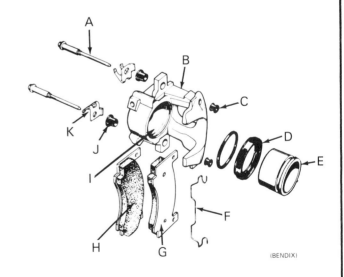

Fig. 21-1. Can you name these parts from memory?

(BENDIX)

BRAKE DISASSEMBLY

2. After drawing a little of the fluid out of the master cylinder (if applicable), unscrew the caliper locating pins, stabilizer bolts, or cap screws so that the caliper can be removed. Since bolt locations and procedures vary, you will need to inspect the construction of your particular unit and decide exactly which fasteners must be removed to free the caliper.

3. If the caliper will NOT slide off the rotor, you may have to use a large screwdriver or C-clamp to push the piston back into its bore. Look at Fig. 21-2.

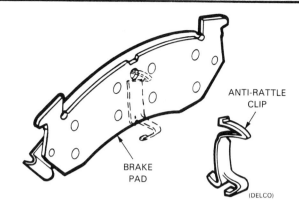

Fig. 21-3. Clip keeps pad from rattling. Note how it fits on pad.

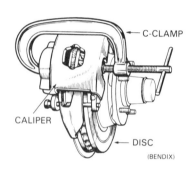

Fig. 21-2. Using a clamp to force brake piston back into bore to free brake pads.

4. How many bolts held the caliper in place?

_____

5. Lay the caliper on the upper control arm, a tie-rod, or hang it on a piece of mechanic's wire. The weight of the caliper should NOT be hung on the rubber brake hose or hose damage may occur.

6. Now, remove the brake pads, retaining clips, anti-rattle clips, etc. If anti-rattle clips are used on the pads, note how the clips fit into place. One example is given in Fig. 21-3.

7. Does your unit use anti-rattle clips?

_____

How do they fit into place? _____

_____

_____

PART INSPECTION

8. INSPECT the condition of all of the parts to be reused (clips, bolts, retainers, etc.). They should be checked for wear, breakage, distortion, etc. Also, look around the edge of the caliper piston. If leakage is present, the caliper must be rebuilt or replaced.

9. Explain the condition of your brake parts.

_____

_____

_____

_____

10. What is the maximum and minimum thickness of your brake pad linings?

_____

_____

_____

_____

REBUILDING CALIPER

11. OPTIONAL! If you have your instructor's approval, you may disassemble and rebuild the caliper. If NOT approved, skip over steps 12 through 19 of this Job.

12. Disconnect the rubber brake hose at the caliper, not at the steel brake line. Be careful not to lose the special sealing flat washer on the end of the rubber brake hose fitting. Drain the fluid from the caliper.

13. As in Fig. 21-4, position rags or a small block of wood inside the caliper. Then, KEEPING YOUR HANDS OUT OF THE WAY, slowly apply air pressure to the inside of the caliper cylinder.

    WARNING! Too much air pressure can cause the piston to shoot out of the caliper with tremendous force.

    If the piston is frozen and will NOT come out with moderate air pressure, tap on the piston lightly with a soft hammer or mallet and try again.

    In extreme cases, you can reinstall the caliper on the car and force the piston out with brake system pressure.

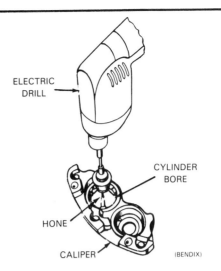

Fig. 21-5. If cylinder condition is good, crocus cloth can be used instead of a hone.

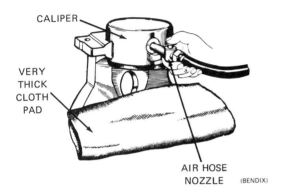

Fig. 21-4. Only apply enough air pressure to slowly push piston out of its bore. Keep your hands clear and wear eye protection.

14. Now, remove the dust boot and piston seal from the caliper. During a real repair, these parts would always be replaced.

15. Inspect the condition of the caliper cylinder bore. Check it for scratches, pits, and scoring. Crocus cloth may be used to clean up minor imperfections (gumming, discoloration, etc.). You may need to hone the cylinder. See Fig. 21-5.

    If excessive honing is required, the caliper must be replaced!

    After honing or sanding, clean the cylinder.

16. Using a ruler or sliding caliper, estimate the diameter of the caliper cylinder.

    CALIPER CYLINDER BORE
    DIAMETER   = _____

17. Lubricate the caliper bore, piston, and seal with clean brake fluid. Then, fit the seal into it's groove in the cylinder.

18. Now, slide the dust boot over the piston, Fig. 21-6. Then, hold the piston and boot over the bore and use your fingers to work the boot bead into place. A driving tool may be needed. Depending upon the type of brake, you may need to change your procedures slightly.

    If you are having problems, ask your instructor for help.

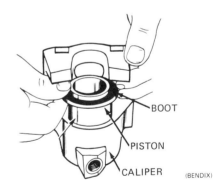

Fig. 21-6. Before pushing piston all the way into bore, fit boot into its grooves.

19. After fitting the dust boot into position, push the piston down into it's bore. You may need to use a C-clamp to push the piston fully into place. See Fig. 21-7.

    Be careful not to "cock" the piston sideways during installation or it may be damaged.

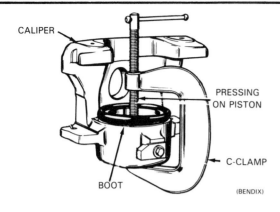

Fig. 21-7. Make sure the piston is not "cocked" sideways during installation.

CHECKING ROTOR

20. Inspect the condition of your rotor, Fig. 21-8. It should be free of heavy scoring and runout. Normally, unless the rotor has grooves deeper than .015 in. (0.38 mm) or runout in excess of around .004 in. (0.102 mm), manufacturers recommend that you avoid turning the rotor. "Cutting" a rotor on a lathe, when it is not needed, will only increase the chances of the rotor developing runout or warpage.

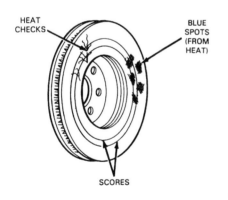

Fig. 21-8. Rotor problems. Blue spots and minor scoring can be removed. A crack or a series of cracks requires disc replacement.

21. Measure the thickness of your rotor. Look up and compare its thickness to specifications. Quite often, the minimum thickness is marked on the side of the rotor or disc.

22. Optional! Use a dial indicator to measure rotor runout as described in the textbook.

23. Record the following measurements.
   A. Actual Rotor Thickness = _____
   B. Minimum Thickness Spec. = _____
   C. Rotor Runout = _____

BLEED BRAKES

24. If applicable, bleed the system of air, as described in the textbook. Also, look at Fig. 21-9. With the system pressurized or with someone pumping the brake pedal, open the bleeder screw until all of the air bubbles are removed from the system. The jar and rubber hose will help prevent a mess on the floor and re-entry of air.

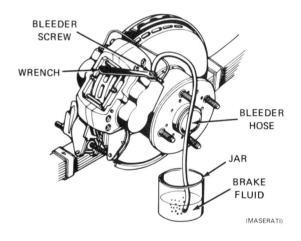

Fig. 21-9. Bleeding a disc brake caliper. Attach one end of bleeder hose to bleeder screw and submerge other in a partially filled jar of brake fluid.

25. Fill the master cylinder with fluid and check that you have a solid brake pedal.

26. Clean your work area and have your instructor sign this Job.

INSTRUCTOR'S SIGNATURE

Job 22

WHEEL BEARING SERVICE

Name _____

Date _____ Period _____

Instructor _____

INTRODUCTION: Wheel bearings have the tough job of supporting the weight of the vehicle while spinning for thousands of miles. Open bearings must be periodically serviced by disassembly, cleaning, and repacking with new grease. Sealed bearings must be replaced when worn and noisy. A worn bearing can cause loose wheels, tire wear, handling problems, erratic brake application, lowered gas mileage, bearing seizure, and ultimately, the loss of a wheel while driving.

OBJECTIVE: Given the proper tools and equipment, you will learn to service both open and sealed wheel bearings.

TOOLS AND EQUIPMENT: You will need a basic set of hand tools, torque wrenches, grease cap pliers, a parts cleaning tank, wheel bearing grease, a stool creeper, a lug wrench, an air nozzle, cotter pins, a ruler, shop rags, a seal driver, and a hydraulic press with appropriate adaptors.

INSTRUCTIONS: Ask your instructor which vehicles and parts will be used during this job. You should have access to a vehicle with tapered roller bearings on the front wheels. You will also need a steering knuckle with a pressed-in sealed bearing. The first part of the job is for a serviceable bearing that can be disassembled. The second section summarizes how to service a sealed bearing.

REVIEW OF PARTS

1. Without using your textbook, see how many of the front wheel, hub, and bearing assembly parts you can identify, Fig. 22-1. If you cannot remember the names of some of the parts, restudy the textbook.

A. _____
B. _____
C. _____
D. _____
E. _____
F. _____
G. _____
H. _____
I. _____
J. _____
K. _____
L. _____

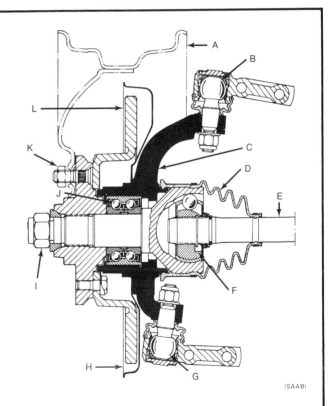

(SAAB)

Fig. 22-1. Name the parts of this wheel assembly to prepare you for the Job.

TAPERED ROLLER BEARING SERVICE

2. Since they require different service procedures, look on the inside of the front wheel. Determine whether your hub uses drum or disc brakes.

3. What type of brakes are used on your hub?

_____

_____

_____

_____

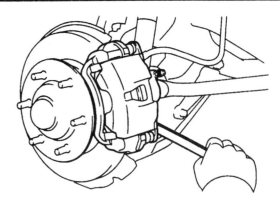

Fig. 22-3. If you have disc brakes, you will have to remove bolts securing caliper before removing hub.

REMOVE WHEEL

4. Loosen the wheel lug nuts one half turn but DO NOT REMOVE THEM ALL THE WAY. Then, raise and secure the car on jack stands. Block the wheels so that the car cannot roll off of the stands.

5. Before removing the wheel and tire, mark one of the lug studs and the wheel with chalk or crayon. See Fig. 22-2. This will let you install the wheel exactly as it was removed. If the wheel and tire were balanced on the car, it could be thrown out of balance if installed in a different position.

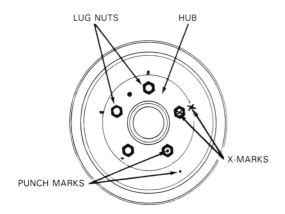

LUG NUTS   HUB

X-MARKS

PUNCH MARKS

Fig. 22-2. Lug studs and wheel should be marked with chalk, crayon, or with center punch marks.

REMOVE HUB

6. If you have disc brakes, you must remove the brake caliper before removing the rotor and hub! The caliper is usually fastened to the spindle with two or three bolts, Fig. 22-3.

7. Using your dust cover pliers or channel locks, remove the dust cap. Then, use your diagonal cutters to straighten and remove the cotter pin. Place all of the parts into the bottom of the stool creeper, parts tray, can, or wheel cover.

8. Unscrew and remove the adjusting nut and wiggle the tire or hub sideways. This will make the safety washer and outer bearing pop out for removal.

9. Thread the adjusting nut onto the end of the spindle without the safety washer and outer bearing. Slide the hub assembly briskly off of the spindle while placing a slight downward pressure on the hub. This is an extremely fast and efficient method of removing the inner grease seal and bearing.

10. Whenever a drum or rotor is removed, you should inspect the brake linings for wear. As a general rule, brake linings should be at least 1/8 in. (3.18 mm) thick at their thinnest point.

11. What is the minimum measured thickness of your brake linings? _____

_____

12. Are your linings worn enough to need replacement? Explain! _____

_____

_____

_____

13. CAUTION! Brake lining dust contains asbestos which is a powerful cancer causing substance. Avoid using air to blow the asbestos dust off of the brake parts. Instead, use a special vacuum machine if available. In any case, wear a painters mask to prevent the dust from entering your lungs. Use a rag to wipe the spindle clean.

14. If you were to disassemble both front wheel bearing assemblies, keep your right and left side bearings separated, Fig. 22-4. Wheel bearings are matched to their cup. Placing a bearing in a different cup can cause problems.

(SHELL)

Fig. 22-4. Always keep identical wheel bearing from right and left sides of car separated. They must be returned to same cup.

15. Submerse and clean your bearings in part cleaning solvent. Blow them dry with compressed air, but do NOT allow them to spin. If spun, a wheel bearing can explode with tremendous force. The rollers can shoot out as if shot from a gun. Remember to wear eye protection.

16. Inspect your bearings and cup for faults, Fig. 22-5. Look at them closely. Rotate and inspect each bearing roller. Run your finger over the surface of the bearing cups as you check for imperfections. The slightest amount of roughness can cause bearing noise and ultimate failure.

17. Can you detect any problem with your bearings or cups?_____

_____

_____

18. Pack your wheel bearings with grease. Work grease into the bearing rollers with your fingers. Then, lay them on a clean rag or paper towel.

19. Inspect the inner lip of the grease seal for splits or tears, see Fig. 22-6. To check the seal for wear, slide it over the enlarged portion of the spindle. The seal should fit snugly over the spindle.

    Note! During an actual repair, you would normally replace a grease seal.

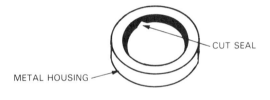

CUT SEAL

METAL HOUSING

Fig. 22-6. Inspect inner rubber lip of grease seal for damage and wear.

20. Can you find any problem with your grease seal? _____

_____

_____

DULLED CUP AND ROLLERS

WEAR

SHINY LINES

BRINELLING

DARKENED AND BURNED

HEAT DISCOLORATION

PITTED SURFACE

FATIGUE SPALLING

(CADILLAC)

Fig. 22-5. Typical bearing conditions. Study them!

21. If your instructor gives the OK, wipe out the inside of the hub to remove all of the old grease. Coat the inside of the hub with new grease to a depth even with the bearing cups, Fig. 22-7. DO NOT overfill the hub or upon operation, the heat and expansion will force the grease out of the hub and possibly onto the brake linings.

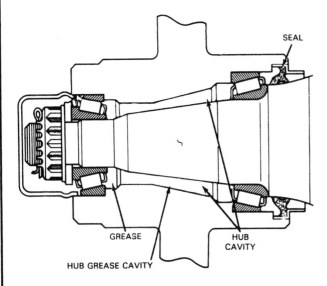

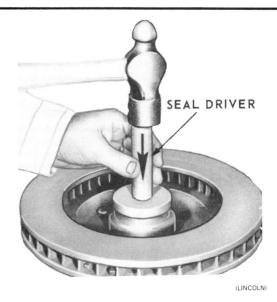

Fig. 22-8. If a seal driver is not available, seal can be tapped in with just a ball peen hammer.

Fig. 22-7. Fill hub grease cavity to this depth. Place a LIGHT coating in dust cap.

HUB AND TAPERED ROLLER BEARING ASSEMBLY

22. Lay your greased inner bearing onto it's cup and use, if available, a seal driver and a ball peen hammer to install the inner grease seal, Fig. 22-8. Lightly tap the seal squarely into place. Make sure you do NOT dent or bend the seal housing.

23. Slide the hub assembly onto the spindle. Install the outer bearing, safety washer, and adjusting nut. Be careful not to damage the grease seal on the threads of the spindle.

24. Following one of the procedures in either Fig. 22-9 or 22-10, adjust your wheel bearings. A torque wrench and socket will be needed to properly set the bearings.

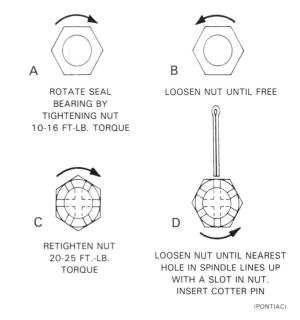

Fig. 22-9. Recommended four step procedure used on cars with only slotted nut.

25. Install a new cotter pin and bend it around the outside of the adjusting nut.

26. Always double check the installation of the cotter pin. If the cotter pin is left out or installed improperly, the front wheel of the car may fall off.

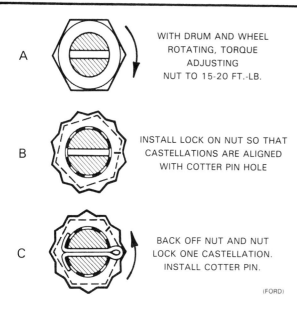

Fig. 22-10. Three step procedure used on cars with a locknut.

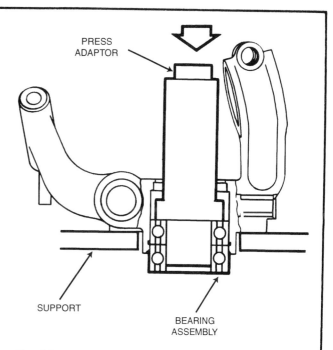

Fig. 22-11. Remove the bearing from the steering knuckle with an arbor press and a special bearing adapter tool.

7. Being careful not to dent it, tap the dust cap into the hub with a ball peen hammer. If you dent the cap, straighten it by hammering on the inside of the cap with a blunt driver and a hammer.

8. Obtain a steering knuckle with a pressed-in sealed bearing from your instructor.

9. Remove any dust covers or snap rings in the steering knuckle.

0. Place the knuckle in an appropriate press.

1. Using the proper adapters, press the bearing out of the steering knuckle. See Fig. 22-11.

2. Clean the steering knuckle and study it for cracks and wear. Does the knuckle show signs of wear or damage? If so, explain. _____
_____
_____

3. Inspect all parts removed from the steering knuckle. Replace worn or dented dust covers and wear plates.

4. Position the bearing assembly on the steering knuckle.

5. Using the proper adapters, press the bearing into the steering knuckle.

36. Install snap rings or dust covers in the correct positions in the steering knuckle.

TORQUING LUG NUTS

37. If applicable, line up your marks and install your wheel and tire. The tapered edge of the lug nuts should face the wheel. This centers the wheel on the hub.

38. Snug the lug nuts with your lug wrench and lower the car to the ground using the reverse order utilized when raising the car.

39. Tightening the lug nuts to specifications. A chart is provided in Fig. 22-12 showing average torque values for various car makes. Proper lug nut torque is very critical, especially on some late model cars using disc brakes.

Overtightened lug nuts can cause the disc to warp. Then, the car will vibrate when the brakes are applied. Torque the lug nuts in the sequence given in Fig. 22-13, which is a crisscross pattern. Go over all of the lug nuts two or three times to double-check their torque.

CAR MAKE	LUG NUT TORQUES IN FT.-LB.		
	COMPACT	INTERMEDIATE	FULL SIZE
FORD	55-65	75-95	80-110
GMC	60-70	75-85	90-130
CHRYSLER	50-55	55-60	60-80

Fig. 22-12. Typical lug nut torques. Use service manual values during actual repairs.

40. How tight did you or would you torque your lug nuts? _____

41. What was the final torque value of your bearing adjusting nut before loosening?

_____

42. Have your instructor initial this sheet for credit.

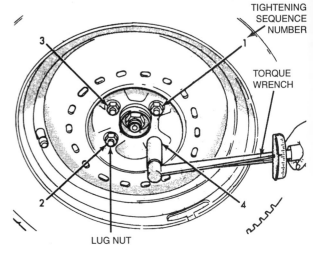

Fig. 22-13. Torque lug nuts in crisscross pattern to help center and evenly tighten wheel.

_____

INSTRUCTOR'S SIGNATURE

Job 23

WHEEL ALIGNMENT

Name _____

Date _____ Period _____

Instructor _____

INTRODUCTION: Have you ever seen a car "dog tracking"? Dog tracking is a condition in which the rear wheels are not aligned with the vehicles centerline. This causes the vehicle to travel down the road with its rear end to one side. As this example points out, wheel alignment is critical to the driveablity and dependability of modern vehicles.

OBJECTIVE: Given the needed tools and equipment, you will be able to realign all four wheels of a vehicle.

TOOLS AND EQUIPMENT: You will need a basic set of hand tools, an alignment machine, a vehicle that requires alignment of all four wheels, and an appropriate service manual.

INSTRUCTIONS: After getting your instructor's approval, proceed to align the four wheels on the vehicle.

SERVICE MANUAL INFORMATION

1. In a service manual for the vehicle at hand, read the service information on four-wheel alignment.

2. What are the alignment specs for your vehicle?

Front wheels:

Right Wheel Caster _____

Left Wheel Caster _____

Right Wheel Camber _____

Left Wheel Camber _____

Toe _____

Rear wheels:

Right Wheel Camber _____

Left Wheel Camber _____

Toe _____

STEERING AND SUSPENSION INSPECTION

3. Position the vehicle on the alignment rack. Have someone guide you as you drive onto the rack.

4. Once in position, place the transmission in Park or place it in gear and block the rear wheels.

5. What kind of alignment equipment do you have in your shop?

_____

_____

_____

6. Have someone turn the steering wheel to the right and then to the left while you check for worn steering parts.

7. Summarize the condition of the following steering parts:

Tie rod ends _____

_____

_____

Rack and pinion assembly _____

_____

_____

Power steering belt and pump _____

_____

_____

Other parts _____
_____
_____

8. Check the suspension system for wear. Summarize the condition of the following suspension system parts:

Ball joints _____
_____
_____

Shock absorbers _____
_____
_____

Control arm bushings_____
_____
_____

Other parts _____
_____
_____

9. Inspect the tires for signs of wear. What does the tire wear pattern tell you about the vehicle's wheel alignment? _____
_____
_____

10. Since the steering and suspension systems must be in good condition before adjusting wheel alignment, replace worn or damaged parts as necessary.

MEASURING ALIGNMENT ANGLES

11. How do you prepare to measure alignment angles? _____
_____
_____

12. Many of today's alignment machines are computerized, Fig. 23-1. They will give instructions, specs, and even pictures of what should be done to align the wheels. Is your alignment machine computerized? _____
_____

13. Read through the operating manual for your alignment machine.

14. Mount the machine attachments on the vehicle as outlined in the operating manual. See Fig. 23-2.

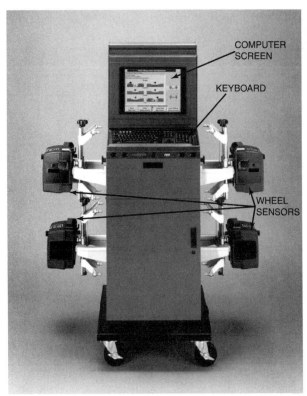

(HUNTER ENGINEERING CO.)

Fig. 23-1. Computerized alignment machine. The sensors are mounted on the vehicle's wheels, and alignment readings are displayed on the screen.

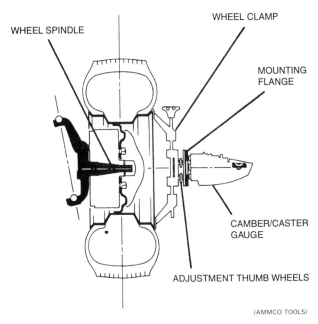

(AMMCO TOOLS)

Fig. 23-2. This alignment tool is properly attached to the wheel. Handle these tools with care.

15. Take your readings for four-wheel alignment and record them.

Front wheels:

Right Wheel Caster _____

Left Wheel Caster _____

Right Wheel Camber _____

Left Wheel Camber _____

Toe_____

Rear wheels:

Right Wheel Camber _____

Left Wheel Camber _____

Toe_____

16. How much do these readings vary from specs?

Front wheels:

Caster Difference_____

Camber Difference _____

Toe Difference _____

Rear Wheels:

Camber Difference _____

Toe Difference_____

ADJUSTING WHEEL ALIGNMENT

Note: Make the following adjustments only if the alignment measurements taken previously are not within specifications. Remember, however, that toe must be adjusted last, as it is affected by the other alignment angles. Refer to the appropriate service manual for information on how to make adjustments on the vehicle at hand.

17. Adjust rear camber. Explain how this is accomplished on the vehicle at hand. _____

_____

_____

_____

18. Adjust rear toe. Fig. 23-3 shows one method of adjusting rear toe. Explain how this is done on the vehicle at hand. _____

_____

_____

_____

19. Adjust front caster. How would this be done on the vehicle at hand? _____

_____

_____

_____

_____

TO ADJUST, LOOSEN JAM NUT
AND ROTATE TIE ROD.

JAM NUT

(HUNTER ENGINEERING CO.)

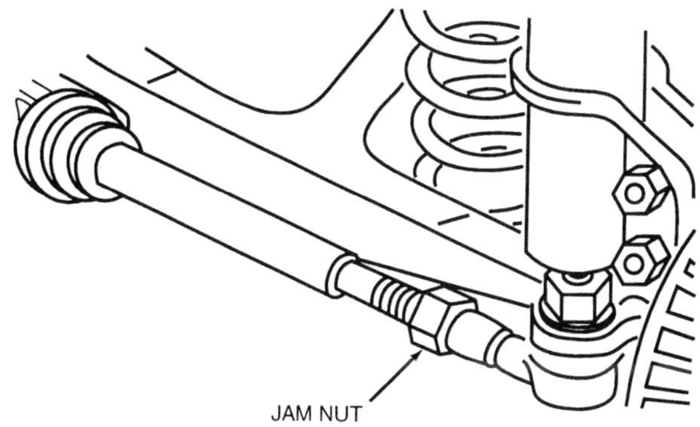

Fig. 23-3. Rotate the strut rod to set rear toe to specifications.

20. Adjust front camber. Fig. 23-4 shows two camber adjustment methods. Explain the adjustment method used on the vehicle at hand.

_____

_____

_____

_____

PIVOT STRUT

A

ADJUSTMENT SLOT

5 mm

FILE SHADED AREA AT STRUT MOUNTS (3)

B

STRUT

LEFT SIDE

FRONT

(HUNTER ENGINEERING CO.)

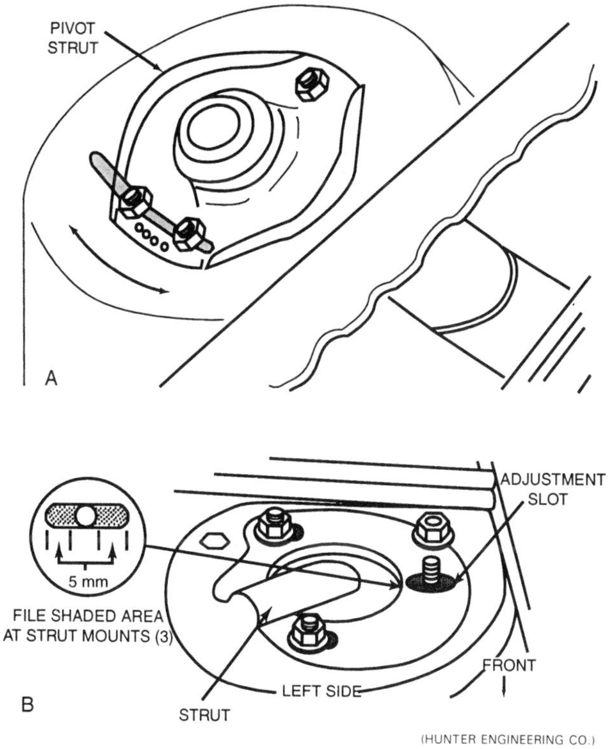

Fig. 23-4. Camber adjustment methods. A — By pivoting the strut. B — By sliding the strut sideways.

21. Finally, adjust front toe, Fig. 23-5. How do you adjust toe on the vehicle at hand?

_____

_____

_____

_____

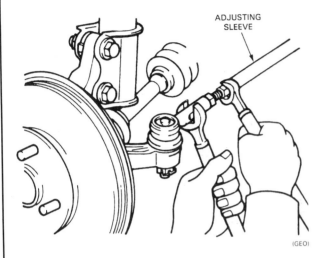

Fig. 23-5. Adjusting front toe-in. Turn the adjusting sleeve as specified in the service manual.

22. Is the steering wheel still centered when the front wheels are straight ahead? See Fig. 23-6. If not, how would you correct this problem?

_____

_____

_____

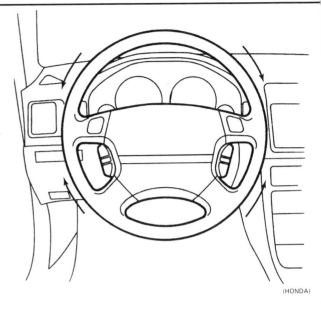

Fig. 23-6. The steering wheel spoke should be straight when the tie rods are adjusted correctly.

23. Make sure all steering and suspension system fasteners are retorqued to specifications.

24. Have your instructor check your work.

_____

INSTRUCTOR'S SIGNATURE

Job 24

CHECKING FLUID LEVELS

Name _____

Date _____ Period _____

Instructor _____

INTRODUCTION: If a car's oils and fluids are not serviced properly, the useful life of the vehicle will be reduced. When a mechanic checks a fluid level (engine oil, coolant, power steering fluid, differential lubricant), it is a form of preventive maintenance.

Anytime a low fluid level, dirty oil, or other problem is found, it tells the mechanic something about the condition of the car. For example, an excessively low fluid level may indicate a serious leak. Then, the mechanic would know to inspect other areas to find the source of the problem. This type maintenance can prevent costly on-the-road breakdowns.

OBJECTIVE: Given the tools and equipment listed below, you will learn to check the fluids in an automobile.

TOOLS AND EQUIPMENT: Check out a pair of safety glasses, standard screwdriver, set of hand wrenches, 3/8 drive ratchet, ruler, shop rag, battery hydrometer, antifreeze tester, and an automobile.

INSTRUCTIONS: Ask your instructor for any added details for the job. You may have to work on a shop owned or an actual customer car.

BRAKE FLUID

. Locate the brake master cylinder on your car. It is normally bolted to the firewall on the driver's side of the car.

. Clean and remove the master cylinder cover. If spring clips are used, pry them off with a screwdriver. A wrench is needed if the cover is bolted in place.

Inspect the level and condition of the brake fluid. Typically, the brake fluid should NOT be more than 1/4 in. (6.4 mm) down in the reservoir. See Fig. 24-1.

WARNING! Keep oil, dirt, and grease out of the brake fluid. Oil and grease can ruin the cups in a brake system.

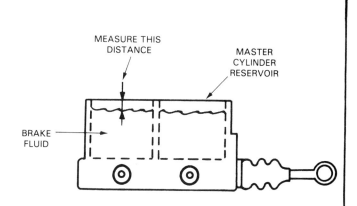

Fig. 24-1. Brake fluid must be kept at specified level for car to be in safe operating condition. Always refer to a service manual for exact specs on filling.

4. Is your master cylinder full or low? _____
   Explain. _____
   _____
   _____
   _____
   _____

OIL DIPSTICK SHOWS ALMOST 1/2 QUART LOW.

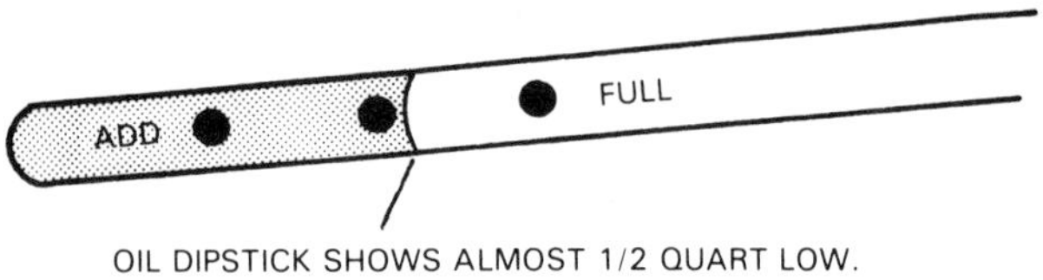

Fig. 24-2. When adding oil to an engine, only add enough to bring oil up to full mark on dipstick.

5. When the brake fluid becomes low in a short period of time, inspect the entire brake system for leaks. Check the wheel cylinders, brake lines, and back of the master cylinder for wetness. Brake fluid will show up as a dark, damp spot.

6. To improve your troubleshooting ability, memorize the smell of brake fluid. Then, if fluid leakage is found, you can quickly smell and identify the leak.

7. Inspect your brake system for leaks. Look behind the wheel backing plates, at the brake line fittings, and anywhere else a leak might occur.

8. Could you find any brake system leaks?
   _____ Explain. _____
   _____
   _____
   _____

9. NOTE! If you spill brake fluid, wipe it up immediately. Brake fluid can ruin the paint job on a car. It dissolves paint in a matter of minutes.

ENGINE OIL

10. With the engine off, find the engine oil dipstick. It should be on side or front of engine. Remove dipstick and wipe it off. Then, reinstall dipstick until fully seated.

11. Pull the dipstick back out and hold it over your shop rag. Inspect how far the oil is up on the stick. See Fig. 24-2. The oil should be between the full and add marks.
    Memorize the smell of engine oil. This will help you when diagnosing leaks.

12. When the oil level is even with the add mark on the dipstick, you usually need to add one quart of oil. If the oil is midway between the add and full marks, one-half quart is needed. Be careful never to add too much oil to an engine or oil foaming and other problems may result.

13. How was the level of oil in your engine?
    _____ Explain._____
    _____
    _____
    _____
    _____

14. If this is an actual customer car and oil is needed, remove the breather cap. The cap is usually on the valve cover. Pour in the correct type motor oil. Then, reinstall the breather cap.

15. Where would you add oil on this engine?
    _____
    _____
    _____
    _____

BATTERY

16. Inspect the battery. The top of the battery should be clean and dry. Moisture on the battery case top can cause battery leakage (current shorts from one cell to another across top of dirty battery). Also, check the condition of the battery terminals. They should be uncorroded, clean, and tight. Corroded terminals may keep the engine from cranking properly.

17. Describe the outer condition or cleanliness or your battery case and terminals. Could you find any other problems?

_____

_____

_____

_____

_____

18. What is battery leakage? _____

_____

_____

ENGINE COOLANT

19. Determine whether your car has a closed or an open cooling system, Fig. 24-3. A closed system will have a plastic reservoir tank on one side of the radiator. The radiator cap may also be labeled – DO NOT OPEN.

    To check the coolant level in a closed system, inspect the amount of coolant in the plastic reservoir tank. Compare the level with the marks on the side of the tank.

    To check the coolant level in an open system, first make sure the radiator is cool. If warm, DO NOT remove the radiator cap. Hot coolant could blow into your face, causing serious injury. The coolant in an open system should be about one inch down in the radiator, Fig. 20-3.

    If either type cooling system needs coolant, add a mixture of 50% antifreeze. This is the most efficient mixture.

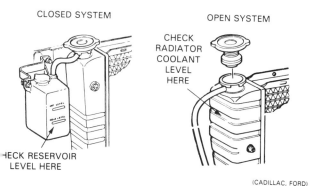

CLOSED SYSTEM   OPEN SYSTEM

CHECK RADIATOR COOLANT LEVEL HERE

CHECK RESERVOIR LEVEL HERE

(CADILLAC, FORD)

Fig. 24-3. Note the difference between closed and open cooling systems. You do not have to remove radiator cap to check coolant level in closed system.

20. How was the level of coolant in your cooling system? _____

_____

_____

_____

_____

21. Check out an antifreeze tester. Draw coolant into the tester. Use the directions with the particular tester to determine the freeze-up protection of the coolant.

22. Also, inspect the coolant for rust or discoloration. After prolonged use, antifreeze can break down and become very corrosive. It can cause rapid rust formation and damage to the cooling system. For this reason, antifreeze must be drained and replaced at recommended intervals.

    A leak in a cooling system will usually be easy to see. The area around the leak will often be a bright, rust color or the color of the antifreeze.

23. To increase your troubleshooting skills, memorize the smell of antifreeze. Then, when a leak is found, the smell will tell you whether it is antifreeze or another fluid.

24. How much freeze-up protection does your coolant provide for the system? _____

_____

_____

_____

25. Is your coolant rusty or could you find any leaks? _____ Explain._____

_____

_____

_____

_____

POWER STEERING FLUID

26. Locate the power steering pump. It is normally on the lower front of the engine. With the engine off, remove the power steering pump cap and wipe off the dipstick. Reinsert dipstick and pull it back out. Holding it over your shop rag, inspect the level of fluid. The fluid should be between the full and add marks, as in Fig. 24-4.

If needed, add enough recommended power steering fluid (usually automatic transmission fluid) to fill to the add mark. Do NOT add too much, or fluid will blow out the pump after engine starting.

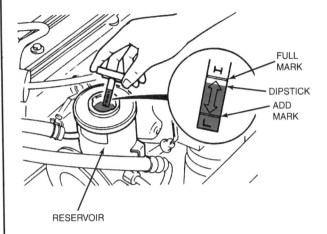

Fig. 24-4. Power steering fluid dipstick is normally attached to cap on pump. If needed, add recommended type fluid, usually automatic transmission fluid.

27. If the power steering pump is excessively low, check the power steering system for leaks. Look under the pump, around line fittings and any other component containing fluid.

28. Did your power steering fluid level check OK? Explain._____

_____

_____

_____

_____

AUTOMATIC TRANSMISSION FLUID

29. To check the automatic transmission fluid, start and warm the engine. Move the transmission selector through the gears. Apply the parking brake and then shift the transmission into park and block the wheels. Leave the engine running.

   Remove and wipe off the transmission dipstick. It will usually be at the rear of the engine on one side. Reinsert the dipstick and pull it back out. Hold it over your rag while you check the fluid level on the stick. Refer to Fig. 24-5.

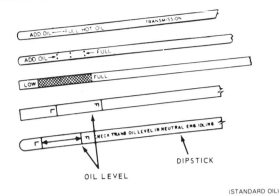

Fig. 24-5. Note different types of markings on these automatic transmission dipsticks. Some only show one pint from add to full, others show a quart from add to full. Only add enough to reach full mark.

30. When adding fluid to an automatic transmission, make sure you have the correct type of fluid. Different transmissions require different types. Always install the type fluid recommended by the manufacturer.

   Also, do NOT overfill the transmission. Overfilling can cause fluid foaming, poor transmission operation, and seal leakage.

31. Study the smell of automatic transmission fluid. If the fluid smells burned, then the bands or clutches inside the transmission may be worn and damaged.

32. Describe the condition and level of fluid in your automatic transmission. _____

_____

_____

_____

_____

DIFFERENTIAL LUBRICANT

33. OPTIONAL! Ask your instructor for approval before completing the last section of this job.

34. After getting your instructor's OK, raise the car on a lift or secure it on jack stands.

   Remove the differential filler plug, NOT the drain plug. The filler plug will be on the front or rear of the housing, about halfway up on the differential. This is pictured in Fig. 24-6.

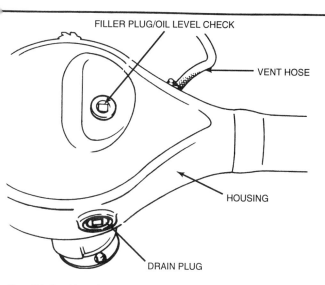

Fig. 24-6. Note locations of filler and drain plugs in this differential.

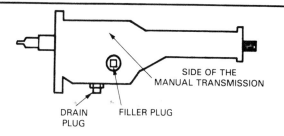

Fig. 24-7. Filler plug is on side of manual transmission. Drain plug will be on bottom. Only remove filler plug when checking level.

35. The differential fluid should be approximately 1/2 in. (12.7 mm) below the filler hole. This can vary with some cars so always refer to a service manual for an exact specification. Stick your finger in the filler hole to check the lubricant level.

    If needed, add just enough recommended differential lubricant to meet factory recommendations. Memorize the smell of differential fluid so that you can quickly diagnose leaks.

36. Was the lubricant in your differential low? _____ Explain._____
    _____
    _____
    _____

MANUAL TRANSMISSION LUBRICANT

37. OPTIONAL! Check the lubricant in a manual transmission. If your car has an automatic, you may need another car or a shop training unit.

    Remove the filler plug on the side of the transmission. This is pictured in Fig. 24-7. Insert your finger into the hole. The lubricant should be slightly below or almost even with the filler hole.

    If needed, add the recommended type gear oil for the particular transmission. Also, learn to identify the smell of gear oil.

38. How was the lubricant level in the manual transmission?_____
    _____
    _____
    _____
    _____

39. OPTIONAL! Use the directions in a service manual to check the lubricant level in a manual steering gearbox.

40. Check the windshield washer solvent. It will be in a plastic reservoir on one side of the engine compartment. The solvent should be almost even with the full mark on the side of the container.

    In cold weather, only add the recommended type solution to the windshield washer tank. If water is added, it could freeze and damage the windshield washer reservoir and pump.

41. Ask your instructor to sign this job for credit.

_____
INSTRUCTOR'S SIGNATURE